ADVANCES IN INEQUALITIES
FOR SPECIAL FUNCTIONS

Advances in Mathematical Inequalities
SEVER S. DRAGOMIR (SERIES EDITOR)

Advances in Inequalities from Probability Theory and Statistics
Neil S. Barnett and Sever S. Dragomir
1-60021-943-8

Advances in Inequalities for Special Functions
Pietro Cerone and Sever S. Dragomir
1-60021-919-5

Inequalities for Random Variables over a Finite Interval
Neil S. Barnett; Pietro Cerone and Sever S. Dragomir
1-60021-909-8

Advances in Inequalities for Series
Sever S. Dragomir and Anthony Sofo
1-60021-920-9

ADVANCES IN INEQUALITIES FOR SPECIAL FUNCTIONS

PIETRO CERONE AND SEVER S. DRAGOMIR
Editors

Nova Science Publishers, Inc.
New York

Library of Congress Cataloging-in-Publication Data

Advances in inequalities for special functions / Pietro Cerone and Sever S. Dragomir, editors.
    p. cm.
  Includes index.
  ISBN-13: 978-1-60021-919-1 (hardcover)
  ISBN-10: 1-60021-919-5 (hardcover)
  1. Functions, Special. 2. Inequalities (Mathematics) I. Dragomir, Sever Silvestru. II. Cerone, Pietro.
QA351.A375 2008
515'.5--dc22

2007030612

Published by Nova Science Publishers, Inc. ✦ New York

Contents

Preface

This book is the first in a collection of research monographs that are devoted to presenting recent research, development and use of Mathematical Inequalities for Special Functions. All the papers incorporated in the book have peen peer-reviewed and they cover a range of topics that include both survey material of previously published works as well as new results.

In his presentation on special functions approximations and bounds via integral representation, Pietro Cerone utilizes the classical Steffensen inequality and bounds for the Čebyšev functional to obtain bounds for some classical special functions. The methodology relies on determining bounds on integrals of products of functions. The techniques are used to obtain novel and useful bounds for the Bessel function of the first kind, the Beta function, the Zeta function and Mathieu series.

Pietro Cerone & Sever S. Dragomir then survey some recent results of the authors concerning inequalities for Dirichlet series with positive terms. Applications for the Zeta function and other related functions are also provided.

Stamatis Koumandos then investigates the monotonicity of the mean value function of normalized Bessel functions of the first kind while Milan Merkle surveys the tools and techniques that are shown useful in producing inequalities for the Euler gamma function via convexity.

It has been over 150 years since the first formulation of the Sturm comparison theorem concerning solutions of second order linear differential equations. In these years the theorem has been extended to higher order differential equations, to partial differential equations and to difference equations. The aim of the paper authored by Andrea Laforgia & Pierpaolo Natalini is to present a survey of the most important inequalities and monotonicity properties of the zeros of Bessel functions. The results are obtained as a consequence of the Sturm comparison theorem. The notion of hyperharmonic numbers is rather new. In his contribution, Some Inequalities for Hyperharmonic Series, István Mezö establishes some new inequalities for these numbers as well as an upper bound for Ramsey numbers.

Further, Edward Newman establishes some new Hermite-Hadamard type inequalities for double Dirichlet averages of univariate functions and investigates their applications to special functions with emphasis on Lauricellas hypergeometric function FB and Jacobi polynomials while Baburao G. Pachpatte obtains some new inequalities of Hermite-Hadamard type for the product of two convex respectively two logarithmic convex functions.

In his contribution on certain special functions of Number Theory and Mathematical Analysis, József Sándor offers a survey of results on certain special number theoretical functions as well as their real variable analogues that have been initiated by the author.

In his paper Tibor K. Pogány investigates the growth rates of the Weierstrass functions $\wp'(z)$ and $\wp(z)$ while Mehmet Zeki Sarikaya and Hüseyin Yildirim explore properties of the operator $\oplus_B^k$ Related to the Bessel-wave equation and the Laplacian-Bessel operator.

Finally, on utilising the concept of majorant sequence some new inequalities for Walsh polynomials with p-times complex semi-monotone and p-times complex monotone sequence are obtained by Zivorad Tomovski. Inequalities for p-times monotone sequences of nonnegative real numbers are also obtained. These results generalize some inequalities for Walsh polynomials with semi-monotone and semi-convex coefficients, obtained by the author in an earlier paper.

We hope that you find the volume interesting, stimulating and suggestive of new ideas for future research in the highly dynamic field of Special Function Theory.

P. Cerone and S. S. Dragomir, Editors.

In: Advances in Inequalities for Special Functions
Editors: P. Cerone and S. S. Dragomir, pp. 1–35

ISBN 978-1-60021-919-1
© 2008 Nova Science Publishers, Inc.

Special Functions Approximations and Bounds via Integral Representation

P. Cerone

School of Computer Science and Mathematics
Victoria University, PO Box 14428
MCMC 8001, Victoria, Australia
E-mail address: pietro.cerone@vu.edu.au

ABSTRACT. The Steffensen inequality and bounds for the Čebyšev functional are utilised to obtain bounds for some classical special functions. The methodology relies on determining bounds on integrals of products of functions. The above techniques are used to obtain novel and useful bounds for the Bessel function of the first kind, the Beta function, the Zeta function and Mathieu series.

1991 Mathematics Subject Classification: Primary 26D15, 26D20; Secondary 26D10.

Key words and phrases: Čebyšev functional, Grüss inequality, Bessel, Beta and Zeta function bounds, Mathieu series.

1 INTRODUCTION AND REVIEW OF SOME RECENT RESULTS

There are a number of results that provide bounds for integrals of products of functions. The main techniques that shall be employed in the current article involve the Steffensen inequality and a variety of bounds related to the Čebyšev functional. There have been some developments in both of these in the recent past with which the current author has been involved. These have been put to fruitful use in a variety of areas of applied mathematics including quadrature rules, in the approximation of integral transforms, as well as in applied probability problems (see [30], [20] and [12]).

It is intended that in the current article the techniques will be utilised to obtain useful bounds for special functions. The methodologies will be demonstrated through obtaining bounds for the Bessel function of the first kind, the Beta function, the Zeta function and Mathieu series.

It is instructive to introduce some techniques for approximating and bounding integrals of the product of functions. We first present inequalities due to Steffensen and then review bounds for the Čebyšev functional.

The following theorem is due to Steffensen [52] (see also [12] and [17]).

Theorem 1.1. *Let* $h : [a, b] \to \mathbb{R}$ *be a nonincreasing mapping on* $[a, b]$ *and* $g : [a, b] \to \mathbb{R}$ *be an integrable mapping on* $[a, b]$ *with*

$$-\infty < \phi \leq g(t) \leq \Phi < \infty \quad \text{for all } x \in [a, b],$$

then

$$(1.1) \qquad \phi \int_a^{b-\lambda} h(x)\, dx + \Phi \int_{b-\lambda}^b h(x)\, dx \le \int_a^b h(x)\, g(x)\, dx$$

$$\le \Phi \int_a^{a+\lambda} h(x)\, dx + \phi \int_{a+\lambda}^b h(x)\, dx,$$

where

$$(1.2) \qquad \lambda = \int_a^b G(x)\, dx, \quad G(x) = \frac{g(x) - \phi}{\Phi - \phi}, \quad \Phi \ne \phi.$$

Remark 1.1. *We note that the result (1.1) may be rearranged to give Steffensen's better known result that*

$$(1.3) \qquad \int_{b-\lambda}^b h(x)\, dx \le \int_a^b h(x)\, G(x)\, dx \le \int_a^{a+\lambda} h(x)\, dx,$$

where λ is as given by (1.2) and $0 \le G(x) \le 1$.

Equation (1.3) has a very pleasant interpretation, as observed by Steffensen, that if we divide by λ then

$$(1.4) \qquad \frac{1}{\lambda} \int_{b-\lambda}^b h(x)\, dx \le \frac{\int_a^b G(x)\, h(x)\, dx}{\int_a^b G(x)\, dx} \le \frac{1}{\lambda} \int_a^{a+\lambda} h(x)\, dx.$$

Thus, the weighted integral mean of $h(x)$ is bounded by the integral means over the end intervals of length λ, the total weight.

Now, for two measurable functions $f, g : [a, b] \to \mathbb{R}$, define the functional, which is known in the literature as Čebyšev's functional, by

$$(1.5) \qquad T(f, g) := \mathcal{M}(fg) - \mathcal{M}(f)\, \mathcal{M}(g),$$

where the integral mean is given by

$$(1.6) \qquad \mathcal{M}(f) := \frac{1}{b-a} \int_a^b f(x)\, dx.$$

The integrals in (1.5) are assumed to exist.

The weighted Čebyšev functional is defined by

$$(1.7) \qquad T(f, g; p) := \mathcal{M}(fg; p) - \mathcal{M}(f; p)\, \mathcal{M}(g; p),$$

where the weighted integral mean $\mathcal{M}(f; p)$ is given by

$$(1.8) \qquad P \cdot \mathcal{M}(f; p) = \int_a^b p(x)\, f(x)\, dx, \quad P = \int_a^b p(x)\, dx$$

with the weight P satisfying $0 < P < \infty$.

We note that

$$T(f, g; 1) \equiv T(f, g) \quad \text{and} \quad \mathcal{M}(f; 1) \equiv \mathcal{M}(f).$$

We further note that bounds for (1.5) and (1.7) may be looked upon as approximating the integral mean of the product of functions in terms of the product of integral means which are more easily calculated explicitly. Bounds are perhaps best procured from identities. It is worthwhile noting that a number of identities relating to the Čebyšev functional already exist (The reader is referred to [42] Chapters IX and X.). Korkine's identity is well known, see [42, p. 296] and is given by

$$(1.9) \qquad T(f,g) = \frac{1}{2(b-a)^2} \int_a^b \int_a^b (f(x) - f(y))(g(x) - g(y)) \, dx \, dy.$$

It is identity (1.9) that is often used to prove an inequality due to Grüss for functions bounded above and below, [42]. Namely, the Grüss inequality [38] is given by

$$(1.10) \qquad |T(f,g)| \leq \frac{1}{4} (\Phi_f - \phi_f)(\Phi_g - \phi_g),$$

where $\phi_f \leq f(x) \leq \Phi_f$ for $x \in [a,b]$, with ϕ_f, Φ_f constants and similarly for $g(x)$.

The interested reader is also referred to Dragomir [29] and Fink [35] for extensive treatments of the Grüss and related inequalities.

Identity (1.9) may also be used to prove the Čebyšev inequality which states that for $f(\cdot)$ and $g(\cdot)$ synchronous, namely $(f(x) - f(y))(g(x) - g(y)) \geq 0$, a.e. $x, y \in [a,b]$, then

$$(1.11) \qquad T(f,g) \geq 0.$$

As mentioned earlier, there are many identities involving the Čebyšev functional (1.5) or more generally (1.7). Recently, Cerone [12] obtained, for $f, g : [a,b] \to \mathbb{R}$ where f is of bounded variation and g continuous on $[a,b]$, the identity

$$(1.12) \qquad T(f,g) = \frac{1}{(b-a)^2} \int_a^b \psi(t) \, df(t),$$

where

$$(1.13) \qquad \psi(t) = (t-a) G(t,b) - (b-t) G(a,t)$$

with

$$(1.14) \qquad G(c,d) = \int_c^d g(x) \, dx.$$

The following theorem was proved in [12].

Theorem 1.2. *Let $f, g : [a,b] \to \mathbb{R}$, where f is of bounded variation and g is continuous on $[a,b]$. Then*

$$(1.15) \qquad (b-a)^2 |T(f,g)| \leq \begin{cases} \sup_{t \in [a,b]} |\psi(t)| \bigvee_a^b (f), \\ L \int_a^b |\psi(t)| \, dt, & \text{for } f \ L - Lipschitzian, \\ \int_a^b |\psi(t)| \, df(t), & \text{for } f \ monotonic \ nondecreasing. \end{cases}$$

where $\bigvee_a^b (f)$ is the total variation of f on $[a,b]$.

The bounds for the Čebyšev functional were utilised to procure approximations to moments and moment generating functions in [12] and [22].

The reader is referred to [30] and the references therein for applications to numerical quadrature of trapezoidal and Ostrowski functionals, which were shown to be related to the Čebyšev functional in [16].

For other Grüss type inequalities, see the books [8] and [42], and the papers [19], [21], [25], [28], [29], where further references are given.

Recently, Cerone and Dragomir [19] – [21] have pointed out generalisations of the above results for integrals defined on two different intervals $[a, b]$ and $[c, d]$ and more generally in a measurable space setting (see also, [7] and [15]).

The functional $T(f, g; p)$ defined in (1.7) satisfies a number of identities including that due to Sonin [47]

$$(1.16) \qquad P \cdot |T(f, g; p)| = \left| \int_a^b p(x)(f(x) - \gamma)(g(x) - \mathcal{M}(g; p)) \, dx \right|$$

to give

$$(1.17) \qquad P \cdot |T(f, g; p)| \leq \begin{cases} \displaystyle\inf_{\gamma \in \mathbb{R}} \|f(\cdot) - \gamma\| \int_a^b p(x) |g(x) - \mathcal{M}(g; p)| \, dx, \\[2em] \displaystyle\left(\int_a^b p(x)(f(x) - \mathcal{M}(f; p))^2 \, dx \right)^{\frac{1}{2}} \\[2em] \qquad \times \left(\int_a^b p(x)(g(x) - \mathcal{M}(g; p))^2 \, dx \right)^{\frac{1}{2}}, \end{cases}$$

where

$$(1.18) \qquad \int_a^b p(x)(h(x) - \mathcal{M}(h; p))^2 \, dx = \int_a^b p(x) h^2(x) \, dx - P \cdot \mathcal{M}^2(h; p)$$

and P is as defined in (1.8). Further, it may be easily shown by direct calculation that,

$$(1.19) \qquad \inf_{\gamma \in \mathbb{R}} \left[\int_a^b p(x)(f(x) - \gamma)^2 \, dx \right] = \int_a^b p(x)(f(x) - \mathcal{M}(f; p))^2 \, dx.$$

Some of the above results are used to find bounds for the Bessel function (Section 2), the Beta function (Section 3), the Zeta function (Section 4) and Mathieu series (Section 5).

2   Bounding the Bessel Function

In this section we investigate techniques for determining bounds on the Bessel function of the first kind (see also [13], [14]).

In Abramowitz and Stegun [1] equation (9.1.21) defines the Bessel of the first kind

$$(2.1) \qquad J_\nu(z) = \gamma_\nu(z) \int_0^1 \left(1 - t^2\right)^{\nu - \frac{1}{2}} \cos(zt) \, dt, \quad \mathrm{Re}(\nu) > -\frac{1}{2},$$

where

$$(2.2) \qquad \gamma_\nu(z) = \frac{2\left(\frac{z}{2}\right)^\nu}{\sqrt{\pi} \Gamma\left(\nu + \frac{1}{2}\right)}.$$

For the current work the interest is in both z and ν real.

Theorem 2.1. *For z real then*

(2.3)
$$\frac{1}{2}B\left(\frac{1}{2},\nu+\frac{1}{2}\right) - B\left(\frac{1}{2},\nu+\frac{1}{2};(1-\lambda)^2\right)$$
$$\leq \frac{J_\nu(z)}{\gamma_\nu(z)}$$
$$\leq B\left(\frac{1}{2},\nu+\frac{1}{2};\lambda^2\right) - \frac{1}{2}B\left(\frac{1}{2},\nu+\frac{1}{2}\right), \quad \nu > \frac{1}{2}$$

and

(2.4)
$$B\left(\frac{1}{2},\nu+\frac{1}{2};\lambda^2\right) - \frac{1}{2}B\left(\frac{1}{2},\nu+\frac{1}{2}\right)$$
$$\leq \frac{J_\nu(z)}{\gamma_\nu(z)}$$
$$\leq \frac{1}{2}B\left(\frac{1}{2},\nu+\frac{1}{2}\right) - B\left(\frac{1}{2},\nu+\frac{1}{2};(1-\lambda)^2\right), \quad -\frac{1}{2} < \nu < \frac{1}{2},$$

where

(2.5) $$B(\alpha,\beta;x) = \int_0^x u^{\alpha-1}(1-u)^{\beta-1}\,du, \qquad \text{the incomplete Beta function,}$$

(2.6) $$B(\alpha,\beta) = B(\alpha,\beta;1) = \frac{\Gamma(\alpha)\Gamma(\beta)}{\Gamma(\alpha+\beta)}, \qquad \text{the Beta function,}$$

and

(2.7) $$2\lambda - 1 = \frac{\sin z}{z}.$$

Proof. Consider the case $\nu > \frac{1}{2}$ then $h(t) = \left(1-t^2\right)^{\nu-\frac{1}{2}}$ is nonincreasing for $t \in [0,1]$. Further, taking $g(t) = \cos zt$ we have that $-1 \leq g(t) \leq 1$ for $t \in [0,1]$ and, from (1.2)

$$\lambda = \frac{1}{2}\int_0^1 (\cos zt + 1)\,dt = \frac{1}{2}\left(1 + \frac{\sin z}{z}\right).$$

Thus, from Theorem 1.1, we have

$$-\int_0^{1-\lambda}\left(1-t^2\right)^{\nu-\frac{1}{2}}dt + \int_{1-\lambda}^1\left(1-t^2\right)^{\nu-\frac{1}{2}}dt$$
$$\leq \frac{J_\nu(z)}{\gamma_\nu(z)}$$
$$\leq \int_0^\lambda\left(1-t^2\right)^{\nu-\frac{1}{2}}dt - \int_\lambda^1\left(1-t^2\right)^{\nu-\frac{1}{2}}dt,$$

that is,

(2.8)
$$\int_0^1\left(1-t^2\right)^{\nu-\frac{1}{2}}dt - 2\int_0^{1-\lambda}\left(1-t^2\right)^{\nu-\frac{1}{2}}dt$$
$$\leq \frac{J_\nu(z)}{\gamma_\nu(z)}$$
$$\leq 2\int_0^\lambda\left(1-t^2\right)^{\nu-\frac{1}{2}}dt - \int_0^1\left(1-t^2\right)^{\nu-\frac{1}{2}}dt.$$

If we let

$$(2.9) \qquad G(\alpha) = \int_0^\alpha \left(1 - t^2\right)^{\nu - \frac{1}{2}} dt$$

then (2.8) becomes

$$(2.10) \qquad G(1) - 2G(1 - \lambda) \leq \frac{J_\nu(z)}{\gamma_\nu(z)} \leq 2G(\lambda) - G(1).$$

A simple change of variable $u = t^2$ in (2.9) gives

$$G(\alpha) = \frac{1}{2} \int_0^{\alpha^2} u^{-\frac{1}{2}} \left(1 - u\right)^{\nu - \frac{1}{2}} du$$

and so

$$(2.11) \qquad G(\alpha) = \frac{1}{2} B\left(\frac{1}{2}, \nu + \frac{1}{2}, \alpha^2\right),$$

where $B(\alpha, \beta; x)$ is the incomplete beta function as given by (2.5).

Thus substituting (2.11) into (2.10) produces (2.3).

For $-\frac{1}{2} < \nu < \frac{1}{2}$ then $h(t)$ is nondecreasing for $t \in [0,1]$ and thus the inequalities in (2.2) are reversed, or equivalently, the bounds are swapped to produce (2.4). $\qquad \square$

Remark 2.1. *If we take $\nu = \frac{1}{2}$ in either (2.3) or (2.4) then equality is obtained. Namely,*

$$\frac{J_{\frac{1}{2}}(z)}{\gamma_{\frac{1}{2}}(z)} = \frac{\sin z}{z}.$$

Remark 2.2. *We note from (2.1) that we may obtain a classical bound (see [1, p. 362]) for $J_\nu(z)$, namely*

$$|J_\nu(z)| \leq \frac{2 \left(\frac{|z|}{2}\right)^\nu}{\sqrt{\pi} \Gamma\left(\nu + \frac{1}{2}\right)} \int_0^1 \left(1 - t^2\right)^{\nu - \frac{1}{2}} dt,$$

where from (2.9) and (2.11)

$$(2.12) \qquad \int_0^1 \left(1 - t^2\right)^{\nu - \frac{1}{2}} dt = \frac{1}{2} B\left(\frac{1}{2}, \nu + \frac{1}{2}\right) = \frac{1}{2} \cdot \frac{\Gamma\left(\frac{1}{2}\right) \Gamma\left(\nu + \frac{1}{2}\right)}{\Gamma(\nu + 1)}$$

to give

$$(2.13) \qquad |J_\nu(z)| \leq \left|\frac{z}{2}\right|^\nu \frac{1}{\Gamma(\nu + 1)}.$$

The following theorem gives a bound on the deviation of the Bessel function from an approximant. This is accomplished via bounds on the Čebyšev functional for which there are numerous results.

Theorem 2.2. *The following result holds for the Bessel function of the first kind* $J_\nu(z)$. *Namely,*

$$(2.14) \quad \left| J_\nu(z) - \frac{\left(\frac{z}{2}\right)^\nu}{\Gamma(\nu+1)} \cdot \frac{\sin z}{z} \right|$$

$$\leq \left(\frac{|z|}{2}\right)^\nu \left[\frac{2}{\sqrt{\pi}} \cdot \frac{\Gamma(2\nu)}{\Gamma^2\left(\nu+\frac{1}{2}\right)\Gamma\left(2\nu+\frac{1}{2}\right)} - \frac{1}{\Gamma^2(\nu+1)} \right]^{\frac{1}{2}}$$

$$\times \left[\left(\frac{\cos z}{4}\right)^2 + \frac{1}{2} - \left(\frac{\sin z}{z} - \frac{\cos z}{4}\right)^2 \right]^{\frac{1}{2}}.$$

Proof. From (2.1) and (2.2) consider,

$$(2.15) \qquad Q_\nu(z) = \frac{J_\nu(z)}{\gamma_\nu(z)} = \int_0^1 \left(1-t^2\right)^{\nu-\frac{1}{2}} \cos(zt)\,dt.$$

Let $f(t) = \left(1-t^2\right)^{\nu-\frac{1}{2}}$ and $g(t) = \cos zt$.
   Now,

$$(2.16) \qquad \mathcal{M}(g) = \int_0^1 \cos(zt)\,dt = \frac{\sin z}{z}$$

and from (2.12)

$$(2.17) \qquad \mathcal{M}(f) = \int_0^1 \left(1-t^2\right)^{\nu-\frac{1}{2}}dt = \frac{1}{2}B\left(\frac{1}{2}, \nu+\frac{1}{2}\right) = \frac{\sqrt{\pi}}{2} \cdot \frac{\Gamma\left(\nu+\frac{1}{2}\right)}{\Gamma(\nu+1)}.$$

   Thus, from (1.17)

$$(2.18) \quad \left| Q_\nu(z) - \frac{\sqrt{\pi}}{2} \cdot \frac{\Gamma\left(\nu+\frac{1}{2}\right)}{\Gamma(\nu+1)} \cdot \frac{\sin z}{z} \right| \leq \left(\int_0^1 f^2(t)\,dt - \mathcal{M}^2(f) \right)^{\frac{1}{2}}$$

$$\times \left(\int_0^1 g^2(t)\,dt - \mathcal{M}^2(g) \right)^{\frac{1}{2}}.$$

   We have, from (2.17),

$$(2.19) \qquad \int_0^1 f^2(t)\,dt = \int_0^1 \left(1-t^2\right)^{2\nu-1}dt = \frac{\sqrt{\pi}}{2} \cdot \frac{\Gamma(2\nu)}{\Gamma\left(2\nu+\frac{1}{2}\right)}$$

and

$$(2.20) \qquad \int_0^1 g^2(t)\,dt = \int_0^1 \cos^2(zt)\,dt = \frac{1}{2}\left(1 + \frac{\sin z}{z} \cdot \cos z\right).$$

   Substitution of (2.19) and (2.20) gives

$$(2.21) \quad \left| Q_\nu(z) - \frac{\sqrt{\pi}}{2} \cdot \frac{\Gamma\left(\nu+\frac{1}{2}\right)}{\Gamma(\nu+1)} \cdot \frac{\sin z}{z} \right|$$

$$\leq \left[\frac{\sqrt{\pi}}{2} \cdot \frac{\Gamma(2\nu)}{\Gamma\left(2\nu+\frac{1}{2}\right)} - \frac{\pi}{4} \cdot \left(\frac{\Gamma\left(\nu+\frac{1}{2}\right)}{\Gamma(\nu+1)}\right)^2 \right]^{\frac{1}{2}}$$

$$\times \left[\left(\frac{\cos z}{4}\right)^2 + \frac{1}{2} - \left(\frac{\sin z}{z} - \frac{\cos z}{4}\right)^2 \right]^{\frac{1}{2}},$$

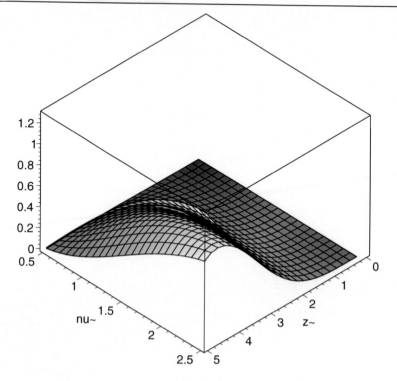

FIGURE 1: Visual representation of the left and right hand expression given by (2.14) for $0.5 \leq \nu \leq 2.5$ and $0 \leq z \leq 5$.

and so (2.14) is obtained on multiplication of (2.21) by $|\gamma_\nu(z)|$.   □

Remark 2.3. *Figure 1 presents a visual depiction of both the left and right hand sides of (2.14) for $0.5 < \nu < 2.5$ ad $0 \leq z \leq 5$ while Figure 2 presents the difference of the left hand side from the right hand side. It may clearly be seen that the bound is better for lower values of z and ν as expected.*

Figure 3 shows the difference between the classical upper bound and $|J_\nu(z)|$ as given by (2.13). Figure 4 provides a comparison to Figure 3 where the upper bound is procured from the result (2.14). It may clearly be noticed from these two figures that the current results are better than the classical result given by (2.13).

3   BOUNDING THE BETA FUNCTION

The incomplete beta function is defined by

$$(3.1) \qquad B(x, y; z) = \int_0^z t^{x-1}(1-t)^{y-1}\, dt, \quad 0 < z \leq 1.$$

We shall restrict our attention to $x > 1$ and $y > 1$.

In this region we observe that

$$(3.2) \qquad 0 \leq t^{x-1} \leq z^{x-1} \quad \text{and} \quad (1-z)^{y-1} \leq (1-t)^{y-1} \leq 1$$

with t^{x-1}, an increasing function and $(1-t)^{y-1}$, a decreasing function, for $t \in [0, z]$.

The following theorem follows from utilizing Steffensen's result as depicted in Theorem 1.1 [13].

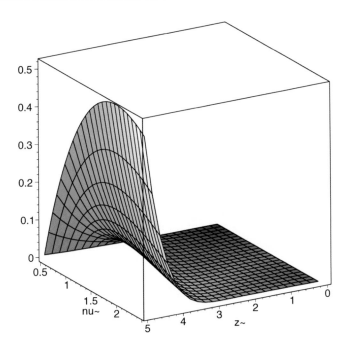

FIGURE 2: Plot of the left from the right hand side of the expressions given by (2.14) for $0.5 \leq \nu \leq 2.5$ and $0 \leq z \leq 5$.

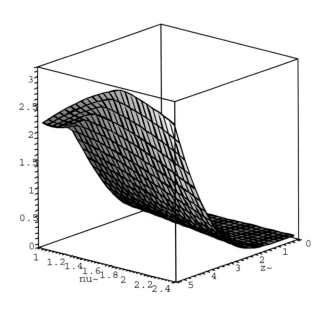

FIGURE 3: Plot of $\left|\frac{z}{2}\right|^{\nu} / \Gamma(\nu + 1) - |J_{\nu}(z)|$ from (2.13) for $1 \leq \nu \leq 2.5$ and $0 \leq z \leq 5$.

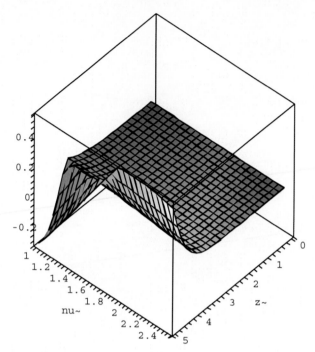

FIGURE 4: Plot of $\left[\left(\frac{z}{2}\right)^{\nu}/\Gamma\left(\nu+1\right)\right]\cdot\frac{\sin z}{z}+b\left(\nu,z\right)-\left|J_{\nu}\left(z\right)\right|$ for $1\leq\nu\leq2.5$ and $0\leq z\leq5$ where $b\left(\nu,z\right)\equiv$ bound from (2.14).

Theorem 3.1. *For $x>1$ and $y>1$ with $0\leq z\leq1$ we have the incomplete Beta function defined by (3.1) satisfying the following bounds*

$$(3.3) \qquad \max\left\{L_1\left(z\right),L_2\left(z\right)\right\}\leq B\left(x,y;z\right)\leq\min\left\{U_1\left(z\right),U_2\left(z\right)\right\},$$

where

$$(3.4) \qquad L_1\left(z\right)=\frac{z^{x-1}}{y}\left[\left(1-z+\frac{z}{x}\right)^y-\left(1-z\right)^y\right], \quad U_1\left(z\right)=\frac{z^{x-1}}{y}\left[1-\left(1-\frac{z}{x}\right)^y\right]$$

and

$$(3.5) \qquad L_2\left(z\right)=\frac{\lambda_2^x\left(z\right)}{x}+\left(1-z\right)^{y-1}\frac{z^x-\lambda_2^x\left(z\right)}{x},$$

$$U_2\left(z\right)=\left(1-z\right)^{y-1}\frac{\left(x-\lambda_2\left(z\right)\right)^x}{x}+\frac{z^x-\left(z-\lambda_2\left(z\right)\right)^x}{x}$$

with

$$(3.6) \qquad \lambda_2\left(z\right)=\frac{1-\left(1-z\right)\left[1-z\left(1-y\right)\right]}{y\left[1-\left(1-z\right)^{y-1}\right]}.$$

Proof. If we take $h\left(t\right)=\left(1-t\right)^{y-1}$ and $g\left(t\right)=t^{x-1}$, then for $y>1$ and $x>1$, $h\left(t\right)$ is a decreasing function of t and $0\leq g\left(t\right)\leq z^{x-1}$. Thus, from (1.1)

$$(3.7) \qquad z^{x-1}\int_{z-\lambda_1}^{z}\left(1-t\right)^{y-1}dt\leq\int_0^z t^{x-1}\left(1-t\right)^{y-1}dt\leq z^{x-1}\int_0^{\lambda_1}\left(1-t\right)^{y-1}dt,$$

where

$$\lambda_1 = \lambda_1(z) = \int_0^z \frac{t^{x-1}}{z^{x-1}} dt = \frac{z}{x}.$$

Now,

$$\int_0^{\lambda_1} (1-t)^{y-1} dt = \frac{1 - (1-\lambda_1)^y}{y}$$

and

$$\int_{z-\lambda_1}^z (1-t)^{y-1} dt = \frac{(1-z+\lambda_1)^y - (1-z)^y}{y},$$

so that, from (3.7),

$$(3.8) \qquad \frac{z^{x-1}}{y} \left[\left(1 - z + \frac{z}{x}\right)^y - (1-z)^y \right] \le B(x, y; z) \le \frac{z^{x-1}}{y} \left[1 - \left(1 - \frac{z}{x}\right)^y \right].$$

If $h(t)$ is an increasing function then the inequalities in (1.1) are reversed. Thus, if $h(t) = t^{x-1}$ and $g(t) = (1-t)^{y-1}$, then for $x > 1$ and $y > 1$, $h(t)$ is an increasing function of t and $(1-z)^{y-1} \le g(t) \le 1$. From (1.1) we have

$$(3.9) \qquad \int_0^{\lambda_2} t^{x-1} dt + (1-z)^{y-1} \int_{\lambda_2}^z t^{x-1} dt$$

$$\le \int_0^z t^{x-1}(1-t)^{y-1} dt$$

$$\le (1-z)^{y-1} \int_0^{z-\lambda_2} t^{x-1} dx + \int_{z-\lambda_2}^z t^{x-1} dx,$$

where

$$\lambda_2 = \lambda_2(z) = \int_0^z \frac{(1-t)^{y-1} - (1-z)^{y-1}}{1 - (1-z)^{y-1}} dt = \frac{1 - (1-z)[1 - z(1-y)]}{y \left[1 - (1-z)^{y-1} \right]}$$

as given by (3.6).

Hence, from (3.9)

$$(3.10) \qquad \frac{\lambda_2^x(z)}{x} + (1-z)^{y-1} \frac{z^x - \lambda_2^x(z)}{x}$$

$$\le B(x, y; z)$$

$$\le (1-z)^{y-1} \frac{(x - \lambda_2(z))^x}{x} + \frac{z^x - (z - \lambda_2(z))^x}{x}.$$

Combining the results (3.8) and (3.10) produces the result (3.4) with obvious use of notation.   □

Corollary 3.2. *For $x > 1$ and $y > 1$ we have the Beta function*

$$B(x, y) = \int_0^1 t^{x-1}(1-t)^{y-1} dt,$$

which is symmetric in x and y, satisfies the following bounds,

$$(3.11) \qquad \max \left\{ \frac{1}{xy^x}, \frac{1}{yx^y} \right\} \le B(x, y)$$

$$\le \min \left\{ \frac{1}{y} \left[1 - \left(1 - \frac{1}{x}\right)^y \right], \frac{1}{x} \left[1 - \left(1 - \frac{1}{y}\right)^x \right] \right\}.$$

Proof. Put $z = 1$ in (3.6) to give $\lambda_2(1) = \frac{1}{y}$ followed by the obvious correspondences from (3.3) – (3.5). $\square$

The following theorem relates to the Beta function and is a correction of the result in [13].

Theorem 3.3. *For $x > 1$ and $y > 1$ the following bounds hold for the Beta function, namely,*

$$(3.12) \qquad 0 \le \frac{1}{xy} - B(x,y) \le 2\min\{A(x), A(y)\},$$

where

$$(3.13) \qquad A(x) = \frac{x-1}{x^{\left(1+\frac{x}{x-1}\right)}}$$

Proof. We have from (1.16) – (1.17) with $p(\cdot) \equiv 1$,

$$0 \le |T(f,g)| = |\mathcal{M}(fg) - \mathcal{M}(f)\mathcal{M}(g)|$$
$$\le \mathcal{M}(|f(\cdot) - \gamma||g(\cdot) - \mathcal{M}(g)|).$$

That is,

$$(3.14) \qquad |T(f,g)| \le \inf_{\gamma} \|f(\cdot) - \gamma\|_{\infty}\, \mathcal{M}|g(\cdot) - \mathcal{M}(g)|$$

If we take $f(t) = t^{x-1}$, $g(t) = (1-t)^{y-1}$ then $\mathcal{M}(f) = \frac{1}{x}$ and $\mathcal{M}(g) = \frac{1}{y}$, so that we have from (3.14)

$$(3.15) \qquad 0 \le \frac{1}{xy} - B(x,y)$$

$$\le \inf_{\gamma}\left[\sup_{t\in[0,1]}\left|t^{x-1} - \gamma\right|\right]\int_0^1 \left|(1-t)^{y-1} - \frac{1}{y}\right|dt$$

$$= \inf_{\gamma}[\max\{\gamma, 1-\gamma\}]\int_0^1 \left|(1-t)^{y-1} - \frac{1}{y}\right|dt.$$

Now,

$$\inf_{\gamma}[\max\{\gamma, 1-\gamma\}] = \inf_{\gamma}\left[\frac{1}{2} + \left|\gamma - \frac{1}{2}\right|\right] = \frac{1}{2}$$

and

$$\int_0^1 \left|(1-t)^{y-1} - \frac{1}{y}\right|dt = \int_0^1 \left|u^{y-1} - \frac{1}{y}\right|du$$

$$= \int_0^{u_*}\left(\frac{1}{y} - u^{y-1}\right)du + \int_{u_*}^1\left(u^{y-1} - \frac{1}{y}\right)du$$

$$= \frac{1}{y}\left[u_* - u_*^y - (u_*^y - u_*)\right]$$

$$= \frac{2}{y}u_*\left(1 - u_*^{y-1}\right),$$

where $u_*^{y-1} = \frac{1}{y}$.

Thus

$$0 \leq \frac{1}{xy} - B(x,y) \leq 2\frac{\left(1 - \frac{1}{y}\right)}{y^{\frac{y}{y-1}}} = 2A(y),$$

where $A(y)$ is as given by (3.13).

We may interchange the role of x and y because of the symmetry and so (3.12) results. $\square$

The following pleasing result is valid ([13]).

Theorem 3.4. *For $x > 1$ and $y > 1$ we have*

(3.16)
$$0 \leq \frac{1}{xy} - B(x,y) \leq \frac{x-1}{x\sqrt{2x-1}} \cdot \frac{y-1}{y\sqrt{2y-1}}$$
$$\leq 0.090169437\ldots,$$

where the upper bound is obtained at $x = y = \frac{3+\sqrt{5}}{2} = 2.618033988\ldots$.

Proof. We have from $(1.17) - (1.19)$

$$(b-a)\,|T(f,g)| \leq \left(\int_a^b f^2(t)\,dt - \mathcal{M}^2(f)\right)^{\frac{1}{2}} \times \left(\int_a^b g^2(t)\,dt - \mathcal{M}^2(g)\right)^{\frac{1}{2}}.$$

That is, taking $f(t) = t^{x-1}$, $g(t) = (1-t)^{y-1}$ then

(3.17)
$$0 \leq \frac{1}{xy} - B(x,y) \leq \left(\int_0^1 t^{2x-2}dt - \frac{1}{x^2}\right)^{\frac{1}{2}} \times \left(\int_0^1 (1-t)^{2y-2}\,dt - \frac{1}{y^2}\right)^{\frac{1}{2}}.$$

Now,

$$\int_0^1 t^{2x-2}dt = \frac{1}{2x-1} \quad \text{and} \quad \int_0^1 (1-t)^{2y-2}\,dt = \frac{1}{2y-1}$$

and so from (3.17) we have the first inequality in (3.16).

Now, consider

(3.18)
$$C(x) = \frac{x-1}{x\sqrt{2x-1}}.$$

The maximum occurs when $x = x^* = \frac{3+\sqrt{5}}{2}$ to give $C(x^*) = 0.3002831\ldots$. Hence, because of the symmetry we have the upper bound as stated in (3.16). $\square$

Remark 3.1. *In a recent paper Alzer [3] shows that*

(3.19)
$$0 \leq \frac{1}{xy} - B(x,y) \leq b_A = \max_{x \geq 1}\left(\frac{1}{x^2} - \frac{\Gamma^2(x)}{\Gamma(2x)}\right) = 0.08731\ldots,$$

where 0 and b_A are shown to be the best constants. This uniform bound of Alzer is only smaller for a small area around $\left(\frac{3+\sqrt{5}}{2}, \frac{3+\sqrt{5}}{2}\right)$ while the first upper bound in (3.16) provides a better bound over a much larger region of the $x - y$ plane.

Figure 5 shows a plot of the upper bound (3.16) and the best uniform bound b_A as defined in (3.19).

Figure 6 demonstrates the cross-section through $x = y$ showing the small interval for which $b_A < C^2(x)$. The worst upper bound from (3.16) occurs at $x = y = \frac{3+\sqrt{5}}{2}$ and is given as the second upper bound in (3.16). This is represented, by the symbol $+$, in the region $C(x)\,C(y) = b_A$ shown in Figure 7.

We may state the following corollary given the results above.

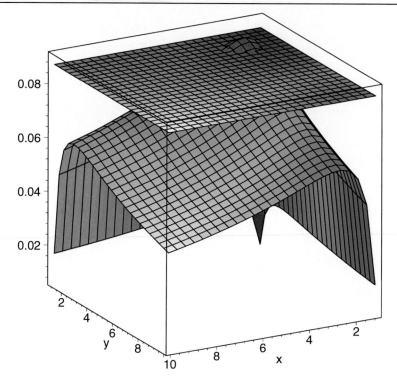

FIGURE 5: Three dimensional plot of $C(x)C(y)$ and b_A where $C(x)$ is defined in (3.18) and $b_A = 0.08731\ldots$ from (3.19).

Corollary 3.5. *For $x > 1$ and $y > 1$ we have*

$$0 \le \frac{1}{xy} - B(x,y) \le \min\{C(x)C(y), b_A\},$$

where $C(x)$ is defined by (3.18) and b_A by (3.19).

Remark 3.2. *The upper bound in Theorem 3.3 seems not to be as good as that given in Theorem 3.4.*

4   BOUNDS FOR THE EULER ZETA AND RELATED FUNCTIONS

The Zeta function ([10])

$$(4.1) \qquad \zeta(x) := \sum_{n=1}^{\infty} \frac{1}{n^x}, \qquad x > 1$$

was originally introduced in 1737 by the Swiss mathematician Leonhard Euler (1707-1783) for real x who proved the identity

$$(4.2) \qquad \zeta(x) := \prod_{p} \left(1 - \frac{1}{p^x}\right)^{-1}, \qquad x > 1,$$

where p runs through all primes. It was Riemann who allowed x to be a complex variable z and showed that even though both sides of (4.1) and (4.2) diverge for $\text{Re}(z) \le 1$, the

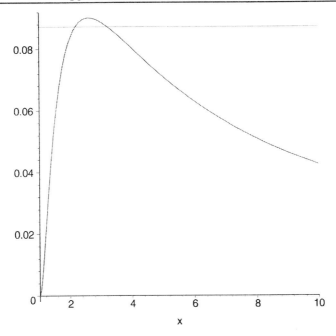

FIGURE 6: The curve defined by $C^2(x) = \frac{(x-1)^2}{x^2(2x-1)}$ and $b_A = 0.08731\ldots$, from (3.18) and (3.19).

function has a continuation to the whole complex plane with a simple pole at $z = 1$ with residue 1. The function plays a very significant role in the theory of the distribution of primes (see [5], [6], [26], [31], [39] and [53]). One of the most striking properties of the zeta function, discovered by Riemann himself, is the functional equation

$$(4.3) \qquad \zeta(z) = 2^z \pi^{z-1} \sin\left(\frac{\pi z}{2}\right) \Gamma(1-z)\zeta(1-z)$$

that can be written in symmetric form to give

$$(4.4) \qquad \pi^{-\frac{z}{2}}\Gamma\left(\frac{z}{2}\right)\zeta(z) = \pi^{-\left(\frac{1-z}{2}\right)}\Gamma\left(\frac{1-z}{2}\right)\zeta(1-z).$$

In addition to the relation (4.3) between the zeta and the gamma function, these functions are also connected via the integrals [31]

$$(4.5) \qquad \zeta(x) = \frac{1}{\Gamma(x)}\int_0^\infty \frac{t^{x-1}dt}{e^t - 1}, \qquad x > 1,$$

and

$$(4.6) \qquad \zeta(x) = \frac{1}{C(x)}\int_0^\infty \frac{t^{x-1}dt}{e^t + 1}, \qquad x > 0,$$

where

$$(4.7) \qquad C(x) := \Gamma(x)\left(1 - 2^{1-x}\right) \quad \text{and} \quad \Gamma(x) = \int_0^\infty e^{-t}t^{x-1}dt.$$

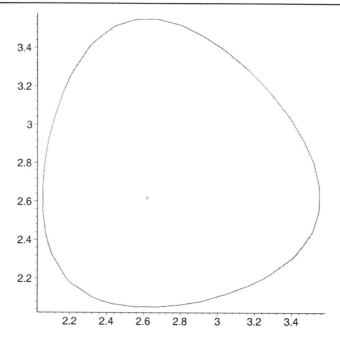

FIGURE 7: Region over which $C(x)C(y) > b_A$ where $C(x)$ is as defined in (3.18) and b_A is the best uniform bound of Alzer given by (3.19).

In the series expansion

$$(4.8) \qquad \frac{te^{xt}}{e^t - 1} = \sum_{m=0}^{\infty} B_m(x) \frac{t^m}{m!},$$

where $B_m(x)$ are the Bernoulli polynomials (after Jacob Bernoulli), $B_m(0) = B_m$ are the Bernoulli numbers. They occurred for the first time in the formula [1, p. 804]

$$(4.9) \qquad \sum_{k=1}^{m} k^n = \frac{B_{n+1}(m+1) - B_{n+1}}{n+1}, \qquad n, m = 1, 2, 3, \dots .$$

One of Euler's most celebrated theorems discovered in 1736 (Institutiones Calculi Differentialis, Opera (1), Vol. 10) is

$$(4.10) \qquad \zeta(2n) = (-1)^{n-1} \frac{2^{2n-1}\pi^{2n}}{(2n)!} B_{2n}; \qquad n = 1, 2, 3, \dots .$$

The Zeta function is also explicitly known at the non-positive integers by

$$\zeta(-n) = (-1)^n \frac{B_{n+1}}{n+1}, \qquad \text{for } n = 1, 2, \dots$$

The result may also be obtained in a straight forward fashion from (4.6) and a change of variable on using the fact that

$$(4.11) \qquad B_{2n} = (-1)^{n-1} \cdot 4n \int_0^\infty \frac{t^{2n-1}}{e^{2\pi t} - 1} dt$$

from Whittaker and Watson [57, p. 126].

We note here that

$$\zeta(2n) = A_n \pi^{2n},$$

where

$$A_n = (-1)^{n-1} \cdot \frac{n}{(2n+1)!} + \sum_{j=1}^{n-1} \frac{(-1)^{j-1}}{(2j+1)!} A_{n-j}$$

and $A_1 = \frac{1}{3!}$.

Further, the Zeta function for even integers satisfy the relation (Borwein et al. [6], Srivastava [48])

$$\zeta(2n) = \left(n + \frac{1}{2}\right)^{-1} \sum_{j=1}^{n-1} \zeta(2j)\zeta(2n - 2j), \quad n \in \mathbb{N}\setminus\{1\}.$$

Despite several efforts to find a formula for $\zeta(2n+1)$, (for example [49, 50]), there seems to be no elegant closed form representation for the zeta function at the odd integer values. Several series representations for the value $\zeta(2n + 1)$ have been proved by Srivastava and co-workers in particular, see [48], [51].

There is also an integral representation for $\zeta(n + 1)$ namely,

$$(4.12) \qquad \zeta(2n + 1) = (-1)^{n+1} \cdot \frac{(2\pi)^{2n+1}}{2\delta(n+1)!} \int_0^\delta B_{2n+1}(t) \cot(\pi t)\, dt,$$

where $\delta = 1$ or $\frac{1}{2}$ ([1, p. 807]). Recently, Cvijović and Klinkowski [27] have given the integral representations

$$(4.13) \qquad \zeta(2n + 1) = (-1)^{n+1} \cdot \frac{(2\pi)^{2n+1}}{2\delta(1 - 2^{-2n})(2n+1)!} \int_0^\delta B_{2n+1}(t)\tan(\pi t)\, dt,$$

and

$$(4.14) \qquad \zeta(2n + 1) = (-1)^n \cdot \frac{\pi^{2n+1}}{4\delta(1 - 2^{-(2n+1)})(2n)!} \int_0^\delta E_{2n}(t)\csc(\pi t)\, dt.$$

Both series representations and the integral representations (4.12) – (4.13) are however somewhat difficult in terms of computational aspects and time considerations.

We note that there are functions that are closely related to $\zeta(x)$. Namely, the Dirichlet $\eta(\cdot)$ and $\lambda(\cdot)$ functions given by

$$(4.15) \qquad \eta(x) = \sum_{n=1}^\infty \frac{(-1)^{n-1}}{n^x} = \frac{1}{\Gamma(x)} \int_0^\infty \frac{t^{x-1}}{e^t + 1}\, dt, \quad x > 0$$

and

$$(4.16) \qquad \lambda(x) = \sum_{n=0}^\infty \frac{1}{(2n+1)^x} = \frac{1}{\Gamma(x)} \int_0^\infty \frac{t^{x-1}}{e^t - e^{-t}}\, dt, \quad x > 0.$$

These are related to $\zeta(x)$ by

$$(4.17) \qquad \eta(x) = \left(1 - 2^{1-x}\right)\zeta(x) \quad \text{and} \quad \lambda(x) = \left(1 - 2^{-x}\right)\zeta(x)$$

satisfying the identity

$$(4.18) \qquad \zeta(x) + \eta(x) = 2\lambda(x).$$

It should be further noted that explicit expressions for both of $\eta\,(2n)$ and $\lambda\,(2n)$ exist as a consequence of the relation to $\zeta\,(2n)$ via (4.17).

The Dirichlet beta function or Dirichlet $L-$function is given by [34]

$$(4.19) \qquad \beta\,(x) = \sum_{n=0}^{\infty} \frac{(-1)^n}{(2n+1)^x}, \quad x > 0$$

where $\beta\,(2) = G$, Catalan's constant.

It is readily observed from (4.16) that $\beta\,(x)$ is the alternating version of $\lambda\,(x)$, however, it cannot be directly related to $\zeta\,(x)$. It is also related to $\eta\,(x)$ in that only the odd terms are summed.

The beta function may be evaluated explicitly at positive odd integer values of x, namely,

$$(4.20) \qquad \beta\,(2n+1) = (-1)^n \frac{E_{2n}}{2\,(2n)!} \left(\frac{\pi}{2}\right)^{2n+1},$$

where E_n are the Euler numbers generated by

$$\operatorname{sech}\,(x) = \frac{2e^x}{e^{2x}+1} = \sum_{n=0}^{\infty} E_n \frac{x^n}{n!}.$$

The Dirichlet beta function may be analytically continued over the whole complex plane by the functional equation

$$\beta\,(1-z) = \left(\frac{2}{\pi}\right)^z \sin\left(\frac{\pi z}{2}\right) \Gamma\,(z)\,\beta\,(z).$$

The function $\beta\,(z)$ is defined everywhere in the complex plane and has no singularities, unlike the Riemann zeta function, $\zeta\,(s) = \sum_{n=1}^{\infty} \frac{1}{n^s}$, which has a simple pole at $s = 1$.

The Dirichlet beta function and the zeta function have important applications in a number of branches of mathematics, and in particular in Analytic number theory. See for example [5], [26], [31].

Further, $\beta\,(x)$ has an alternative integral representation [34, p. 56]. Namely,

$$\beta\,(x) = \frac{1}{2\Gamma\,(x)} \int_0^{\infty} \frac{t^{x-1}}{\cosh\,(t)} dt, \quad x > 0.$$

That is,

$$(4.21) \qquad \beta\,(x) = \frac{1}{\Gamma\,(x)} \int_0^{\infty} \frac{t^{x-1}}{e^t + e^{-t}} dt, \quad x > 0.$$

The function $\beta\,(x)$ is also connected to prime number theory [34] which may perhaps be best summarised by

$$\beta\,(x) = \prod_{\substack{p\ \text{prime} \\ p \equiv 1\,\text{mod}\,4}} \left(1 - p^{-x}\right)^{-1} \cdot \prod_{\substack{p\ \text{prime} \\ p \equiv 3\,\text{mod}\,4}} \left(1 + p^{-x}\right)^{-1} = \prod_{\substack{p\ \text{odd} \\ \text{prime}}} \left(1 - (-1)^{\frac{p-1}{2}} p^{-x}\right)^{-1},$$

where the rearrangement of factors is permitted because of absolute convergence.

The following theorem that was proved in [11] provides sharp bounds for the secant slope of $\beta\,(x)$.

Theorem 4.1. *For real numbers $x > 0$, we have*

$$\frac{c}{3^{x+1}} < \beta(x+1) - \beta(x) < \frac{d}{3^{x+1}}, \tag{4.22}$$

with the best possible constants

$$c = 3\left(\frac{\pi}{4} - \frac{1}{2}\right) = 0.85619449\ldots \quad and \quad d = 2. \tag{4.23}$$

Cerone et al. [18] developed the identity given in the following lemma and the bounds in Theorem 4.3 which are used to obtain approximations to the odd zeta function values in terms of the even function values.

Lemma 4.2. *The following identity involving the Zeta function holds. Namely,*

$$\int_0^\infty \frac{t^x}{(e^t + 1)^2} dt = C(x+1)\zeta(x+1) - xC(x)\zeta(x), \qquad x > 0, \tag{4.24}$$

where $C(x)$ is as given by (4.7).

Based on the identity in Lemma 4.2, the following theorem resulted (see Alzer [2], Cerone et al. [18], and also [10]) where the constants in the bounds of (4.25) were developed.

Theorem 4.3. *For real numbers $x > 0$ we have*

$$\left(\ln 2 - \frac{1}{2}\right) b(x) < \zeta(x+1) - (1 - b(x))\zeta(x) < \frac{b(x)}{2}, \tag{4.25}$$

where

$$b(x) = \frac{1}{2^x - 1}, \tag{4.26}$$

and the constants $\ln 2 - \frac{1}{2}$ and $\frac{1}{2}$ are sharp.

The following is a correction of a result obtained by the author [14] by utilising the Čebyšev functional bounds given by (1.17) and (4.5).

Theorem 4.4. *For $\alpha > 0$ the Zeta function satisfies the inequality*

$$\left|\zeta(\alpha+1) - \frac{2^{\alpha-1}}{\alpha} \cdot \frac{\pi^2}{6}\right| \le \frac{\kappa \cdot 2^{\alpha-\frac{1}{2}}}{\Gamma(\alpha+1)} \left[\Gamma(2\alpha-1) - \Gamma^2(\alpha)\right]^{\frac{1}{2}}, \tag{4.27}$$

where

$$\kappa = \left[\pi^2\left(1 - \frac{\pi^2}{72}\right) - 7\zeta(3)\right]^{\frac{1}{2}} = 0.319846901\ldots \tag{4.28}$$

with equality obtained at $\alpha = 1$.

Remark 4.1. *The plot in Figure 8 demonstrates the attainment of equality at $\alpha = 1$ for the expression given by (4.27). The right hand side of (4.27) provides a bound on the deviation of $\zeta(\alpha+1)$ from its approximant $\frac{2^{\alpha-1}}{\alpha} \cdot \frac{\pi^2}{6}$.*

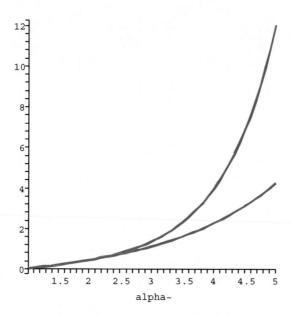

FIGURE 8: Plot of the result (4.27) for $1 \leq \alpha \leq 5$ demonstrating the upper bound for the expression on the left involving Zeta.

Theorem 4.5. *For $\alpha > 1$ and $m = \lfloor \alpha \rfloor$ the zeta function satisfies the inequality*

$$(4.29) \quad \left| \zeta (\alpha + 1) - 2^{\alpha - m} \frac{\Gamma (m + 1)}{\Gamma (\alpha + 1)} \zeta (m + 1) \Gamma (\alpha - m + 1) \right|$$

$$\leq \frac{2^{\left(\alpha - m + \frac{1}{2}\right)}}{\Gamma (\alpha + 1)} \cdot E_m \cdot \left[\Gamma (2\alpha - 2m + 1) - \Gamma^2 (\alpha - m + 1) \right]^{\frac{1}{2}},$$

where

$$(4.30) \qquad E_m^2 = 2^{2m} \Gamma (2m + 1) \left[\lambda (2m) - \lambda (2m + 1) \right] - \frac{1}{2} \Gamma^2 (m + 1) \zeta^2 (m + 1),$$

with $\lambda (\cdot)$ given by (4.16). Equality in (4.29) results when $\alpha = m$.

Proof. Let

$$(4.31) \qquad \tau (\alpha) = \Gamma (\alpha + 1) \zeta (\alpha + 1) = \int_0^\infty \frac{x^\alpha}{e^x - 1} dx$$

$$= \int_0^\infty e^{-\frac{x}{2}} \frac{x^m}{e^{\frac{x}{2}} - e^{-\frac{x}{2}}} \cdot x^{\alpha - m} dx, \quad \alpha > 1$$

where $m = \lfloor \alpha \rfloor$.

Make the associations

$$(4.32) \qquad p (x) = e^{-\frac{x}{2}}, \quad f (x) = \frac{x^m}{e^{\frac{x}{2}} - e^{-\frac{x}{2}}}, \quad g (x) = x^{\alpha - m}$$

then we have from (1.17)

$$(4.33) \quad \begin{cases} P = \int_0^\infty e^{-\frac{x}{2}} dx = 2, \\[2mm] \mathcal{M}(f;p) = \frac{1}{2} \int_0^\infty \frac{e^{-\frac{x}{2}} x^m}{e^{\frac{x}{2}} - e^{-\frac{x}{2}}} dx = \frac{1}{2} \Gamma(m+1) \zeta(m+1), \\[2mm] \mathcal{M}(g;p) = \frac{1}{2} \int_0^\infty e^{-\frac{x}{2}} x^{\alpha-m} dx = 2^{\alpha-m} \Gamma(\alpha - m + 1). \end{cases}$$

Thus, from (1.7), (1.8) and (1.16), we have

$$P \cdot T(f, g; p) = \Gamma(\alpha + 1) \zeta(\alpha + 1) - 2^{\alpha-m} \Gamma(m+1) \zeta(m+1) \Gamma(\alpha - m + 1)$$
$$= \int_0^\infty e^{-\frac{x}{2}} \left(x^{\alpha-m} - \gamma \right) \left(\frac{x^m}{e^{\frac{x}{2}} - e^{-\frac{x}{2}}} - \frac{\Gamma(m+1) \zeta(m+1)}{2} \right) dx.$$

Now, from (1.17) and (1.18), the best value for γ when utilising the Euclidean norm is the integral mean and so we have from (1.17),

$$\left| \Gamma(\alpha + 1) \zeta(\alpha + 1) - 2^{\alpha-m} \Gamma(m+1) \zeta(m+1) \Gamma(\alpha - m + 1) \right|$$
$$\leq \left(\int_0^\infty e^{-\frac{x}{2}} \left(x^{\alpha-m} - 2^{\alpha-m} \Gamma(\alpha - m + 1) \right)^2 dx \right)^{\frac{1}{2}}$$
$$\times \left(\int_0^\infty e^{-\frac{x}{2}} \left(\frac{x^m}{e^{\frac{x}{2}} - e^{-\frac{x}{2}}} - \frac{\Gamma(m+1) \zeta(m+1)}{2} \right)^2 dx \right)^{\frac{1}{2}}.$$

That is, on using (1.18), we have

$$(4.34) \quad \left| \Gamma(\alpha + 1) \zeta(\alpha + 1) - 2^{\alpha-m} \Gamma(m+1) \zeta(m+1) \Gamma(\alpha - m + 1) \right|$$
$$\leq E_m^2 \left[\int_0^\infty e^{-\frac{x}{2}} x^{2(\alpha-m)} dx - 2^{2(\alpha-m)+1} \Gamma^2(\alpha - m + 1) \right]^{\frac{1}{2}},$$

where

$$(4.35) \quad E_m^2 = \int_0^\infty e^{-\frac{x}{2}} \frac{x^{2m}}{\left(e^{\frac{x}{2}} - e^{-\frac{x}{2}} \right)^2} dx - 2 \left(\frac{\Gamma(m+1) \zeta(m+1)}{2} \right)^2.$$

Now

$$(4.36) \quad \int_0^\infty e^{-\frac{x}{2}} \left(\frac{x^m}{e^{\frac{x}{2}} - e^{-\frac{x}{2}}} \right)^2 dx = \int_0^\infty e^{-\frac{3}{2}x} x^{2m} \left(1 + 2e^{-x} + 3e^{-2x} + \cdots \right) dx$$
$$= \sum_{n=1}^\infty n \int_0^\infty e^{\left(\frac{2n+1}{2} \right) x} x^{2m} dx$$
$$= \sum_{n=1}^\infty n \frac{2^{2m+1} \Gamma(2m+1)}{(2n+1)^{2m+1}}$$
$$= 2^{2m} \Gamma(2m+1) \sum_{n=1}^\infty \frac{2n}{(2n+1)^{2m+1}}$$
$$= 2^{2m} \Gamma(2m+1) \left[\lambda(2m) - \lambda(2m+1) \right],$$

where $\lambda\left(\cdot\right)$ is as given by (4.16), where we have used (4.7) and have undertaken the permissable interchange of summation and integration.

Substitution of (4.36) into (4.35) and using (4.34) gives the stated results (4.29) and (4.30) after some simplification. □

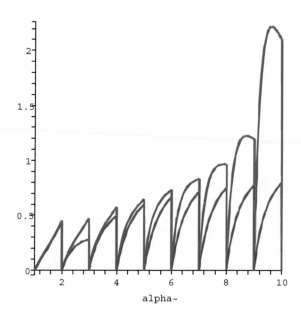

FIGURE 9: Plot of result (4.29) for $0 < \alpha \leq 5$ showing bounds on the error for the expression on the left involving $\zeta\left(\alpha + 1\right)$.

Remark 4.2. *The plot in Figure 9 shows an implementation of (4.29). It demonstrates the attainment of equality for α at the integer values. A deterioration of the bound on the error for increasing α may also be noticed from the figure.*

The following corollary provides upper bounds for the zeta function at odd integers.

Corollary 4.6. *The inequality*

$$(4.37) \qquad \Gamma\left(2m + 1\right)\left[2 \cdot \left(2^{2m} - 1\right)\zeta\left(2m\right) - \left(2^{2m+1} - 1\right)\zeta\left(2m + 1\right)\right]$$
$$- \Gamma^2\left(m + 1\right)\zeta^2\left(m + 1\right) > 0$$

holds for $m = 1, 2, \ldots$.

Proof. From equation (4.30) of Theorem 4.5, we have $E_m^2 > 0$. Utilising the relationship between $\lambda\left(\cdot\right)$ and $\zeta\left(\cdot\right)$ given by (4.17) readily gives the inequality (4.37). □

Remark 4.3. *In (4.37), if m is odd, then $2m$ and $m + 1$ are even so that an expression in the form*

$$(4.38) \qquad \alpha\left(m\right)\zeta\left(2m\right) - \beta\left(m\right)\zeta\left(2m + 1\right) - \gamma\left(m\right)\zeta^2\left(m + 1\right) > 0,$$

results, where

$$\begin{aligned}
\alpha\left(m\right) &= 2\left(2^{2m}-1\right)\Gamma\left(2m+1\right), \\
\beta\left(m\right) &= \left(2^{2m+1}-1\right)\Gamma\left(2m+1\right) \quad and \\
\gamma\left(m\right) &= \Gamma^{2}\left(m+1\right).
\end{aligned}$$

(4.39)

*Thus for m **odd** we have*

(4.40)
$$\zeta\left(2m+1\right) < \frac{\alpha\left(m\right)\zeta\left(2m\right)-\gamma\left(m\right)\zeta^{2}\left(m+1\right)}{\beta\left(m\right)}.$$

That is, for $m=2k-1$, we have from (4.40)

(4.41)
$$\zeta\left(4k-1\right) < \frac{\alpha\left(2k-1\right)\zeta\left(4k-2\right)-\gamma\left(2k-1\right)\zeta^{2}\left(2k\right)}{\beta\left(2k-1\right)}$$

giving for $k=1,2,3$, for example,

$$\zeta\left(3\right) < \frac{\pi^{2}}{7}\left(1-\frac{\pi^{2}}{72}\right) = 1.21667148,$$

$$\zeta\left(7\right) < \frac{2\pi^{6}}{1905}\left(1-\frac{\pi^{2}}{2160}\right) = 1.00887130,$$

$$\zeta\left(11\right) < \frac{62\pi^{10}}{5803245}\left(1-\frac{\pi^{2}}{492150}\right) = 1.00050356,$$

Guo *[37] obtained $\zeta\left(3\right) < \frac{\pi^{4}}{72}$ and the above bound for $\zeta\left(3\right)$ was obtained previously by the author in [14] from (4.28).*

*If m is **even** then for $m=2k$ we have from (4.40)*

(4.42)
$$\zeta\left(4k+1\right) < \frac{\alpha\left(2k\right)\zeta\left(4k\right)-\gamma\left(2k\right)\zeta^{2}\left(2k+1\right)}{\beta\left(2k\right)}, \quad k=1,2,\ldots.$$

We notice that in (4.42), or equivalently (4.38) with $m=2k$ there are two zeta functions with odd arguments. There are a number of possibilities for resolving this, but firstly it should be noticed that $\zeta\left(x\right)$ is monotonically decreasing for $x>1$ so that $\zeta\left(x_{1}\right) > \zeta\left(x_{2}\right)$ for $1 < x_{1} < x_{2}$.

Firstly, we may use a lower bound obtained in [10] as given by

$$L\left(x\right)=\left(1-b\left(x\right)\right)\zeta\left(x\right)+\left(\ln 2-\frac{1}{2}\right)b\left(x\right) \quad or \quad L_{2}\left(x\right)=\frac{\zeta\left(x+2\right)-\frac{b\left(x+1\right)}{2}}{1-b\left(x+1\right)},$$

where $b\left(x\right)$ is given by (4.26).

But from numerical investigation in [10], it seems that $L_{2}\left(x\right) > L\left(x\right)$ for positive integer x and so we have from (4.42)

(4.43)
$$\zeta_{L}\left(4k+1\right) < \frac{\alpha\left(2k\right)\zeta\left(2k\right)-\gamma\left(2k\right)L_{2}^{2}\left(2k\right)}{\beta\left(2k\right)},$$

where we have used the fact that $L_{2}\left(x\right) < \zeta\left(x+1\right)$.

Secondly, since the even argument $\zeta\left(2k+2\right) < \zeta\left(2k+1\right)$, then from (4.42) we have

(4.44)
$$\zeta_{E}\left(4k+1\right) < \frac{\alpha\left(2k\right)\zeta\left(4k\right)-\gamma\left(2k\right)\zeta^{2}\left(2k+2\right)}{\beta\left(2k\right)}.$$

Finally, we have that $\zeta(m+1) > \zeta(2m+1)$ so that from (4.38) we have, with $m = 2k$ on solving the resulting quadratic equation that

$$(4.45) \qquad \zeta_Q(4k+1) < \frac{-\beta(2k) + \sqrt{\beta^2(2k) + 4\gamma(2k)\alpha(2k)\zeta(4k)}}{2\gamma(2k)}.$$

For $k = 1$ we have from (4.43) – (4.45) that

$$\zeta_L(5) < \frac{\pi^4}{93} - \frac{1}{186}\left(\frac{7\pi^4}{540} - \frac{1}{12}\right)^2 = 1.039931461,$$

$$\zeta_E(5) < \frac{\pi^4}{93}\left(1 - \frac{\pi^4}{16200}\right) = 1.041111605,$$

$$\zeta_Q(5) < -93 + \sqrt{8649 + 2\pi^4} = 1.04157688;$$

and for $k = 2$

$$\zeta_L(9) < \frac{17}{160965}\pi^8 - \frac{1}{35770}\left(\frac{31}{28350}\pi^6 - \frac{1}{60}\right)^2 = 1.002082506,$$

$$\zeta_E(9) < \frac{17}{160965}\pi^8\left(1 - \frac{\pi^4}{337650}\right) = 1.0020834954,$$

$$\zeta_Q(9) < -17885 + \frac{1}{3}\sqrt{2878859025 + 34\pi^8} = 1.00208436.$$

It should be noted that the above results give tighter upper bounds for the odd zeta function evaluations than were possible using the methodology utilising techniques based around Theorem 4.3 as demonstrated by the numerics which are presented in Table 1 of [10].

Numerical experimentation using Maple seems to indicate that the upper bounds for

$$\zeta_L(4k+1), \zeta_E(4k+1) \quad and \quad \zeta_Q(4k+1)$$

are in increasing order. Analytic demonstration that $\zeta_L(4k+1)$ is better remains an open problem.

5 Bounds for Mathieu Series

The series, known in the literature as the Mathieu series,

$$(5.1) \qquad S(r) = \sum_{n=1}^{\infty} \frac{2n}{(n^2 + r^2)^2}, \quad r > 0,$$

has been extensively studied in the past since its introduction by Mathieu [41] in 1890, where it arose in connection with work on elasticity of solid bodies. The reader is directed to the references for further illustration.

One of the main questions addressed in relation (5.1) is to obtain sharp bounds. Alzer, Brenner and Ruehr [4] showed that the best constants a and b in

$$(5.2) \qquad \frac{1}{x^2 + a} < S(x) < \frac{1}{x^2 + b}, \quad x \neq 0$$

are $a = \frac{1}{2\zeta(3)}$ and $b = \frac{1}{6}$ where $\zeta(\cdot)$ denotes the Riemann zeta function defined by (4.1). (See also [44], [45], [46], [54], [55] and [58]).

An integral representation for $S(r)$ as given in (5.1) was presented in [33] and [36] as

$$(5.3) \qquad S(r) = \frac{1}{r} \int_0^\infty \frac{x}{e^x - 1} \sin(rx) \, dx.$$

Guo [37] utilised (5.3) to obtain bounds on $S(r)$. Alternate bounds to (5.1) were obtained by Qi and coworkers in [44, 45, 46].

For the generalised Mathieu series

$$(5.4) \qquad S_\mu(r) = \sum_{n=1}^\infty \frac{2n}{(n^2 + r^2)^{1+\mu}}, \qquad r > 0, \ \mu > 0,$$

Cerone and Lenard [24] proved the following two theorems.

Theorem 5.1. *The generalised Mathieu series $S_\mu(r)$ defined by (5.4) may be represented in the integral form*

$$(5.5) \qquad S_\mu(r) = C_\mu(r) \int_0^\infty \frac{x^{\mu+\frac{1}{2}}}{e^x - 1} J_{\mu-\frac{1}{2}}(rx) \, dx, \qquad \mu > 0,$$

where

$$(5.6) \qquad C_\mu(r) = \frac{\sqrt{\pi}}{(2r)^{\mu-\frac{1}{2}} \, \Gamma(\mu+1)}$$

and $J_\nu(z)$ is the νth order Bessel function of the first kind.

Theorem 5.2. *For m a positive integer we have*

$$(5.7) \qquad S_m(r) = \frac{1}{2^{m-1}} \cdot \frac{1}{r^{2m-1}} \cdot \frac{1}{m} \sum_{k=0}^{m-1} \frac{(-1)^{\left\lfloor \frac{3k}{2} \right\rfloor}}{k!} r^k \left[\delta_{k \ even} A_k(r) + \delta_{k \ odd} B_k(r) \right],$$

where

$$(5.8) \qquad A_k(r) = \int_0^\infty \frac{x^{k+1}}{e^x - 1} \sin(rx) \, dx, \qquad B_k(r) = \int_0^\infty \frac{x^{k+1}}{e^x - 1} \cos(rx) \, dx,$$

with $\delta_{condition} = 1$ if condition holds and zero otherwise and $\lfloor x \rfloor$ is the smallest integer part of x.

Bounds on the Čebyšev functional (1.4) – (1.8) may be looked upon as estimating the distance of the weighted mean of the product of two functions from the product of the weighted mean of the two functions. This proves to be quite useful since the individual means are invariably easier to evaluate.

In [24] the author utilised the sharp bounds on the Bessel function $|J_\nu(z)|$ of Landau [40] to procure bounds for the generalised Mathieu series $S_\mu(r)$ given by (5.5).

Here we investigate the bounding of $S_\mu(r)$ as defined by (5.4) through the identities (5.5) – (5.6). We notice that bounding $S_\mu(r)$ is accomplished via $\chi_\mu(r)$ where

$$(5.9) \qquad \chi_\mu(r) := \int_0^\infty \frac{x^{\mu+\frac{1}{2}}}{e^x - 1} J_{\mu-\frac{1}{2}}(rx) \, dx; \qquad \mu, r > 0,$$

since from (5.5)

$$(5.10) \qquad S_\mu(r) = C_\mu(r) \chi_\mu(r),$$

where $C_\mu(r)$ is positive as defined in (5.6).

The following lemma examines the behaviour of $\chi_\mu(r)$ (see also [9]).

Lemma 5.3.

$$(5.11) \quad \left| \chi_\mu(r) - \frac{1}{2} \cdot \frac{(2r)^{\mu-\frac{1}{2}}}{\sqrt{\pi}} \cdot \frac{\Gamma(\mu)}{\left(r^2 + \frac{1}{4}\right)^\mu} \cdot \frac{\pi^2}{6} \right|$$

$$\leq \kappa \left[\frac{\Gamma\left(2\mu - \frac{1}{2}\right) r^{2\mu-1}}{\pi^{\frac{3}{2}}} \int_0^{\frac{\pi}{2}} \frac{\cos^{2\mu-1}\phi}{\left[\left(\frac{1}{4}\right)^2 + r^2\cos^2\phi\right]^{2\mu-\frac{1}{2}}} d\phi - 2K_*^2 \right]^{\frac{1}{2}},$$

where

$$K_* = \frac{(2r)^{\mu-\frac{1}{2}}\Gamma(\mu)}{2\sqrt{\pi}\left(r^2 + \frac{1}{4}\right)^\mu} \quad \text{is defined in (5.20),}$$

and

$$(5.12) \quad \kappa = \left[\pi^2\left(1 - \frac{\pi^2}{72}\right) - 7\zeta(3)\right]^{\frac{1}{2}} = 0.319846901\ldots.$$

Proof. Firstly, we notice that $\chi_\mu(r)$ from (5.9) may be written in the form

$$(5.13) \quad \chi_\mu(r) = \int_0^\infty e^{-\frac{x}{2}} \cdot \frac{x}{e^{\frac{x}{2}} - e^{-\frac{x}{2}}} \cdot x^{\mu-\frac{1}{2}} J_{\mu-\frac{1}{2}}(rx)\, dx.$$

Let

$$(5.14) \quad p(x) = e^{-\frac{x}{2}}, \quad f(x) = \frac{x}{e^{\frac{x}{2}} - e^{-\frac{x}{2}}}, \quad g(x) = x^{\mu-\frac{1}{2}} J_{\mu-\frac{1}{2}}(rx)$$

then from (1.7) – (1.8),

$$(5.15) \quad P = \int_0^\infty p(x)\, dx = \int_0^\infty e^{-\frac{x}{2}}\, dx = 2,$$

$$(5.16) \quad P \cdot \mathcal{M}(f;p) = \int_0^\infty e^{-\frac{x}{2}} \cdot \frac{x}{e^{\frac{x}{2}} - e^{-\frac{x}{2}}}\, dx = \int_0^\infty \frac{x}{e^x - 1}\, dx = \zeta(2) = \frac{\pi^2}{6}$$

and

$$(5.17) \quad P \cdot \mathcal{M}(g;p) = \int_0^\infty e^{-\frac{x}{2}} \cdot x^{\mu-\frac{1}{2}} J_{\mu-\frac{1}{2}}(rx)\, dx = \frac{(2r)^{\mu-\frac{1}{2}}\Gamma(\mu)}{\sqrt{\pi}\left(\left(\frac{1}{2}\right)^2 + r^2\right)^\mu},$$

where we have used (4.5) to procure (5.16), and Watson [56, p. 386]

$$\int_0^\infty e^{-\alpha x} \cdot x^\nu J_\nu(\beta x)\, dx = \frac{(2\beta)^\nu}{\sqrt{\pi}} \cdot \frac{\Gamma\left(\nu + \frac{1}{2}\right)}{\left(\alpha^2 + \beta^2\right)^{\nu+\frac{1}{2}}}, \quad \mathrm{Re}(\nu) > \frac{1}{2}, \quad \mathrm{Re}(\alpha) > |\mathrm{Im}(\beta)|,$$

with $\alpha = \frac{1}{2}$, $\nu = \mu - \frac{1}{2}$, $\beta = r$ to obtain (5.17).

Now, from (1.7) – (1.8) we have on using (5.14) – (5.17)

$$(5.18) \quad \chi_\mu(r) - \frac{1}{2} \cdot \frac{(2r)^{\mu-\frac{1}{2}}}{\sqrt{\pi}} \cdot \frac{\Gamma(\mu)}{\left(r^2 + \frac{1}{4}\right)^\mu} \cdot \frac{\pi^2}{6}$$

$$= \int_0^\infty e^{-\frac{x}{2}} \left(x^{\mu-\frac{1}{2}} J_{\mu-\frac{1}{2}}(rx) - K\right)\left(\frac{x}{e^{\frac{x}{2}} - e^{-\frac{x}{2}}} - \frac{\pi^2}{12}\right) dx.$$

Now, by using the Cauchy-Bunyakovsky-Schwarz inequality, we have from (5.18) and (1.17)

$$(5.19) \quad \left| \chi_\mu (r) - \frac{1}{2} \cdot \frac{(2r)^{\mu - \frac{1}{2}}}{\sqrt{\pi}} \cdot \frac{\Gamma (\mu)}{\left(r^2 + \frac{1}{4}\right)^\mu} \cdot \frac{\pi^2}{6} \right|$$

$$\leq \left(\int_0^\infty e^{-\frac{x}{2}} \left(x^{\mu - \frac{1}{2}} J_{\mu - \frac{1}{2}} (rx) - K \right)^2 dx \right)^{\frac{1}{2}}$$

$$\times \left(\int_0^\infty e^{-\frac{x}{2}} \left(\frac{x}{e^{\frac{x}{2}} - e^{-\frac{x}{2}}} - \frac{\pi^2}{12} \right)^2 dx \right)^{\frac{1}{2}}.$$

As mentioned in Section 1, equation (1.17), the appropriate choice of K is the weighted integral mean as given from (5.17), namely

$$(5.20) \quad K = K_* = \frac{(2r)^{\mu - \frac{1}{2}} \Gamma (\mu)}{2\sqrt{\pi} \left(r^2 + \frac{1}{4}\right)^\mu}.$$

The result given by (1.18) will be utilised to evaluate the two expressions on the right hand side of (5.19).

Thus from (5.19) we have

$$(5.21) \quad \int_0^\infty e^{-\frac{x}{2}} \left(\frac{x}{e^{\frac{x}{2}} - e^{-\frac{x}{2}}} - \frac{\pi^2}{12} \right)^2 dx = \int_0^\infty e^{-\frac{x}{2}} \left(\frac{x}{e^{\frac{x}{2}} - e^{-\frac{x}{2}}} \right)^2 dx - 2 \left(\frac{\pi^2}{12} \right)^2.$$

Now, allowing for the permissable interchange of integration and summation, we have

$$(5.22) \quad \int_0^\infty e^{-\frac{x}{2}} \left(\frac{x}{e^{\frac{x}{2}} - e^{-\frac{x}{2}}} \right)^2 dx = \int_0^\infty e^{-\frac{3x}{2}} \left(\frac{x}{1 - e^{-x}} \right)^2 dx$$

$$= \int_0^\infty e^{-\frac{3x}{2}} x^2 \left(\sum_{n=1}^\infty n e^{-nx} \right) dx$$

$$= \sum_{n=1}^\infty n \int_0^\infty e^{-\left(\frac{2n+1}{2} \right) x} x^2 dx$$

$$= \sum_{n=1}^\infty \frac{n \Gamma (3)}{\left(\frac{2n+1}{2} \right)^3} = \sum_{n=1}^\infty \frac{2n}{\left(n + \frac{1}{2} \right)^3}$$

$$= 2 \sum_{n=1}^\infty \frac{1}{\left(n + \frac{1}{2} \right)^2} - \sum_{n=1}^\infty \frac{1}{\left(n + \frac{1}{2} \right)^3}$$

$$= \pi^2 - 7 \cdot \zeta (3).$$

In (5.22) we have used the fact that

$$\int_0^\infty e^{-\alpha x} x^p dx = \frac{\Gamma (p + 1)}{\alpha^{p+1}}.$$

Hence, from (5.21) and (5.22) we have

$$(5.23) \quad \left[\int_0^\infty e^{-\frac{x}{2}} \left(\frac{x}{e^{\frac{x}{2}} - e^{-\frac{x}{2}}} - \frac{\pi^2}{12} \right)^2 dx \right]^{\frac{1}{2}} = \left[\pi^2 \left(1 - \frac{\pi^2}{72} \right) - 7\zeta (3) \right]^{\frac{1}{2}}.$$

Now, for the first expression on the right hand side of (5.19), we have, on using (5.20) and (1.18)

$$(5.24) \qquad \int_0^\infty e^{-\frac{x}{2}} \left(x^{\mu - \frac{1}{2}} J_{\mu - \frac{1}{2}}(rx) - K_* \right)^2 dx = \int_0^\infty e^{-\frac{x}{2}} x^{2\mu - 1} J_{\mu - \frac{1}{2}}^2(rx)\, dx - 2K_*^2.$$

A result in Watson [56, p. 290] states that

$$(5.25) \qquad \int_0^\infty e^{-2at} J_\alpha(\gamma t) J_\beta(\gamma t) t^{\alpha + \beta} dt$$
$$= \frac{\Gamma\left(\alpha + \beta + \frac{1}{2}\right)}{\pi^{\frac{3}{2}}} \gamma^{\alpha + \beta} \int_0^{\frac{\pi}{2}} \frac{\cos^{\alpha + \beta}\phi \cos(\alpha - \beta)\phi}{(a^2 + \gamma^2 \cos^2\phi)^{\alpha + \beta + \frac{1}{2}}} d\phi$$

and so taking $a = \frac{1}{4}$, $\alpha = \beta = \mu - \frac{1}{2}$ and $\gamma = r$ in (5.25) gives

$$(5.26) \qquad \int_0^\infty e^{-\frac{x}{2}} x^{2\mu - 1} J_{\mu - \frac{1}{2}}^2(rx)\, dx = \frac{\Gamma\left(2\mu - \frac{1}{2}\right) r^{2\mu - 1}}{\pi^{\frac{3}{2}}} \int_0^{\frac{\pi}{2}} \frac{\cos^{2\mu - 1}\phi}{\left(\left(\frac{1}{4}\right)^2 + r^2 \cos^2\phi\right)^{2\mu - \frac{1}{2}}} d\phi.$$

That is,

$$(5.27) \qquad \left[\int_0^\infty e^{-\frac{x}{2}} \left(x^{\mu - \frac{1}{2}} J_{\mu - \frac{1}{2}}(rx) - K_* \right)^2 dx \right]^{\frac{1}{2}}$$
$$= \left[\frac{\Gamma\left(2\mu - \frac{1}{2}\right)}{\pi^{\frac{3}{2}}} r^{2\mu - 1} \int_0^{\frac{\pi}{2}} \frac{\cos^{2\mu - 1}\phi}{\left[\left(\frac{1}{4}\right)^2 + r^2 \cos^2\phi\right]^{2\mu - \frac{1}{2}}} d\phi - 2K_*^2 \right]^{\frac{1}{2}}.$$

Placing (5.27) and (5.23) into (5.19) produces the stated result (5.11). $\square$

Theorem 5.4. *For $\mu > 0$ and $r > 0$ the generalised Mathieu series $S_\mu(r)$ satisfies the following relationship, namely,*

$$(5.28) \qquad \left| S_\mu(r) - \frac{\pi^2}{12\mu \left(r^2 + \frac{1}{4}\right)^\mu} \right|$$

$$\leq \frac{\kappa}{\sqrt{2\mu}} \left[\frac{1}{\sqrt{\pi}} \cdot \frac{\Gamma\left(2\mu - \frac{1}{2}\right)}{4^{2\mu - 1}\Gamma^2(\mu)} \int_0^{\frac{\pi}{2}} \frac{\cos^{2\mu - 1}\phi}{\left[\left(\frac{1}{4}\right)^2 + r^2 \cos^2\phi\right]^{2\mu - 1/2}} d\phi - \frac{1}{\left(r^2 + \frac{1}{4}\right)^{2\mu}} \right]^{\frac{1}{2}}$$

$$= \frac{\kappa}{\sqrt{2\mu}} \left[\frac{4^{-\mu}}{\pi} \cdot B\left(\frac{1}{2}, 2\mu - \frac{1}{2}\right) \cdot \frac{1}{\left(r^2 + \frac{1}{16}\right)^{2\mu - \frac{1}{2}}} - \frac{1}{\left(r^2 + \frac{1}{4}\right)^{2\mu}} \right.$$

$$\left. \times\ {}_2F_1\left(\frac{1}{2}, 2\mu - \frac{1}{2}; \mu + \frac{1}{2}; \frac{r^2}{r^2 + \frac{1}{16}}\right) \right]^{\frac{1}{2}}$$

where κ is as given by (5.12), $B(x, y)$ is the Euler Beta function and ${}_2F_1(a, b; c; x)$ is the hypergeometric function.

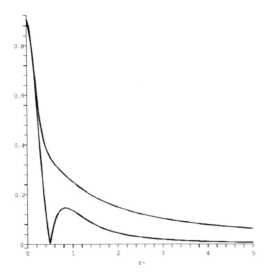

FIGURE 10: Visual representation of (5.31) for $0 \leq r \leq 5$.

Proof. From (5.10) we have, since $C_\mu(r)$, as defined by (5.6), is positive so that using Lemma 5.3 readily produces the result

$$(5.29) \quad \left| S_\mu(r) - \frac{\pi^2}{12\mu \left(r^2 + \frac{1}{4}\right)^\mu} \right|$$

$$\leq \frac{\kappa}{\sqrt{2\mu}} \left[\frac{1}{\sqrt{\pi}} \cdot \frac{\Gamma\left(2\mu - \frac{1}{2}\right)}{4^{2\mu-1}\Gamma^2(\mu)} \int_0^{\frac{\pi}{2}} \frac{\cos^{2\mu-1}\phi \, d\phi}{\left[\left(\frac{1}{4}\right)^2 + r^2 \cos^2\phi\right]^{2\mu-1/2}} - \frac{1}{\left(r^2 + \frac{1}{4}\right)^{2\mu}} \right]^{\frac{1}{2}}$$

upon simplification.

Further, utilising the Maple computer algebra package, it may be shown that

$$(5.30) \quad \int_0^{\frac{\pi}{2}} \frac{\cos^{2\mu-1}\phi}{\left[\left(\frac{1}{4}\right)^2 + r^2 \cos^2\phi\right]^{2\mu-1/2}} d\phi$$

$$= \frac{\sqrt{\pi}}{2} \cdot \frac{\Gamma(\mu)}{\Gamma\left(\mu + \frac{1}{2}\right)} \cdot \frac{1}{\left(r^2 + \frac{1}{16}\right)^{2\mu-1/2}}$$

$$\times {}_2F_1\left(\frac{1}{2}, 2\mu - \frac{1}{2}; \mu + \frac{1}{2}; \frac{r^2}{r^2 + \frac{1}{16}}\right),$$

where

$${}_2F_1(a, b; c; x) = \sum_{k=0}^\infty \frac{(a)_k (b)_k}{(c)_k} \cdot \frac{x^k}{k!}$$

and $(\alpha)_k = \frac{\Gamma(\alpha+k)}{\Gamma(\alpha)}$, the Pochhammer function.

Now, substitution of (5.30) into (5.29) produces the bound in (5.28) in terms of the well-known Euler Beta function B and the Hypergeometric function ${}_2F_1$, where we have used the

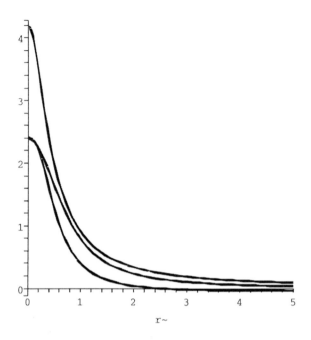

FIGURE 11: Upper and lower bounds from (5.31) for the Mathieu series $S(r)$.

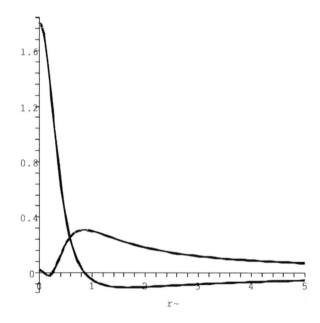

FIGURE 12: Difference between the upper and lower bounds from (5.2) and (5.31).

duplication formula $\sqrt{\pi}\Gamma\left(2x\right) = 2^{2x-1}\Gamma\left(x\right)\Gamma\left(x + \frac{1}{2}\right)$ and the definition of the Euler Beta function $B\left(x, y\right) = \frac{\Gamma(x)\Gamma(y)}{\Gamma(x+y)}$. $\qquad\square$

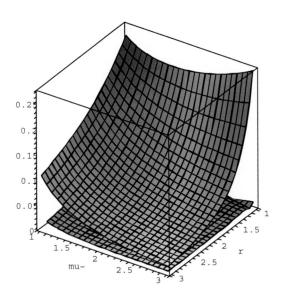

FIGURE 13: Demonstration of the result (5.28) for $1 \le r, \mu \le 3$.

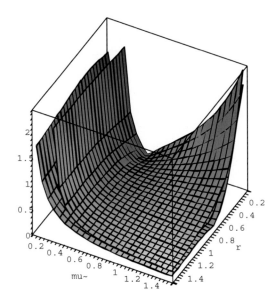

FIGURE 14: Pictorial demonstration of the result (5.28) for $0.1 \le r, \mu \le 1.5$.

Corollary 5.5. *The following bounds are valid for $S(r)$ the Mathieu series. That is,*

$$(5.31) \qquad \left| \sum_{n=1}^{\infty} \frac{2n}{(n^2+r^2)^2} - \frac{\pi^2}{12\left(r^2+\frac{1}{4}\right)} \right| \leq 2\sqrt{2} \cdot \kappa \left\{ \frac{2}{1+(4r)^2} - \frac{1}{\left[1+(2r)^2\right]^2} \right\}^{\frac{1}{2}},$$

where κ is as given by (5.12).

Proof. Let $\mu = 1$ in (5.28) and using (5.1) and (5.4) gives the above result (5.31), on noting that

$$2^6 \int_0^{\frac{\pi}{2}} \frac{\cos\phi}{\left[1+(4r\cos\phi)^2\right]^{\frac{3}{2}}} d\phi = \frac{64}{1+(4r)^2}$$

and after some simplification. $\qquad \square$

Remark 5.1. *Figures 10 and 11 provide a visual representation involving the Matthieu series $S(r)$ and its bounds derived from the first inequality in (5.28) with $\mu = 1$. The bounds extracted from (5.31) may be compared with the classical bounds from (5.2) for the Mathieu series.*

The plots presented in Figure 12 show the difference between the upper and lower bounds from (5.2) and (5.31). The upper bound for $S(r)$ from (5.31) is better for $0 < r < 0.85566$ whereas the lower bound is better only for $0.0816295 < r < 0.2482358$. The bounds provided by (5.2) seem to be superior for the remainder of the r values. It must be remembered however that (5.31) is a consequence of the more general result given by the first inequality in (5.28).

Remark 5.2. *Figures 13 and 14 show the left hand side of (5.28) being covered by the bound provided by the right hand side of (5.28). The two figures are provided to cater for the different vertical scale.*

6 CONCLUDING REMARKS

In the paper the usefulness of some recent results in the analysis of inequalities, has been demonstrated through application to some special functions. Although these techniques have been applied in a variety of areas of applied mathematics, their application to special functions does not seem to have received much attention to date. There are many special functions which may be represented as the integral of products of functions. The investigation in the current article has restricted itself to the investigation of the Bessel function of the first kind, the Beta function, the Zeta function and Mathieu series.

It may be surmised from the above investigations that the accuracy of the bounds over particular regions of parameters cannot be ascertained *a priori*. It has been demonstrated, however, that some useful bounds may be obtained which seem hitherto not to have been discovered. The approach of utilising developments in the field of inequalities to special functions has been shown to have the potential for further development.

REFERENCES

[1] M. Abramowitz and I.A. (Eds.), *Handbook of Mathematical Functions with Formulas, Graphs and Mathematical Tables*, National Bureau of Standards, Applied Mathematics Series, **55**, 4th printing, Washington, 1965.

[2] H. Alzer, Remark on a double-inequality for the Euler zeta function, *Expositiones Mathematicae*, **23**(4) (2005), 349–352.

[3] H. Alzer, Sharp inequalities for the Beta function, *Indag. Math.* (N.S.), **12** (2001), 15-21.

[4] H. Alzer, J.L. Brenner, and O.G. Ruehr, On Mathieu's inequality, *J. Math. Anal. Appl.*, **218** (1998), 607–610.

[5] T.M. Apostol, *Analytic Number Theory*, Springer, New York, 1976.

[6] J.M. Borwein, D.M. Bradley and R.E. Crandall, Computational strategies for the Riemann zeta function, *J. of Comput. and Applied Math.*, **121** (2000), 247–296.

[7] I. Budimir, P. Cerone and J.E. Pečarić, Inequalities related to the Chebyshev functional involving integrals over different intervals, *J. Ineq. Pure and Appl. Math.*, **2**(2) Art. 22, (2001). [ONLINE http://jipam.vu.edu.au/v2n2/].

[8] P.S. Bullen, *A Dictionary of Inequalities*, Addison Wesley Longman Limited, 1998.

[9] P. Cerone, Bounding Mathieu type series, *RGMIA Res. Rep. Coll.*, **6**(3) (2003), Article 7. [ONLINE]

[10] P. Cerone, Bounds for Zeta and related functions, *J. Ineq. Pure & Appl. Math.*, **6**(5) Art. 134, (2005). [ONLINE http://jipam.vu.edu.au/article.php?sid=608].

[11] P. Cerone, On a double inequality for the Dirichlet beta function, submitted.

[12] P. Cerone, On an identity for the Chebychev functional and some ramifications, *J. Ineq. Pure and Appl. Math.*, **3**(1) Art. 4, (2002). [ONLINE http://jipam.vu.edu.au/v3n1/].

[13] P. Cerone, On applications of the integral of products of functions and its bounds, *RGMIA Res. Rep. Coll.*, **6**(4) (2003), Article 4. [ONLINE]

[14] P. Cerone, On odd zeta and other special functions bounds, *Inequality Theory and Applications*, Nova Science Publishers, N.Y., in press.

[15] P. Cerone, On some results involving the Čebyšev functional and its generalisations, *J. Ineq. Pure & Appl. Math.*, **4**(3) Art. 54, (2003). [ONLINE http://jipam.vu.edu.au/v4n3/124_02.html].

[16] P. Cerone, On relationships between Ostrowski, trapezoidal and Chebychev identities and inequalities, *Soochow J. Math.*, **28**(3) (2002), 311-328.

[17] P. Cerone, On some generalisatons of Steffensen's inequality and related results, *J. Ineq. Pure and Appl. Math.*, **2**(3) Art. 28, (2001). [ONLINE http://jipam.vu.edu.au/v2n3/].

[18] P. Cerone, M.A. Chaudhry, G. Korvin and A. Qadir, New inequalities involving the zeta function, *J. Inequal. Pure Appl. Math.*, **5**(2) (2004), Art. 43. [ONLINE:]

[19] P. Cerone and S. Dragomir, A refinement of the Grüss inequality and applications, *Tamkang J. Math.*, in press.

[20] P. Cerone and S. Dragomir, New upper and lower bounds for the Čebyšev functional, *J. Ineq. Pure & Appl. Math.*, **3**(5) Art. 77, (2002). [ONLINE http://jipam.vu.edu.au/v3n5/].

[21] P. Cerone and S. Dragomir, Generalisations of the Grüss, Chebychev and Lupaş inequalities for integrals over different intervals, *Int. J. Appl. Math.*, **6**(2) (2001), 117-128.

[22] P. Cerone and S.S. Dragomir, On some inequalities arising from Montgomery's identity, *J. Comput. Anal. Applics.*, **5**(4) (2003), 341-362.

[23] P. Cerone and S.S. Dragomir, On some inequalities for the expectation and variance, *Korean J. Comput. Appl. Math.*, **8**(2) (2001), 357-380.

[24] P. Cerone and C. Lenard, On integral forms of generalised Mathieu series, *J. Inequal. Pure Appl. Math.*, **4**(5) (2003), Art. 100, 1-11. [ONLINE:]

[25] X.L. Cheng and J. Sun, A note on the perturbed trapezoid inequality, *J. Ineq. Pure and Appl. Math.*, **3**(2) Art. 29, (2002). [ONLINE http://jipam.vu.edu.au/v3n2/046_01.html].

[26] J.B. Conrey, The Riemann hypothesis, *Notices of the AMS* (2003), 341–353.

[27] D. Cvijović and J. Klinowski, Integral representations of the Riemann zeta function for odd-integer arguments, *J. of Comput. and Applied Math.*, **142**(2) (2002). 435–439.

[28] S.S. Dragomir, A generalisation of Grüss' inequality in inner product spaces and applications, *J. Math. Anal. Appl.*, **237** (1999), 74–82.

[29] S.S. Dragomir, Some integral inequalities of Grüss type, *Indian J. of Pure and Appl. Math.*, **31**(4) (2000), 397-415.

[30] S.S. Dragomir and Th.M. Rassias (Ed.), *Ostrowski Type Inequalities and Applications in Numerical Integration,* Kluwer Academic Publishers, 2002.

[31] H.M. Edwards, *Riemann's Zeta Function,* Academic Press, New York, 1974.

[32] A. Elbert, Asymptotic expansion and continued fraction for Mathieu's series, *Period. Math. Hungar.*, **13**(1) (1982), 1–8.

[33] O. E. Emersleben, Über die Reihe $\sum_{k=1}^{\infty} k(k^2+c^2)^{-2}$, *Math. Ann.*, **125** (1952), 165–171.

[34] S.R. Finch, *Mathematical Constants,* Cambridge Univ. Press, Cambridge, 2003.

[35] A.M. Fink, A treatise on Grüss' inequality, *Analytic and Geometric Inequalites and Applications, Math. Appl.*, **478** (1999), Kluwer Academic Publishers, Dordrecht, 93-114.

[36] I. Gavrea, Some remarks on Mathieu's series, *Mathematical Analysis and Approximation Theory*, 113-117, Burg Verlag, 2002.

[37] B.-N. Guo, Note on Mathieu's inequality, *RGMIA Res. Rep. Coll.*, **3**(3) (2000), Article 5. [ONLINE http://rgmia.vu.edu.au/v3n3.html].

[38] G. Grüss, Über das Maximum des absoluten Betrages von $\frac{1}{b-a}\int_a^b f(x)g(x)dx - \frac{1}{(b-a)^2}\int_a^b f(x)dx \int_a^b g(x)dx$, *Math. Z.* , **39**(1935), 215-226.

[39] J. Havil, *Gamma: Exploring Euler's constant,* Princeton University Press, New Jersey, 2003.

[40] L. Landau, Monotonicity and bounds on Bessel functions, *Electronic J. of Differential Equations.* (2002), 147-154.

[41] E. Mathieu, *Traité de physique mathématique, VI–VII: Théorie de l'élasticité des corps solides*, Gauthier-Villars, Paris, 1890.

[42] D.S. Mitrinović, J.E. Pečarić and A.M. Fink, *Classical and New Inequalities in Analysis*, Kluwer Academic Publishers, Dordrecht, 1993.

[43] J. Pečarić, F. Proschan and Y. Tong, *Convex Functions, Partial Orderings and Statistical Applications*, Academic Press, San Diego, 1992.

[44] F. Qi, Inequalities for Mathieu's series, *Internat. J. Pure Appl. Math.* (2003), in press.

[45] F. Qi, Integral expressions and inequalities of Mathieu type series, *RGMIA Res. Rep. Coll.*, **6**(2) (2003), Article 5. Available online at http://rgmia.vu.edu.au/v6n2.html

[46] F. Qi and Ch.-P. Chen, Notes on double inequalities of Mathieu's series, *RGMIA Res. Rep. Coll.*, **4**(2) (2001), Article 3. Available online at http://rgmia.vu.edu.au/v4n2.html

[47] N.Ja. Sonin, O nekotoryh neravenstvah otnosjaščihsjak opredelennym integralam, *Zap. Imp. Akad. Nauk po Fiziko-matem, Otd.t.*, **6** (1898), 1-54.

[48] H.M. Srivastava, Certain classes of series associated with the Zeta and related functions, *Appl. Math. & Comput.*, **141** (2003), 13–49.

[49] H.M. Srivastava, Some rapidly converging series for $\zeta(2n+1)$, *Proc. Amer. Math. Soc.*, **127** (1999), 385–3996.

[50] H.M. Srivastava, Some families of rapidly convergent series representation for the zeta function, *Taiwanese J. Math.*, **4** (2000), 569–596.

[51] H.M. Srivastava and J. Choi, Series associated with the zeta and related functions, Kluwer Acad. Publ., Dordrecht/Boston/London (2001), pp. 388.

[52] J.F. Steffensen, On certain inequalities between mean values and their application to actuarial problems, *Skandinavisk Aktuarietidskrift*, (1918), 82-97.

[53] E.C. Titchmarsh, *The Theory of the Riemann Zeta Function*, Oxford Univ. Press, London, 1951.

[54] Z. Tomovski and K. Trenčevski, On an open problem of Bai-Ni Guo and Feng Qi, *J. Inequal. Pure Appl. Math.*, **4**(2) (2003), In press. Available online at http://jipam.vu.edu.au/v4n2/102_02.html.

[55] Ch.-L. Wang and X.-H. Wang, A refinement of the Mathieu inequality, *Univ. Beograd. Publ. Elektroteh. Fak. Ser. Mat. No.* **716-734** (1981), 22-24.

[56] G.N. Watson, A treatise on the theory of Bessel functions, (1966) 2nd Edn., Cambridge University Press.

[57] E.T. Whittaker and G.N. Watson, *A Course of Modern Analysis*, Cambridge University Press, Cambridge, 1978.

[58] J.E. Wilkins, Jr., Solution of Problem 97-1, *Siam Rev.*.

In: Advances in Inequalities for Special Functions   ISBN 978-1-60021-919-1
Editors: P. Cerone and S. S. Dragomir, pp. 37–65   © 2008 Nova Science Publishers, Inc.

Inequalities for Positive Dirichlet Series

P. Cerone and S. S. Dragomir

School of Computer Science and Mathematics
Victoria University, PO Box 14428
Melbourne VIC 8001, Australia
E-mail addresses: {pietro.cerone,sever.dragomir}@vu.edu.au

ABSTRACT. In this paper we survey some recent results of the authors concerning inequalities for Dirichlet series with positive terms. Applications for the Zeta function are also provided.

1991 Mathematics Subject Classification: Primary 26D15, 11M38, 11M41.

Key words and phrases: Dirichlet series, Zeta function, Lambda function, Logarithmic convexity.

1 INTRODUCTION

We consider the following Dirichlet series:

$$\psi(s) := \sum_{n=1}^{\infty} \frac{a_n}{n^s} \tag{1.1}$$

for which we assume that the coefficients $a_n \geq 0$ for $n \geq 1$ and the series is uniformly convergent for $s > 1$.

It is obvious that in this class we can find the *Zeta function*

$$\zeta(s) := \sum_{n=1}^{\infty} \frac{1}{n^s} \tag{1.2}$$

and the *Lambda function*

$$\lambda(s) := \sum_{n=0}^{\infty} \frac{1}{(2n+1)^s} = \left(1 - 2^{-s}\right) \zeta(s), \tag{1.3}$$

where $s > 1$.

If $\Lambda(n)$ is the *von Mangoldt function*, where

$$\Lambda(n) := \begin{cases} \log p, & n = p^k \quad (p \text{ prime}, k \geq 1) \\ 0, & \text{otherwise}, \end{cases} \tag{1.4}$$

then [4, p. 3]:

$$-\frac{\zeta'(s)}{\zeta(s)} = \sum_{n=1}^{\infty} \frac{\Lambda(n)}{n^s}, \quad s > 1. \tag{1.5}$$

If $d(n)$ is the number of divisors of n, we have [4, p. 35] the following relationships with the Zeta function:

$$(1.6) \qquad \zeta^2(s) = \sum_{n=1}^{\infty} \frac{d(n)}{n^s},$$

$$(1.7) \qquad \frac{\zeta^3(s)}{\zeta(2s)} = \sum_{n=1}^{\infty} \frac{d(n^2)}{n^s},$$

$$(1.8) \qquad \frac{\zeta^4(s)}{\zeta(2s)} = \sum_{n=1}^{\infty} \frac{d^2(n)}{n^s},$$

and [4, p. 36]

$$(1.9) \qquad \frac{\zeta^2(s)}{\zeta(2s)} = \sum_{n=1}^{\infty} \frac{2^{\omega(n)}}{n^s}, \quad s > 1,$$

where $\omega(n)$ is the number of distinct prime factors of n.

Further, if $\varphi(n)$ denotes *Euler's function* defined by

$$\varphi(n) = n \prod_{p|n} \left(1 - \frac{1}{p}\right),$$

where the product is over all prime divisors of n, then

$$(1.10) \qquad \frac{\zeta(s-1)}{\zeta(s)} = \sum_{n=1}^{\infty} \frac{\varphi(n)}{n^s}, \quad s > 2.$$

For $a \in \mathbb{R}$ we define

$$\sigma_a(n) = \sum_{d|n} d^a$$

and in particular $\sigma(n) = \sigma_1(n) = \sum_{d|n} d$, is the sum of the divisors of n, then [4, p. 37] these are related to the Zeta function by

$$\zeta(s)\zeta(s-a) = \sum_{n=1}^{\infty} \frac{\sigma_a(n)}{n^s}, \quad s > \max\{1, a+1\};$$

and

$$\frac{\zeta(s)\zeta(s-a)\zeta(s-b)\zeta(s-a-b)}{\zeta(2s-a-b)} = \sum_{n=1}^{\infty} \frac{\sigma_a(n)\sigma_b(n)}{n^s},$$

where $s > \max\{1, a+1, b+1, a+b+1\}$.

The main aim of the present paper is to survey some recent results obtained by the authors concerning various inequalities and functional properties of Dirichlet series with positive terms. Numerous particular cases for the Zeta funcion are also pointed out.

2 SOME CONVEXITY PROPERTIES

2.1 Inequalities for Log-convex Functions

In what follows, we will denote an interval of real numbers by I. A function $f : I \to (0, \infty)$ is said to be *logarithmic convex* or *log-convex* for short if $\log f$ is convex, or, equivalently, if for any $x, y \in I$ and $t \in [0, 1]$ one has the inequality [6, p. 7]

$$(2.1) \qquad f\left(tx + (1 - t)y\right) \le \left[f\left(x\right)\right]^{t} \left[f\left(y\right)\right]^{1-t}.$$

We note that if f and g are convex and g is increasing, then $g \circ f$ is convex; moreover, since $f = \exp\left(\log f\right)$, it follows that a log-convex function is convex, but the converse may not necessarily be true [6, p. 7]. This follows directly from (2.1) because, by the arithmetic-geometric mean inequality, we have

$$(2.2) \qquad \left[f\left(x\right)\right]^{t} \left[f\left(y\right)\right]^{1-t} \le tf\left(x\right) + (1 - t)f\left(y\right)$$

for all $x, y \in I$ and $t \in [0, 1]$.

The following result may be stated [1]:

Proposition 2.1. *Let $f : I \subseteq \mathbb{R} \to (0, \infty)$ be a log-convex function. If $x \in I$ and $h > 0$ are such that $x + h, x + 2h \in I$, then*

$$(2.3) \qquad f\left(x + h\right) \le \sqrt{f\left(x\right)f\left(x + 2h\right)}.$$

Proof. Since $\ln f\left(\cdot\right)$ is convex, then for any $x_3 > x_2 > x_1$ we have

$$\frac{\ln f\left(x_3\right) - \ln f\left(x_2\right)}{x_3 - x_2} \ge \frac{\ln f\left(x_2\right) - \ln f\left(x_1\right)}{x_2 - x_1}$$

giving the inequality:

$$\ln \left[\frac{f\left(x_3\right)}{f\left(x_2\right)}\right]^{\frac{1}{x_3 - x_2}} \ge \ln \left[\frac{f\left(x_2\right)}{f\left(x_1\right)}\right]^{\frac{1}{x_2 - x_1}}$$

which is clearly equivalent to:

$$(2.4) \qquad \left[\frac{f\left(x_3\right)}{f\left(x_2\right)}\right]^{\frac{1}{x_3 - x_2}} \ge \left[\frac{f\left(x_2\right)}{f\left(x_1\right)}\right]^{\frac{1}{x_2 - x_1}}.$$

Now, if in (2.4) we choose $x_3 = x + 2h$, $x_2 = x + h$ and $x_1 = x$, then by (2.4) we deduce the desired result (2.3). $\qquad \square$

Remark 2.1. *If $f : [a, \infty) \to (0, \infty)$ is log-convex, then obviously*

$$(2.5) \qquad f\left(x + h\right) \le \sqrt{f\left(x\right)f\left(x + 2h\right)}$$

for any $x \ge a$, $h \ge 0$ and in particular

$$(2.6) \qquad f\left(x + 1\right) \le \sqrt{f\left(x\right)f\left(x + 2\right)}, \quad \text{for any } x \ge a.$$

Proposition 2.2. *If $f : I \subseteq \mathbb{R} \to (0, \infty)$ is log-convex and differentiable on $\mathring{I}$, then for $x \in \mathring{I}$ and $h > 0$, with $x + h \in \mathring{I}$, we have:*

$$(2.7) \qquad \exp\left[h \cdot \frac{f'\left(x + h\right)}{f\left(x + h\right)}\right] \ge \frac{f\left(x + h\right)}{f\left(x\right)} \ge \exp\left[h \cdot \frac{f'\left(x\right)}{f\left(x\right)}\right].$$

Proof. Since $\ln f$ is convex and differentiable, then for $x_2, x_1 \in \overset{\circ}{I}$, $x_2 > x_1$ we have

$$[\ln f(x)]'_{x=x_2} \geq \frac{\ln f(x_2) - \ln f(x_1)}{x_2 - x_1} \geq [\ln f(x)]'_{x=x_1}$$

which is clearly equivalent to

$$(x_2 - x_1)\frac{f'(x_2)}{f(x_2)} \geq \ln\left[\frac{f(x_2)}{f(x_1)}\right] \geq (x_2 - x_1)\frac{f'(x_1)}{f(x_1)}$$

and so

$$(2.8) \qquad \exp\left[(x_2 - x_1)\frac{f'(x_2)}{f(x_2)}\right] \geq \frac{f(x_2)}{f(x_1)} \geq \exp\left[(x_2 - x_1)\frac{f'(x_1)}{f(x_1)}\right].$$

Now, if we take in (2.8) $x_2 = x + h$, $x_1 = x$, then we get (2.7). $\qquad\square$

Remark 2.2. *If $f : [a, \infty) \to [0, \infty)$ is log-convex and differentiable, then:*

$$(2.9) \qquad \exp\left[\frac{f'(x+1)}{f(x+1)}\right] \geq \frac{f(x+1)}{f(x)} \geq \exp\left[\frac{f'(x)}{f(x)}\right],$$

for any $x \in [a, \infty)$.

Another result is as follows.

Proposition 2.3. *Let $f : I \subseteq \mathbb{R} \to (0, \infty)$ be a log-convex function which is differentiable on $\overset{\circ}{I}$. If $\alpha, \beta \geq 0$ and $\alpha + \beta = 1$ then for all $x_1, x_2 \in \overset{\circ}{I}$ we have:*

$$(2.10) \qquad (1 \leq) \frac{[f(x_1)]^\alpha [f(x_2)]^\beta}{f(\alpha x_1 + \beta x_2)} \leq \exp\left\{\alpha\beta(x_2 - x_1)\left[\frac{f'(x_2)}{f(x_2)} - \frac{f'(x_1)}{f(x_1)}\right]\right\}.$$

Proof. We have

$$(2.11) \qquad \ln f(\alpha x_1 + \beta x_2) - \ln f(x_1) \geq (\alpha x_1 + \beta x_2 - x_1)\frac{f'(x_1)}{f(x_1)}$$

$$= \beta(x_2 - x_1)\frac{f'(x_1)}{f(x_1)}$$

and

$$(2.12) \qquad \ln f(\alpha x_1 + \beta x_2) - \ln f(x_2) \geq (\alpha x_1 + \beta x_2 - x_2)\frac{f'(x_2)}{f(x_2)}$$

$$= -\alpha(x_2 - x_1)\frac{f'(x_2)}{f(x_2)}.$$

We multiply (2.11) and (2.12) with $\alpha \geq 0$ and $\beta \geq 0$ respectively and add the obtained results to get:

$$\ln f(\alpha x_1 + \beta x_2) - \alpha \ln f(x_1) - \beta \ln f(x_2) \geq -\alpha\beta(x_2 - x_1)\left[\frac{f'(x_2)}{f(x_2)} - \frac{f'(x_1)}{f(x_1)}\right]$$

which implies that

$$\alpha \ln f(x_1) + \beta \ln f(x_2) - \ln f(\alpha x_1 + \beta x_2) \leq \alpha\beta(x_2 - x_1)\left[\frac{f'(x_2)}{f(x_2)} - \frac{f'(x_1)}{f(x_1)}\right]$$

which is equivalent with (2.10). $\qquad\square$

Corollary 2.4. *If $f : I \subseteq \mathbb{R} \to \mathbb{R}$ is log-convex and differentiable then for any $\alpha \in \overset{\circ}{I}$ and $h > 0$ with $x + h \in \overset{\circ}{I}$, we have:*

$$(2.13) \qquad (1 \leq) \frac{[f(x)]^\alpha [f(x+h)]^\beta}{f(x+\beta h)} \leq \exp\left\{ \alpha\beta h \left[\frac{f'(x+h)}{f(x+h)} - \frac{f'(x)}{f(x)} \right] \right\}$$

for any $\alpha, \beta > 0$ with $\alpha + \beta = 1$.

Remark 2.3. *If $\alpha = \beta = \frac{1}{2}$, then we have*

$$(2.14) \qquad (1 \leq) \frac{\sqrt{f(x) f(x+h)}}{f\left(x+\frac{h}{2}\right)} \leq \exp\left\{ \frac{1}{4} h \left[\frac{f'(x+h)}{f(x+h)} - \frac{f'(x)}{f(x)} \right] \right\}.$$

Now, if $h = 2k$, $k > 0$, then we get from (2.14):

$$(2.15) \qquad (1 \leq) \frac{\sqrt{f(x) f(x+2k)}}{f(x+k)} \leq \exp\left\{ \frac{1}{2} k \left[\frac{f'(x+2k)}{f(x+2k)} - \frac{f'(x)}{f(x)} \right] \right\},$$

and in particular

$$(2.16) \qquad (1 \leq) \frac{\sqrt{f(x) f(x+2)}}{f(x+1)} \leq \exp\left\{ \frac{1}{2} \left[\frac{f'(x+2)}{f(x+2)} - \frac{f'(x)}{f(x)} \right] \right\}.$$

The inequality (2.15) is a reverse of (2.3) while (2.16) is a reverse of (2.6).

Now consider the function $\varphi : I \to \mathbb{R}$, $\varphi(x) = \frac{f'(x)}{f(x)}$, and assume that f is twice differentiable on $\overset{\circ}{I}$. Then

$$(2.17) \qquad \varphi'(x) = \frac{f''(x) f'(x) - [f'(x)]^2}{[f(x)]^2}, \quad x \in \overset{\circ}{I}.$$

The following corollary of Proposition 2.3 may be stated as well.

Corollary 2.5. *Let $f : I \subseteq \mathbb{R} \to \mathbb{R}$ be a log-convex function that is also twice differentiable on $\overset{\circ}{I}$. Assume that there exists a constant $K > 0$ such that*

$$(2.18) \qquad (0 \leq) \frac{f''(x) f(x) - [f'(x)]^2}{[f(x)]^2} \leq K \quad \text{for any } x \in \overset{\circ}{I}.$$

Then for any $x_1, x_2 \in \overset{\circ}{I}$ and $\alpha, \beta > 0$ with $\alpha + \beta = 1$, we have:

$$(2.19) \qquad (1 \leq) \frac{[f(x_1)]^\alpha [f(x_2)]^\beta}{f(\alpha x_1 + \beta x_2)} \leq \exp\left[\alpha\beta K (x_2 - x_1)^2 \right].$$

Proof. Follows by Proposition 2.3 on applying Lagrange's mean value theorem for the function φ defined by (2.17). □

Remark 2.4. *If we choose $x_1 = x$, $x_2 = x + h \in \overset{\circ}{I}$ $(h > 0)$, then we get from (2.19):*

$$(2.20) \qquad (1 \leq) \frac{[f(x)]^\alpha [f(x+h)]^\beta}{f(x+\beta h)} \leq \exp\left(\alpha\beta K h^2 \right)$$

and in particular:

$$(2.21) \qquad (1 \leq) \frac{\sqrt{f(x) f(x+2k)}}{f(x+k)} \leq \exp\left(K k^2 \right)$$

for x, $x + k$, $x + 2k \in \overset{\circ}{I}$ $(k > 0)$.

Finally, (2.21) provides the inequality:

$$(2.22) \qquad (1 \leq) \frac{\sqrt{f(x)f(x+2)}}{f(x+1)} \leq \exp K$$

if x, $x + 1$, $x + 2 \in \overset{\circ}{I}$.

2.2   Applications for Dirichlet Series with Positive Terms

In [3], A. Gut observed that the Zeta function is log-convex for $s > 1$. However, as in the case of the present authors, he was unable to locate the results in an earlier paper.

Utilising a simpler argument than Gut, we are able to prove the logarithmic convexity of Dirichlet series with positive terms, as follows [1]:

Proposition 2.6. *The function ψ defined by (1.1) is log-convex on $(1, \infty)$.*

Proof. Let $s_1, s_2 \in (1, \infty)$ and $\alpha, \beta \geq 0$ with $\alpha + \beta = 1$. Utilising the Hölder inequality for $p = \frac{1}{\alpha}$, $q = \frac{1}{\beta}$ $(\alpha > 0)$ we have:

$$\begin{aligned}
\psi(\alpha s_1 + \beta s_2) &= \sum_{n=1}^{\infty} \frac{a_n}{n^{\alpha s_1 + \beta s_2}} = \sum_{n=1}^{\infty} \frac{a_n}{(n^{s_1})^{\alpha}(n^{s_2})^{\beta}} \\
&\leq \left[\sum_{n=1}^{\infty} a_n \left(\frac{1}{(n^{s_1})^{\alpha}} \right)^p \right]^{\frac{1}{p}} \left[\sum_{n=1}^{\infty} a_n \left(\frac{1}{(n^{s_2})^{\beta}} \right)^q \right]^{\frac{1}{q}} \\
&= \left(\sum_{n=1}^{\infty} \frac{a_n}{n^{s_1}} \right)^{\alpha} \left(\sum_{n=1}^{\infty} \frac{a_n}{n^{s_2}} \right)^{\beta} \\
&= [\psi(s_1)]^{\alpha} [\psi(s_2)]^{\beta},
\end{aligned}$$

which proves the desired conclusion.   □

Remark 2.5. *It is obvious that all the results stated in Section 2 will hold for the function ψ defined in (1.1). For the sake of brevity, we make some remarks only on the simplest results.*

For instance, we can state that:

$$\psi(s + h) \leq \sqrt{\psi(s)\psi(s + 2h)}$$

for any $s > 1$ and $h > 0$ and in particular

$$(2.23) \qquad \psi(s + 1) \leq \sqrt{\psi(s)\psi(s + 2)}$$

for $s > 1$.

We remark that for $\psi = \zeta$ one obtains from (2.23) that

$$(2.24) \qquad \frac{\zeta(s + 1)}{\zeta(s)} \leq \frac{\zeta(s + 2)}{\zeta(s + 1)} \quad \text{for } s > 1.$$

This inequality is an improvement of a recent result due to Laforgia and Natalini [5] who proved that

$$\frac{\zeta(s + 1)}{\zeta(s)} \leq \frac{s + 1}{s} \cdot \frac{\zeta(s + 2)}{\zeta(s + 1)} \quad \text{for } s > 1.$$

Their arguments make use of an integral representation and Turán-type inequalities.

Remark 2.6. *If we apply the inequality (2.23) for* $\lambda(s) = \frac{2^s - 1}{2^s} \zeta(s)$, $s > 1$, *we have*

$$(2.25) \qquad \frac{\left(2^{s+1} - 1\right)^2}{\left(2^s - 1\right)\left(2^{s+2} - 1\right)} \leq \frac{\zeta(s)\zeta(s+2)}{\zeta^2(s+1)}, \quad \text{for } s > 1.$$

Since a simple calculation shows that

$$1 \leq \frac{\left(2^{s+1} - 1\right)^2}{\left(2^s - 1\right)\left(2^{s+2} - 1\right)}, \quad \text{for } s > 1$$

it follows that (2.25) is a better inequality than (2.24). which is equivalent with

$$(2.26) \qquad 1 \leq \frac{\zeta(s)\zeta(s+2)}{\zeta^2(s+1)}, \quad s > 1.$$

Now, if we apply the same inequality (2.23) for the functions $\psi(s) = \frac{\zeta(s)}{\zeta(s+1)}$, $s > 1$ *and* $\psi(s) = \zeta(s+1)\zeta(s)$, $s > 1$, *then we get*

$$(2.27) \qquad \frac{\zeta(s)}{\zeta(s+3)} \geq \left[\frac{\zeta(s+1)}{\zeta(s+2)}\right]^3, \quad s > 1$$

and

$$(2.28) \qquad \frac{\zeta(s)}{\zeta(s+1)} \geq \frac{\zeta(s+2)}{\zeta(s+3)}, \quad s > 1.$$

Remark 2.7. *The above result (2.24) may be useful for some alternating Dirichlet series. For instance, if we consider the **Eta function** defined by*

$$(2.29) \qquad \eta(s) := \sum_{n=1}^{\infty} \frac{(-1)^{n-1}}{n^s}$$

and use the representation

$$(2.30) \qquad \eta(s) = \left(1 - 2^{1-s}\right)\zeta(s), \quad \text{for } s > 1,$$

then on utilising the inequality for Zeta

$$(2.31) \qquad \zeta^2(s+1) \leq \zeta(s)\zeta(s+2), \quad \text{for } s > 1,$$

we can easily deduce that

$$(2.32) \qquad \frac{\left(1 - 2^{1-s}\right)\left(1 - 2^{-1-s}\right)}{\left(1 - 2^{-s}\right)^2} \leq \frac{\eta(s)\eta(s+2)}{\eta^2(s+1)},$$

for any $s > 1$.

Conjecture 2.7. *We conjecture that the function* $\eta : (1, \infty) \to \mathbb{R}$ *is logarithmic concave on this interval.*
Since, for $s > 1$, $\psi(s) := \ln\eta(s) = \ln\left(1 - 2^{1-s}\right) + \ln\zeta(s)$ *and*

$$\psi'(s) = \frac{\zeta'(s)}{\zeta(s)} + \frac{\ln 2}{2^{s-1} - 1},$$

$$\psi''(s) = \frac{\zeta''(s)\zeta(s) - \left[\zeta'(s)\right]^2}{\left[\zeta(s)\right]^2} - \frac{2^{s-1}(\ln 2)^2}{\left(2^{s-1} - 1\right)^2},$$

hence the logarithmic concavity of η will be equivalent with the inequality:

$$\text{(2.33)} \qquad \frac{\zeta''(s)\,\zeta(s) - [\zeta'(s)]^2}{[\zeta(s)]^2} \leq \frac{2^{s-1}\,(\ln 2)^2}{(2^{s-1} - 1)^2}$$

for $s > 1$.

The logarithmic concavity of η would also imply

$$\text{(2.34)} \qquad \frac{\eta(s)\,\eta(s+2)}{\eta^2(s+1)} \leq 1, \quad s > 1$$

which seems to be satisfied as may be seen from computer experimentation with Maple.

If, however, we assume more about the positive sequence a_n, then we obtain some other results as follows [1].

Theorem 2.8. *If the sequence $(a_n)_{n \in \mathbb{N}}$ is monotonic nonincreasing, then*

$$\text{(2.35)} \qquad \frac{\psi(s+h)}{\psi(s)} \geq \exp\left[h \cdot \frac{\zeta'(s)}{\zeta(s)}\right]$$

for any $s > 1$ and $h > 0$.

If $(a_n)_{n \in \mathbb{N}}$ is monotonic nondecreasing, then

$$\text{(2.36)} \qquad \exp\left[h \cdot \frac{\zeta'(s+h)}{\zeta(s+h)}\right] \geq \frac{\psi(s+h)}{\psi(s)},$$

for any $s > 1$ and $h > 0$.

Proof. From Proposition 2.2 we always have the double inequality

$$\text{(2.37)} \qquad \exp\left[h \cdot \frac{\psi'(s+h)}{\psi(s+h)}\right] \geq \frac{\psi(s+h)}{\psi(s)} \geq \exp\left[h \cdot \frac{\psi'(s)}{\psi(s)}\right]$$

for any $s > 1$ and $h > 0$.

Observe that for $s > 1$

$$\psi'(s) = -\sum_{n=1}^{\infty} a_n \frac{\ln n}{n^s}.$$

Since the sequence $(\ln n)_{n \in \mathbb{N}}$ is increasing, then assuming that $(a_n)_{n \in \mathbb{N}}$ is nonincreasing and applying Čebyšev's inequality to asynchronous sequences, we have:

$$\text{(2.38)} \qquad \sum_{n=1}^{\infty} \frac{1}{n^s} \cdot \sum_{n=1}^{\infty} \frac{a_n \ln n}{n^s} \leq \sum_{n=1}^{\infty} \frac{a_n}{n^s} \cdot \sum_{n=1}^{\infty} \frac{\ln n}{n^s}$$

for $s > 1$.

Further,

$$\zeta'(s) = -\sum_{n=1}^{\infty} \frac{\ln n}{n^s}, \quad s > 1$$

and so from (2.38) we get

$$-\frac{\sum_{n=1}^{\infty} \frac{a_n \ln n}{n^s}}{\sum_{n=1}^{\infty} \frac{a_n}{n^s}} \geq -\frac{\sum_{n=1}^{\infty} \frac{\ln n}{n^s}}{\sum_{n=1}^{\infty} \frac{1}{n^s}}$$

which is exactly

(2.39)
$$\frac{\psi'(s)}{\psi(s)} \geq \frac{\zeta'(s)}{\zeta(s)}, \quad s > 1,$$

that is of interest in itself.

Utilising the second inequality in (2.37) and (2.39) we deduce (2.35). The inequality (2.36) can be proved in a similar manner and the details are omitted. □

Remark 2.8. *Utilising the inequality (2.9) and the fact that (see (1.5))*

$$\frac{\zeta'(s)}{\zeta(s)} = -\sum_{n=1}^{\infty} \frac{\Lambda(n)}{n^s}, \quad s > 1,$$

we may also state the following result for the Zeta function

(2.40)
$$\exp\left[-\sum_{n=1}^{\infty} \frac{\Lambda(n)}{n^{s+1}}\right] \geq \frac{\zeta(s+1)}{\zeta(s)} \geq \exp\left[-\sum_{n=1}^{\infty} \frac{\Lambda(n)}{n^s}\right]$$

for any $s > 1$.

The following result may also be stated [1].

Theorem 2.9. *If $s > \frac{3}{2}$, $h > 0$ and $\alpha, \beta \geq 0$ with $\alpha + \beta = 1$, then*

(2.41)
$$(1 \leq) \frac{[\psi(s)]^{\alpha} [\psi(s+h)]^{\beta}}{\psi(s+\beta h)}$$
$$\leq \exp\left\{\alpha\beta h \left[\frac{\psi\left(s-\frac{1}{2}\right)\psi\left(s+h+\frac{1}{2}\right) - \psi\left(s+h-\frac{1}{2}\right)\psi\left(s+\frac{1}{2}\right)}{\psi(s+h)\psi(s)}\right]\right\}.$$

Proof. Utilising Corollary 2.4 for the log-convex function ψ, we can state that:

(2.42)
$$\frac{[\psi(s)]^{\alpha} [\psi(s+h)]^{\beta}}{\psi(s+\beta h)} \leq \exp\left\{\alpha\beta h \left[\frac{\psi'(s+h)}{\psi(s+h)} - \frac{\psi'(s)}{\psi(s)}\right]\right\}$$

for $s > 1$.

Let $k \geq 1$ and consider the expression for $s > 1$

$$\delta_k := \frac{\sum_{n=1}^{k} a_n \frac{\ln n}{n^s}}{\sum_{n=1}^{k} \frac{a_n}{n^s}} - \frac{\sum_{n=1}^{k} a_n \frac{\ln n}{n^{s+h}}}{\sum_{n=1}^{k} \frac{a_n}{n^{s+h}}}.$$

Using Korkine's identity we then have:

$$\delta_k = \frac{\sum_{n=1}^{k} \frac{a_n}{n^s} \cdot \frac{1}{n^h} \sum_{n=1}^{k} a_n \frac{\ln n}{n^s} - \sum_{n=1}^{k} \frac{a_n}{n^s} \cdot \sum_{n=1}^{k} \frac{a_n}{n^h} \cdot \frac{\ln n}{n^s}}{\sum_{n=1}^{k} \frac{a_n}{n^s} \cdot \sum_{n=1}^{k} \frac{a_n}{n^{s+h}}}$$

$$= \frac{\frac{1}{2} \sum_{n=1}^{k} \sum_{m=1}^{k} \frac{a_n}{n^s} \cdot \frac{a_m}{m^s} (\ln n - \ln m) \left(\frac{1}{m^h} - \frac{1}{n^h}\right)}{\sum_{n=1}^{k} \frac{a_n}{n^s} \cdot \sum_{n=1}^{k} \frac{a_n}{n^{s+h}}}$$

$$= \frac{\frac{1}{2} \sum_{n=1}^{k} \sum_{m=1}^{k} \frac{a_n}{n^{s+h}} \cdot \frac{a_m}{m^{s+h}} (\ln n - \ln m) \left(n^h - m^h\right)}{\sum_{n=1}^{k} \frac{a_n}{n^s} \cdot \sum_{n=1}^{k} \frac{a_n}{n^{s+h}}}.$$

The elementary inequality

$$\frac{\ln n - \ln m}{n - m} \leq \frac{1}{\sqrt{nm}} \quad \text{for } n, m \geq 1, \ n \neq m$$

which follows from the fact that the logarithmic mean $\frac{a-b}{\ln a - \ln b}$ is greater than the geometric mean, then gives

$$(2.43) \qquad 0 \leq \delta_k \leq \frac{\frac{1}{2} \sum_{n=1}^{k} \sum_{m=1}^{k} \frac{a_n}{n^{s+h}} \cdot \frac{a_m}{m^{s+h}} \frac{(n-m)\left(n^h - m^h\right)}{\sqrt{nm}}}{\sum_{n=1}^{k} \frac{a_n}{n^s} \cdot \sum_{n=1}^{k} \frac{a_n}{n^{s+h}}}$$

$$= \frac{\frac{1}{2} \sum_{n=1}^{k} \sum_{m=1}^{k} \frac{a_n}{n^{s+h+\frac{1}{2}}} \cdot \frac{a_m}{m^{s+h+\frac{1}{2}}} (n-m)\left(n^h - m^h\right)}{\sum_{n=1}^{k} \frac{a_n}{n^s} \cdot \sum_{n=1}^{k} \frac{a_n}{n^{s+h}}}$$

$$= \frac{\sum_{n=1}^{k} \frac{a_n}{n^{s+h+\frac{1}{2}}} n \cdot n^h \sum_{n=1}^{k} \frac{a_n}{n^{s+h+\frac{1}{2}}} - \sum_{n=1}^{k} \frac{a_n}{n^{s+h+\frac{1}{2}}} \cdot n \sum_{n=1}^{k} \frac{a_n}{n^{s+h+\frac{1}{2}}} n^h}{\sum_{n=1}^{k} \frac{a_n}{n^s} \cdot \sum_{n=1}^{k} \frac{a_n}{n^{s+h}}}$$

$$= \frac{\sum_{n=1}^{k} \frac{a_n}{n^{s-\frac{1}{2}}} \cdot \sum_{n=1}^{k} \frac{a_n}{n^{s+h+\frac{1}{2}}} - \sum_{n=1}^{k} \frac{a_n}{n^{s+h-\frac{1}{2}}} \cdot \sum_{n=1}^{k} \frac{a_n}{n^{s+\frac{1}{2}}}}{\sum_{n=1}^{k} \frac{a_n}{n^s} \cdot \sum_{n=1}^{k} \frac{a_n}{n^{s+h}}}$$

$$=: \Delta_k.$$

Since both sequences are uniformly convergent and

$$\lim_{k \to \infty} \delta_k = \frac{\psi'(s+h)}{\psi(s+h)} - \frac{\psi'(s)}{\psi(s)} \geq 0, \quad s > 1, h > 0$$

and

$$\lim_{k \to \infty} \Delta_k = \frac{\psi\left(s - \frac{1}{2}\right) \psi\left(s + h + \frac{1}{2}\right) - \psi\left(s + h - \frac{1}{2}\right) \psi\left(s + \frac{1}{2}\right)}{\psi(s+h) \psi(s)}$$

for $s > \frac{3}{2}$, $h > 0$, then by the inequalities (2.42) and (2.43) we deduce (2.41). $\qquad\square$

Remark 2.9. *We observe that in the above proposition we proved the result*

$$(2.44) \qquad 0 \leq \frac{\psi'(s+h)}{\psi(s+h)} - \frac{\psi'(s)}{\psi(s)} \leq \frac{\psi\left(s - \frac{1}{2}\right) \psi\left(s + h + \frac{1}{2}\right) - \psi\left(s + h - \frac{1}{2}\right) \psi\left(s + \frac{1}{2}\right)}{\psi(s+h) \psi(s)},$$

for any $s > \frac{3}{2}$ and $h > 0$, which is of interest in itself.

Remark 2.10. *In particular, we get for $\alpha + \beta = \frac{1}{2}$ from (2.41):*

$$(2.45) \qquad (1 \leq) \frac{\sqrt{\psi(s) \psi(s+h)}}{\psi\left(s + \frac{h}{2}\right)}$$

$$\leq \exp\left\{\frac{1}{4} h \left[\frac{\psi\left(s - \frac{1}{2}\right) \psi\left(s + h + \frac{1}{2}\right) - \psi\left(s + h - \frac{1}{2}\right) \psi\left(s + \frac{1}{2}\right)}{\psi(s+h) \psi(s)}\right]\right\}$$

for $s > \frac{3}{2}$ and $h > 0$.

Further, choosing $h = 2$ in (2.45) produces

$$(2.46) \qquad (1 \leq) \frac{\sqrt{\psi(s) \psi(s+2)}}{\psi(s+1)}$$

$$\leq \exp\left\{\frac{1}{2} \left[\frac{\psi\left(s - \frac{1}{2}\right) \psi\left(s + \frac{5}{2}\right) - \psi\left(s + \frac{3}{2}\right) \psi\left(s + \frac{1}{2}\right)}{\psi(s+2) \psi(s)}\right]\right\},$$

for $s > \frac{3}{2}$.

2.3 Concavity of the Function $1/\psi$

Consider the Dirichlet series $\psi(s)$ as defined by (1.1).

The following proposition may be stated [1]:

Proposition 2.10. *For the function ψ defined as above, the following statements are equivalent:*

(i) The function $1/\psi$ in concave on $(1, \infty)$;

(ii) For any $s_1, s_2 > 1$ and $\alpha, \beta \geq 0$ with $\alpha + \beta = 1$ we have

$$(2.47) \qquad \psi(\alpha s_1 + \beta s_2) \leq \frac{\psi(s_1)\,\psi(s_2)}{\alpha\psi(s_1) + \beta\psi(s_2)}.$$

(iii) For any $s > 1$ we have

$$(2.48) \qquad \psi''(s)\,\psi(s) \geq 2\left[\psi'(s)\right]^2.$$

(iv) For any $s > 1$ we have

$$(2.49) \qquad \sum_{n=1}^{\infty} \frac{a_n}{n^s} \cdot \sum_{n=1}^{\infty} \frac{a_n\,(\ln n)^2}{n^s} \geq 2 \cdot \left(\sum_{n=1}^{\infty} \frac{a_n \cdot \ln n}{n^s}\right)^2.$$

Proof. By the definition of concavity we have that $1/\psi$ is concave if and only if for any $s_1, s_2 > 1$ and $\alpha, \beta \geq 0$ with $\alpha + \beta = 1$

$$\frac{1}{\psi(\alpha s_1 + \beta s_2)} \geq \frac{\alpha}{\psi(s_1)} + \frac{\beta}{\psi(s_2)},$$

which is exactly (2.47).

Finally, $1/\psi$ is concave if and only if $\frac{d^2}{ds^2}\left(\frac{1}{\psi(s)}\right) \leq 0$ and since

$$\frac{d}{ds}\left(\frac{1}{\psi(s)}\right) = -\frac{\psi'(s)}{\psi^2(s)},$$

$$\frac{d^2}{ds^2}\left(\frac{1}{\psi(s)}\right) = -\frac{\psi''(s)\,\psi(s) - 2\left[\psi'(s)\right]^2}{\psi^3(s)}$$

$$= \frac{2\left[\psi'(s)\right]^2 - \psi''(s)\,\psi(s)}{\psi^3(s)}$$

and

$$\psi'(s) = -\sum_{n=1}^{\infty} \frac{a_n \cdot \ln n}{n^s}, \qquad \psi''(s) = \sum_{n=1}^{\infty} \frac{a_n\,(\ln n)^2}{n^s}, \qquad s > 1$$

then $1/\psi$ is concave if and only if either (2.48) or, equivalently (2.49) holds true. $\qquad\square$

Remark 2.11. *If one of the statements (i), (ii) or (iii) holds, then we have the inequality:*

$$(2.50) \qquad \psi(s+1) \leq \frac{2\psi(s)\,\psi(s+2)}{\psi(s) + \psi(s+2)}.$$

for any $s > 1$. This inequality, if true, would improve the known fact from (2.23) that:

$$(2.51) \qquad \psi(s+1) \leq \sqrt{\psi(s)\psi(s+2)}, \quad s > 1$$

since, by the harmonic mean – geometric mean inequality we know that

$$(2.52) \qquad \frac{2\psi(s)\psi(s+2)}{\psi(s) + \psi(s+2)} \leq \sqrt{\psi(s)\psi(s+2)}, \quad s > 1.$$

Conjecture 2.11. *Based on some numerical experiments conducted with a computer program, we conjecture that any Dirichlet series ψ with nonnegative coefficients has the property that the function $1/\psi$ is concave where it is defined.*

The following result gives an answer to the conjecture above in the case of the *Zeta function.*

Theorem 2.12. *The function $1/\zeta$ is concave on the interval $(1, \infty)$*

Proof. We use the following identities

$$(2.53) \qquad \frac{\zeta'(s)}{\zeta(s)} = -\sum_{n=2}^{\infty} \frac{\Lambda(n)}{n^s}, \quad \text{(see for example [3, Eq. (5.2)])}$$

$$(2.54) \qquad \ln\zeta(s) = \sum_{n=2}^{\infty} \frac{\Lambda(n)}{n^s \ln n}, \quad \text{(see [3, Eq. (3.2)])}$$

and

$$(2.55) \qquad \frac{\zeta''(s)\zeta(s) - [\zeta'(s)]^2}{[\zeta(s)]^2} = \sum_{n=2}^{\infty} \frac{\Lambda(n)\ln n}{n^s}, \quad \text{(see [3, Eq. (5.5)])},$$

where $s > 1$ and $\Lambda(n)$ is the von Mangold function defined by (1.4).

Utilising the Schwarz inequality

$$\sum_{m=1}^{k} p_m \sum_{m=1}^{k} p_m \alpha_k^2 \geq \left(\sum_{m=1}^{k} p_m \alpha_m \right)^2$$

with $p_m \geq 0$, $\alpha_m \in \mathbb{R}$, $m \in \{1, \dots, k\}$, we may state from (2.55)

$$(2.56) \qquad \sum_{n=2}^{\infty} \frac{\Lambda(n)\ln n}{n^s} = \sum_{n=2}^{\infty} \frac{\Lambda(n)}{n^s \cdot \ln n} \cdot (\ln n)^2$$

$$\geq \frac{\left(\sum_{n=2}^{\infty} \frac{\Lambda(n)}{n^s \cdot \ln n} \cdot \ln n \right)^2}{\sum_{n=2}^{\infty} \frac{\Lambda(n)}{n^s \cdot \ln n}} = \frac{\left(\sum_{n=2}^{\infty} \frac{\Lambda(n)}{n^s} \right)^2}{\sum_{n=2}^{\infty} \frac{\Lambda(n)}{n^s \cdot \ln n}}$$

for $s > 1$, which by the identities (2.53) – (2.55), is equivalent with

$$(2.57) \qquad \frac{\zeta''(s)\zeta(s) - [\zeta'(s)]^2}{[\zeta(s)]^2} \geq \frac{\left[\frac{\zeta'(s)}{\zeta(s)} \right]^2}{\ln\zeta(s)}, \quad s > 1,$$

giving the interesting result

$$(2.58) \qquad \zeta''(s)\,\zeta(s) - \left[\zeta'(s)\right]^2 \geq \frac{\left[\zeta'(s)\right]^2}{\ln \zeta(s)} \quad (> 0),$$

for any $s \in (1, \infty)$.

Now, we observe that for $s \in \left[\zeta^{-1}(e), \infty\right)$ we have that $\zeta(s) \geq 1$ and then by (2.58) we get

$$(2.59) \qquad \zeta''(s)\,\zeta(s) \geq 2\left[\zeta'(s)\right]^2$$

which is equivalent with the fact that $1/\zeta$ is concave on the interval $\left[\zeta^{-1}(e), \infty\right)$.

Finally, a simple Maple program (see Figure 1) shows that the plot of the difference $\zeta''(s)\,\zeta(s) - 2\left[\zeta'(s)\right]^2$ for $s \in (1, \zeta^{-1}(e))$ is above the constant $12.60536482 \,(= \zeta''(s_0)\,\zeta(s_0) - 2\left[\zeta'(s_0)\right]^2$ where $s_0 = \zeta^{-1}(e))$, and therefore the inequality (2.58) is trivially satisfied on this interval as well. $\qquad\qquad\qquad\qquad\qquad\qquad\qquad\qquad\qquad\qquad\qquad\square$

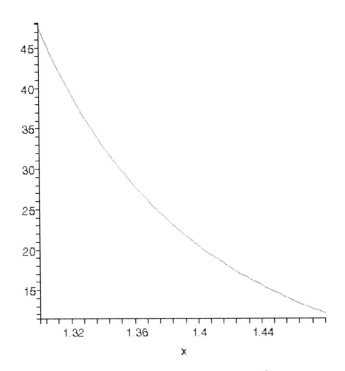

FIGURE 1: The plot for $\zeta''(x)\,\zeta(x) - 2\left[\zeta'(x)\right]^2$ on $(1, \zeta^{-1}(e))$.

The concavity of $\frac{1}{\zeta}$ implies from Proposition 2.10 that $\zeta(s+1)$ is bounded by the harmonic mean of $\zeta(s)$ and $\zeta(s+2)$. Namely,

Corollary 2.13. *For any $s > 1$ we have that*

$$(2.60) \qquad \zeta(s+1) \leq \frac{2\zeta(s)\,\zeta(s+2)}{\zeta(s) + \zeta(s+2)} \quad \left(\leq \sqrt{\zeta(s)\,\zeta(s+2)}\right).$$

In particular, for any $n \in \mathbb{N}$, $n \geq 1$ we have

$$(2.61) \qquad \zeta(2n+1) \leq \frac{2\zeta(2n)\zeta(2n+2)}{\zeta(2n)+\zeta(2n+2)} \quad \left(\leq \sqrt{\zeta(2n)\zeta(2n+2)} \right).$$

3 Inequalities for Dirichlet Series with Positive Terms

3.1 General Results

We consider the Dirichlet series given by (1.1). We assume that the series which defines ψ is uniformly convergent for $s > 1$.

The following result may be stated [2]:

Proposition 3.1. *Let $\alpha, \beta > 1$ with $\alpha^{-1} + \beta^{-1} = 1$. If $s, p, q \in \mathbb{R}$ are such that $s+p+q > 1$, $s + p\alpha > 1$ and $s + q\beta > 1$, then*

$$(3.1) \qquad \psi(s+p+q) \leq [\psi(s+p\alpha)]^{\frac{1}{\alpha}} [\psi(s+q\beta)]^{\frac{1}{\beta}}.$$

Proof. We use Hölder's inequality to state that:

$$\psi(s+p+q) = \sum_{n=1}^{\infty} \frac{a_n}{n^s} \cdot \frac{1}{n^p} \cdot \frac{1}{n^q}$$

$$\leq \left[\sum_{n=1}^{\infty} \frac{a_n}{n^s} \cdot \left(\frac{1}{n^p} \right)^{\alpha} \right]^{\frac{1}{\alpha}} \left[\sum_{n=1}^{\infty} \frac{a_n}{n^s} \cdot \left(\frac{1}{n^q} \right)^{\beta} \right]^{\frac{1}{\beta}}$$

$$= \left(\sum_{n=1}^{\infty} \frac{a_n}{n^{s+\alpha p}} \right)^{\frac{1}{\alpha}} \left(\sum_{n=1}^{\infty} \frac{a_n}{n^{s+\beta q}} \right)^{\frac{1}{\beta}}$$

$$= [\psi(s+p\alpha)]^{\frac{1}{\alpha}} [\psi(s+q\beta)]^{\frac{1}{\beta}},$$

which proves the desired inequality (3.1). □

Remark 3.1. *We observe that for $\alpha = \beta = 2$, we obtain from (3.1) the following inequality*

$$(3.2) \qquad \psi^2(s+p+q) \leq \psi(s+2p)\psi(s+2q),$$

provided the real numbers s, p, q satisfy the conditions $s + p + q, s + 2p, s + 2q > 1$. In its turn, the inequality (3.2), and in fact (3.1), is a generalisation of the following result

$$(3.3) \qquad \psi^2(s+1) \leq \psi(s)\psi(s+2),$$

provided $s > 1$.

We remark that for $\psi = \zeta$ one obtains from (3.3) that

$$(3.4) \qquad \frac{\zeta(s+1)}{\zeta(s)} \leq \frac{\zeta(s+2)}{\zeta(s+1)} \quad \text{for } s > 1.$$

This inequality is an improvement of a recent result due to Laforgia and Natalini [5] who proved that

$$\frac{\zeta(s+1)}{\zeta(s)} \leq \frac{s+1}{s} \cdot \frac{\zeta(s+2)}{\zeta(s+1)} \quad \text{for } s > 1.$$

Their arguments make use of an integral representation of the Zeta function and Turán-type inequalities.

It should be further noted that, if $s = 2n$, $n \in \mathbb{N}$, then (3.4) shows that

$$\zeta(2n+1) \leq \sqrt{\zeta(2n)\,\zeta(2n+2)},$$

demonstrating that Zeta at the odd integers is bounded above by the geometric mean of its immediate even Zeta values.

The following result also holds [2]:

Proposition 3.2. *If $a > 1$, $b, c \in \mathbb{R}$ such that $bc \geq (\leq) 0$ and $a + b$, $a + c$, $a + b + c > 1$, then:*

$$(3.5) \qquad \psi(a)\,\psi(a+b+c) \geq (\leq)\, \psi(a+b)\,\psi(a+c).$$

Proof. Consider the sequence $\alpha_n := n^b$, $n \geq 1$, $b \in \mathbb{R}$. It is clear that α_n is increasing if $b > 0$ and decreasing if $b < 0$. Therefore, the sequences $\frac{1}{n^b}, \frac{1}{n^c}$ are synchronous if $bc \geq 0$ and asynchronous when $bc < 0$.

Utilising Čebyšev's inequality for synchronous (asynchronous) sequences, we have:

$$
\begin{aligned}
\psi(a)\,\psi(a+b+c) &= \sum_{n=1}^{\infty} \frac{a_n}{n^a} \cdot \sum_{n=1}^{\infty} \frac{a_n}{n^a} \cdot \frac{1}{n^b} \cdot \frac{1}{n^c} \\
&\geq (\leq) \sum_{n=1}^{\infty} \frac{a_n}{n^a} \cdot \frac{1}{n^b} \cdot \sum_{n=1}^{\infty} \frac{a_n}{n^a} \cdot \frac{1}{n^c} \\
&= \psi(a+b)\,\psi(a+c),
\end{aligned}
$$

and the inequality (3.5) is proved. $\qquad\square$

Remark 3.2. *Utilising the inequality (3.5) (for $c = b$) we can state the following result*

$$(3.6) \qquad \psi^2(a+b) \leq \psi(a)\,\psi(a+2b),$$

provided the real numbers a, b are such that $a, a + b, a + 2b > 1$. We also remark that the choice $b = 1$ will produce the same inequality (3.3).

From a different perspective, we can state the following result as well [2]:

Proposition 3.3. *Assume that $m \geq 2$ and $k_1, \ldots, k_m > \frac{1}{2}$. Then*

$$(3.7) \qquad \sum_{1 \leq i < j \leq m} \psi(k_i + k_j) \leq \frac{m-1}{2} \sum_{j=1}^{m} \psi(2k_j).$$

Proof. By the Schwarz inequality:

$$m \sum_{j=1}^{m} z_j^2 \geq \left(\sum_{j=1}^{m} z_j \right)^2$$

we have

$$(3.8) \qquad
\begin{aligned}
m \sum_{j=1}^{m} \frac{1}{n^{2k_j}} &\geq \left(\sum_{j=1}^{m} \frac{1}{n^{k_j}} \right)^2 = \sum_{i=1}^{m} \sum_{j=1}^{m} \frac{1}{n^{k_i + k_j}} \\
&= \sum_{j=1}^{m} \frac{1}{n^{2k_j}} + 2 \sum_{1 \leq i < j \leq m} \frac{1}{n^{k_i + k_j}}
\end{aligned}
$$

giving

$$(3.9) \qquad \frac{m-1}{2} \sum_{j=1}^{m} \frac{1}{n^{2k_j}} \geq \sum_{1 \leq i < j \leq m} \frac{1}{n^{k_i + k_j}}.$$

If we multiply (3.9) by $a_n > 0$ and sum over $n \geq 1$, we get

$$\frac{m-1}{2} \sum_{j=1}^{m} \left(\sum_{n=1}^{\infty} \frac{a_n}{n^{2k_j}} \right) \geq \sum_{1 \leq i < j \leq m} \left(\sum_{n=1}^{\infty} \frac{a_n}{n^{k_i + k_j}} \right)$$

which gives the desired inequality (3.7). $\qquad\qquad\qquad\qquad\qquad\qquad\square$

Remark 3.3. *If $a, b, c > 1$ then from (3.7) applied for $m = 3$ we deduce the following result*

$$(3.10) \qquad \psi\left(\frac{a+b}{2}\right) + \psi\left(\frac{b+c}{2}\right) + \psi\left(\frac{c+a}{2}\right) \leq \psi(a) + \psi(b) + \psi(c).$$

In particular, the choice $a = x, b = x + 2, c = x + 4$ will produce the inequality

$$(3.11) \qquad \psi(x+1) + \psi(x+3) \leq \psi(x) + \psi(x+4),$$

for each $x > 1$.

If more information about the size of k_j, $j = 1, \ldots, m$ is known, then the following reverse of (3.7) may be stated as well [2]:

Proposition 3.4. *Assume that $m \geq 2$ and $\frac{1}{2} < \gamma \leq k_1, \ldots, k_m \leq \Gamma < \infty$. Then*

$$(3.12) \qquad (0 \leq) \frac{m-1}{2} \sum_{j=1}^{m} \psi(2k_j) - \sum_{1 \leq i < j \leq m} \psi(k_i + k_j)$$

$$\leq \frac{m^2}{8} \left[\psi(2\Gamma) + \psi(2\gamma) - 2\psi(\gamma + \Gamma) \right].$$

Proof. We use the following Grüss type inequality:

$$\frac{1}{m} \sum_{j=1}^{m} z_j^2 - \left(\frac{1}{m} \sum_{j=1}^{m} z_j \right)^2 \leq \frac{1}{4} (\Gamma - \gamma)^2,$$

provided $\gamma \leq z_j \leq \Gamma$ for each $j \in \{1, \ldots, m\}$.
   Since $\gamma \leq k_j \leq \Gamma$ for $j \in \{1, \ldots, m\}$, then

$$\frac{1}{m} \sum_{j=1}^{m} \frac{1}{n^{2k_j}} - \frac{1}{m^2} \left(\sum_{j=1}^{m} \frac{1}{n^{k_j}} \right)^2 \leq \frac{1}{4} \left(\frac{1}{n^\gamma} - \frac{1}{n^\Gamma} \right)^2 = \frac{1}{4} \left(\frac{1}{n^{2\gamma}} + \frac{1}{n^{2\Gamma}} - \frac{2}{n^{\gamma + \Gamma}} \right)$$

for $n \geq 1$, which gives

$$\frac{1}{m} \sum_{j=1}^{m} \frac{1}{n^{2k_j}} - \frac{1}{m^2} \left(\sum_{j=1}^{m} \frac{1}{n^{2k_j}} + 2 \sum_{1 \leq i < j \leq m} \frac{1}{n^{k_i + k_j}} \right) \leq \frac{1}{4} \left(\frac{1}{n^{2\gamma}} + \frac{1}{n^{2\Gamma}} - \frac{2}{n^{\gamma + \Gamma}} \right)$$

for $n \geq 1$.

Multiplying with m^2 and re-arranging, we get

$$(3.13) \qquad \frac{m-1}{2} \sum_{j=1}^{m} \frac{1}{n^{2k_j}} - \sum_{1 \leq i < j \leq m} \frac{1}{n^{k_i + k_j}} \leq \frac{m^2}{8} \left(\frac{1}{n^{2\gamma}} + \frac{1}{n^{2\Gamma}} - \frac{2}{n^{\gamma + \Gamma}} \right)$$

for any $n \geq 1$.

Finally, if we multiply (3.13) by $a_n \geq 0$ and sum over $n \geq 1$, we get the desired inequality (3.12). $\qquad \square$

Remark 3.4. *If $R > a, b, c > r > 1$ then from (3.12) applied for $m = 3$ we deduce the following result*

$$(3.14) \qquad 0 \leq \psi(a) + \psi(b) + \psi(c) - \psi\left(\frac{a+b}{2}\right) - \psi\left(\frac{b+c}{2}\right) - \psi\left(\frac{c+a}{2}\right)$$

$$\leq \frac{9}{4} \cdot \left[\frac{\psi(r) + \psi(R)}{2} - \psi\left(\frac{r+R}{2}\right) \right].$$

The following result may be stated as well [2]:

Proposition 3.5. *Assume that $m \geq 1$ and $\frac{1}{2} < \gamma \leq k_1, \ldots, k_m \leq \Gamma < \infty$. Then*

$$(3.15) \qquad \sum_{j=1}^{m} [\psi(k_j + \gamma) + \psi(k_j + \Gamma)] \geq \sum_{j=1}^{m} \psi(2k_j) + m\psi(\gamma + \Gamma).$$

Proof. We have:

$$\left(\frac{1}{n^{\gamma}} - \frac{1}{n^{k_j}} \right) \left(\frac{1}{n^{k_j}} - \frac{1}{n^{\Gamma}} \right) \geq 0$$

for each $j \in \{1, \ldots, m\}$ and $n \geq 1$. This is clearly equivalent to:

$$\frac{1}{n^{\gamma + k_j}} + \frac{1}{n^{\Gamma + k_j}} \geq \frac{1}{n^{2k_j}} + \frac{1}{n^{\gamma + \Gamma}}$$

for $j \in \{1, \ldots, m\}$ and $n \geq 1$.

Summing over j from 1 to m, we get:

$$(3.16) \qquad \sum_{j=1}^{m} \frac{1}{n^{\gamma + k_j}} + \sum_{j=1}^{m} \frac{1}{n^{\Gamma + k_j}} \geq \sum_{j=1}^{m} \frac{1}{n^{2k_j}} + \frac{m}{n^{\gamma + \Gamma}}$$

for each $n \geq 1$.

Multiplying (3.16) with $a_n \geq 0$ and summing over $n \geq 1$, we deduce the desired inequality (3.15). $\qquad \square$

The following result may be stated as well [2]:

Proposition 3.6. *Assume that $m \geq 1$ and $\frac{1}{2} < \gamma \leq k_1, \ldots, k_m \leq \Gamma < \infty$. Then*

$$(3.17) \quad \left(m - \frac{1}{2} \right) \sum_{j=1}^{m} \psi(2k_j) \leq \frac{1}{2} \sum_{j=1}^{m} \left[\frac{\psi(2k_j - \gamma + \Gamma) + \psi(2k_j - \Gamma + \gamma)}{2} \right]$$

$$+ \sum_{1 \leq i < j \leq m} \left[\frac{\psi(k_i + k_j - \Gamma + \gamma) + \psi(k_i + k_j - \gamma + \Gamma)}{2} \right]$$

$$+ \sum_{1 \leq i < j \leq m} \psi(k_i + k_j).$$

Proof. We apply the Polyá-Szegö inequality:

$$(3.18) \qquad (1 \leq) \; \frac{m \sum_{j=1}^{m} z_j^2}{\left(\sum_{j=1}^{m} z_j\right)^2} \leq \frac{(\Gamma + \gamma)^2}{4\gamma\Gamma},$$

provided $\gamma \leq z_j \leq \Gamma$, $j \in \{1, \ldots, m\}$.

Observing that

$$\frac{1}{n^\Gamma} \leq \frac{1}{n^{k_j}} \leq \frac{1}{n^\gamma}, \quad j = 1, \ldots, m$$

then by (3.18) we have

$$m \sum_{j=1}^{m} \frac{1}{n^{2k_j}} \leq \frac{\left(\frac{1}{n^\gamma} + \frac{1}{n^\Gamma}\right)^2}{4 \frac{1}{n^\gamma} \cdot \frac{1}{n^\Gamma}} \left(\sum_{j=1}^{m} \frac{1}{n^{k_j}}\right)^2$$

$$= \frac{1}{4}\left(n^{\Gamma-\gamma} + n^{\gamma-\Gamma} + 2\right)\left[\sum_{j=1}^{m} \frac{1}{n^{2k_j}} + 2 \sum_{1 \leq i < j \leq m} \frac{1}{n^{k_i + k_j}}\right]$$

$$= \frac{1}{4}\left[\sum_{j=1}^{m} \frac{1}{n^{2k_j - \Gamma + \gamma}} + \sum_{j=1}^{m} \frac{1}{n^{2k_j - \gamma + \Gamma}} + 2\sum_{j=1}^{m} \frac{1}{n^{2k_j}}\right]$$

$$+ \frac{1}{2}\left[\sum_{1 \leq i < j \leq m} \frac{1}{n^{k_i + k_j - \Gamma + \gamma}} + \sum_{1 \leq i < j \leq m} \frac{1}{n^{k_i + k_j - \gamma + \Gamma}} + 2\sum_{1 \leq i < j \leq m} \frac{1}{n^{k_i + k_j}}\right],$$

which is clearly equivalent to:

$$(3.19) \quad \left(m - \frac{1}{2}\right)\sum_{j=1}^{m} \frac{1}{n^{2k_j}} \leq \frac{1}{4}\left[\sum_{j=1}^{m} \frac{1}{n^{2k_j - \Gamma + \gamma}} + \sum_{j=1}^{m} \frac{1}{n^{2k_j - \gamma + \Gamma}}\right]$$

$$+ \frac{1}{2}\left[\sum_{1 \leq i < j \leq m} \frac{1}{n^{k_i + k_j - \Gamma + \gamma}} + \sum_{1 \leq i < j \leq m} \frac{1}{n^{k_i + k_j - \gamma + \Gamma}}\right] + \sum_{1 \leq i < j \leq m} \frac{1}{n^{k_i + k_j}}$$

for any $n \geq 1$.

Multiplying (3.19) by $a_n \geq 0$ and summing over n, we deduce the desired result (3.17). $\qquad\square$

3.2   Representations as Double Sums

Consider the sequences

$$(3.20) \qquad I_k^\pm(p, s) := \frac{1}{2}\sum_{n=1}^{k}\sum_{m=1}^{k} \frac{(n^p \pm m^p)^2}{n^s m^s} a_n a_m, \quad k \geq 1$$

where $a_n \geq 0$, $n \geq 1$ and $s, p \in \mathbb{R}$.

The following representation holds [2]:

Proposition 3.7. *If $s > 1$ and $p \in \mathbb{R}$ such that $s - 1 > 2p$ and $s - 1 > p$, then*

$$(3.21) \qquad I^\pm(p, s) := \lim_{k \to \infty} I_k^\pm(p, s) = \psi(s - 2p)\psi(s) \pm [\psi(s - p)]^2 \; (\geq 0).$$

Proof. We observe that

$$I_k^{\pm}(p,s) = \frac{1}{2} \sum_{n=1}^{k} \sum_{m=1}^{k} \left(\frac{n^{2p} \pm 2n^p m^p + m^{2p}}{n^s m^s} \right) a_n a_m$$

$$= \frac{1}{2} \left[\sum_{n=1}^{k} \frac{a_n}{n^{s-2p}} \sum_{m=1}^{k} \frac{a_m}{m^s} \pm 2 \sum_{n=1}^{k} \frac{a_n}{n^{s-p}} \sum_{m=1}^{k} \frac{a_m}{m^{s-p}} + \sum_{n=1}^{k} \frac{a_n}{n^s} \sum_{m=1}^{k} \frac{a_m}{m^{s-2p}} \right].$$

Since, for $s > 1$, $s - 1 > 2p$, $s - 1 > p$,

$$\lim_{k\to\infty} \sum_{n=1}^{k} \frac{a_n}{n^{s-2p}} = \psi(s-2p), \lim_{k\to\infty} \sum_{n=1}^{k} \frac{a_n}{n^{s-p}} = \psi(s-p),$$

$$\text{and} \quad \lim_{k\to\infty} \sum_{n=1}^{k} \frac{a_n}{n^s} = \psi(s)$$

then, the $\lim_{k\to\infty} I_k^{\pm}(p,s)$ exists and the relation (3.21) is proved. $\qquad\square$

Remark 3.5. *We observe that for $s > 1$ and $p = -1$, we have:*

$$(3.22) \qquad \psi(s+2)\psi(s) - [\psi(s+1)]^2 = \frac{1}{2} \lim_{k\to\infty} \sum_{n=1}^{k} \sum_{m=1}^{k} \frac{(n-m)^2}{n^{s+2}m^{s+2}} a_n a_m \geq 0.$$

The following result may be stated [2]:

Proposition 3.8. *Let $\alpha, \beta > 1$ with $\alpha^{-1} + \beta^{-1} = 1$. If $s, p, q, r \in \mathbb{R}$ are such that $s + q + r > 1$, $s + q + r - 1 > 2p$, $s + q + r - 1 > p$ and $s + \alpha q > 1$, $s + \alpha q - 1 > 2p$, $s + \alpha q - 1 > p$, $s + \beta r > 1$, $s + \beta r - 1 > 2p$, $s + \beta r - 1 > p$, then*

$$(3.23) \qquad I^{\pm}(p, s+q+r) \leq \left[I^{\pm}(p, s+\alpha q)\right]^{\frac{1}{\alpha}} \left[I^{\pm}(p, s+\beta r)\right]^{\frac{1}{\beta}}.$$

Proof. Using the representation (3.20), (3.21) and the Hölder inequality for double sums, we have:

$$I^{\pm}(p, s+q+r) = \frac{1}{2} \lim_{k\to\infty} \sum_{n=1}^{k} \sum_{m=1}^{k} \frac{(n^p \pm m^p)^2}{n^{s+q+r} m^{s+q+r}} a_n a_m$$

$$= \frac{1}{2} \lim_{k\to\infty} \sum_{n=1}^{k} \sum_{m=1}^{k} \frac{1}{n^q \cdot m^q} \cdot \frac{1}{n^r \cdot m^r} \cdot \frac{(n^p \pm m^p)^2}{n^s \cdot m^s} a_n a_m$$

$$\leq \left[\frac{1}{2} \lim_{k\to\infty} \sum_{n=1}^{k} \sum_{m=1}^{k} \frac{(n^p \pm m^p)^2}{n^s \cdot m^s} a_n a_m \left(\frac{1}{n^q \cdot m^q} \right)^{\alpha} \right]^{\frac{1}{\alpha}}$$

$$\times \left[\frac{1}{2} \lim_{k\to\infty} \sum_{n=1}^{k} \sum_{m=1}^{k} \frac{(n^p \pm m^p)^2}{n^s \cdot m^s} a_n a_m \left(\frac{1}{n^r \cdot m^r} \right)^{\beta} \right]^{\frac{1}{\beta}}$$

$$= \left[I^{\pm}(p, s+\alpha q)\right]^{\frac{1}{\alpha}} \left[I^{\pm}(p, s+\beta r)\right]^{\frac{1}{\beta}}$$

and the inequality (3.23) is obtained. $\qquad\square$

Remark 3.6. *In particular, if we define:*

(3.24) $$I(s) := \psi(s+2)\psi(s) - [\psi(s+1)]^2 \quad for \ s > 1,$$

then we have:

(3.25) $$I(s+q+r) \le [I(s+\alpha q)]^{\frac{1}{\alpha}} [I(s+\beta r)]^{\frac{1}{\beta}},$$

where $\alpha, \beta > 1$, $\frac{1}{\alpha} + \frac{1}{\beta} = 1$ *and* $s, q, r \in \mathbb{R}$ *with* $s+q+r$, $s+\alpha q$ *and* $s+\beta r > 1$.

The following log-convexity property may be stated [2]:

Proposition 3.9. *Let* $p \in \mathbb{R}$ *and* $s_0 := \max\{1, p+1, 2p+1\}$. *Then the function* $s \mapsto I_k^{\pm}(p, s)$ *is log-convex on the interval* $(s_0, +\infty)$.

Proof. Let $s_1, s_2 \in (s_0, +\infty)$. Then for $\alpha, \beta > 0$, $\alpha + \beta = 1$ by Hölder's inequality for double sums we have

$$
\begin{aligned}
I_k^{\pm}(p, \alpha s_1 + \beta s_2) &= \frac{1}{2} \sum_{n=1}^{k} \sum_{m=1}^{k} \frac{(n^p \pm m^p)^2}{n^{\alpha s_1 + \beta s_2} m^{\alpha s_1 + \beta s_2}} a_n a_m \\
&= \frac{1}{2} \sum_{n=1}^{k} \sum_{m=1}^{k} \frac{(n^p \pm m^p)^2 a_n a_m}{(nm)^{\alpha s_1}(nm)^{\beta s_2}} \\
&\le \left[\frac{1}{2} \sum_{n=1}^{k} \sum_{m=1}^{k} \frac{(n^p \pm m^p)^2 a_n a_m}{[(nm)^{\alpha s_1}]^{1/\alpha}} \right]^{\alpha} \left[\frac{1}{2} \sum_{n=1}^{k} \sum_{m=1}^{k} \frac{(n^p \pm m^p)^2 a_n a_m}{[(nm)^{\beta s_2}]^{1/\beta}} \right]^{\beta} \\
&= \left[I_k^{\pm}(p, s_1) \right]^{\alpha} \left[I_k^{\pm}(p, s_2) \right]^{\beta}
\end{aligned}
$$

for any $k \ge 1$.

Taking the limit over $k \to \infty$, and using the representation (3.21) we deduce the desired result. $\square$

Corollary 3.10. *The function* $I(s) := \psi(s+2)\psi(s) - [\psi(s+1)]^2$ *is log-convex on* $(1, \infty)$.

For given $s, p \in \mathbb{R}$ and $k \in \mathbb{N}$, $k \ge 1$, we consider the sequence

$$\Delta_k(s, p) := \frac{1}{2} \sum_{n=1}^{k} \sum_{m=1}^{k} (a_n - a_m) \left(\frac{1}{m^s} - \frac{1}{n^s} \right) \frac{1}{n^p m^p},$$

where a_n is also a sequence of real numbers.

The following representation result may be stated [2]:

Proposition 3.11. *If* $a_n \ge 0$, $n \in \mathbb{N}$, $n \ge 1$ *and* $p > 1$, $s \in \mathbb{R}$ *such that* $s+p > 1$, *then we have the representation*

(3.26) $$\lim_{k \to \infty} \Delta_k(s, p) = \psi(p)\zeta(s+p) - \zeta(p)\psi(s+p),$$

where ζ *is the Zeta function, i.e.,*

$$\zeta(p) := \sum_{n=1}^{\infty} \frac{1}{n^p}, \quad p > 1.$$

Proof. Observe that, by Korkine's identity, i.e., the equality

$$\sum_{i=1}^{m} p_i \sum_{i=1}^{m} p_i a_i b_i - \sum_{i=1}^{m} p_i a_i \sum_{i=1}^{m} p_i b_i = \frac{1}{2} \sum_{i=1}^{m} \sum_{j=1}^{n} p_i p_j \left(a_i - a_j \right) \left(b_i - b_j \right),$$

we have:

$$\sum_{n=1}^{k} \frac{1}{n^p} \sum_{n=1}^{k} \frac{1}{n^p} \cdot a_n \cdot \frac{1}{n^s} - \sum_{n=1}^{k} \frac{1}{n^p} \cdot a_n \cdot \sum_{n=1}^{k} \frac{1}{n^p} \cdot \frac{1}{n^s}$$

$$= \frac{1}{2} \sum_{i=1}^{m} \sum_{j=1}^{n} \frac{1}{n^p m^p} \left(a_n - a_m \right) \left(\frac{1}{n^s} - \frac{1}{m^s} \right)$$

$$= -\Delta_k \left(s, p \right)$$

for each $k \geq 1$ and p, s as above.

Since

$$\lim_{k \to \infty} \sum_{n=1}^{k} \frac{1}{n^p} = \zeta \left(p \right) \quad \text{and} \quad \lim_{k \to \infty} \sum_{n=1}^{k} \frac{a_n}{n^p} = \psi \left(p \right)$$

then, the $\lim_{k \to \infty} \Delta_k \left(p, s \right)$ exists and the identity (3.26) holds true. □

Corollary 3.12. *If the sequence* $(a_n)_{n \in \mathbb{N}}$ *is decreasing (increasing) then*

(3.27) $$\zeta \left(s + p \right) \psi \left(p \right) \leq (\geq) \zeta \left(p \right) \psi \left(s + p \right)$$

for $p > 1$ *and* $s \in \mathbb{R}$ *such that* $s + p > 1$.

The following result concerning some bounds for the quantity

$$\zeta \left(s + p \right) \psi \left(p \right) - \zeta \left(p \right) \psi \left(s + p \right)$$

in the case when the sequences $(a_n)_{n \in \mathbb{N}}$ satisfy some Lipschitz type conditions may be stated as well [2]:

Proposition 3.13. *Assume that for* $(a_n)_{n \in \mathbb{N}}$ *there exists the constants* $\gamma, \Gamma \in \mathbb{R}$ *such that*

(3.28) $$\gamma \leq \frac{a_n - a_m}{n - m} \leq \Gamma$$

for any $n, m \in \mathbb{N}$, $n \neq m$. *Then for* $p > 2$ *and* $s \in \mathbb{R}$ *such that* , $p + s > 2$

(3.29) $$\gamma \left[\zeta \left(p - 1 \right) \zeta \left(p + s \right) - \zeta \left(p \right) \zeta \left(p + s - 1 \right) \right]$$
$$\leq \zeta \left(s + p \right) \psi \left(p \right) - \zeta \left(p \right) \psi \left(s + p \right)$$
$$\leq \Gamma \left[\zeta \left(p - 1 \right) \zeta \left(p + s \right) - \zeta \left(p \right) \zeta \left(p + s - 1 \right) \right].$$

Proof. With the assumption (3.28) we have

(3.30) $$\frac{1}{2} \gamma \sum_{n=1}^{k} \sum_{m=1}^{k} \left(n - m \right) \left(\frac{1}{m^s} - \frac{1}{n^s} \right) \frac{1}{n^p m^p}$$

$$\leq \Delta_k \left(p, s \right) \leq \frac{1}{2} \Gamma \sum_{n=1}^{k} \sum_{m=1}^{k} \left(n - m \right) \left(\frac{1}{m^s} - \frac{1}{n^s} \right) \frac{1}{n^p m^p}$$

for each $k \in \mathbb{N}$, $k \geq 1$.

Further, utilising Korkine's identity produces

$$I_k := \frac{1}{2} \sum_{n=1}^{k} \sum_{m=1}^{k} (n - m) \left(\frac{1}{m^s} - \frac{1}{n^s} \right) \frac{1}{n^p m^p}$$

$$= \sum_{n=1}^{k} \frac{n}{n^p} \cdot \sum_{n=1}^{k} \frac{1}{n^s} \cdot \frac{1}{n^p} - \sum_{n=1}^{k} \frac{1}{n^p} \sum_{n=1}^{k} \frac{1}{n^p} \cdot n \cdot \frac{1}{n^s}$$

$$= \sum_{n=1}^{k} \frac{1}{n^{p-1}} \sum_{n=1}^{k} \frac{1}{n^{p+s}} - \sum_{n=1}^{k} \frac{1}{n^p} \sum_{n=1}^{k} \frac{1}{n^{p+s-1}}$$

for each $k \in \mathbb{N}$, $k \geq 1$ and so, for $p > 2$, $s \in \mathbb{R}$ with $p + s, p + s - 1 > 1$, we have

$$\lim_{k \to \infty} I_k = \zeta(p - 1) \zeta(p + s) - \zeta(p) \zeta(p + s - 1).$$

Taking the limit in (3.30) we deduce the desired inequality (3.29).   □

The following simple result also holds [2]:

Proposition 3.14. *Let $a_n \geq 0$, $n \in \mathbb{N}$, $n \geq 1$ and $s > 1$.*

(i) If a_n is increasing and

$$M := \sup_{\substack{k \in \mathbb{N} \\ k \geq 1}} \left\{ \frac{1}{k} \sum_{n=1}^{k} a_n \right\},$$

then

(3.31) $$\psi(s) \leq M \cdot \zeta(s).$$

(ii) If a_n is decreasing and

$$m := \inf_{\substack{k \in \mathbb{N} \\ k \geq 1}} \left\{ \frac{1}{k} \sum_{n=1}^{k} a_n \right\}$$

then

(3.32) $$\psi(s) \geq m \cdot \zeta(s).$$

Proof. Utilising Korkine's identity we have for each $k \geq 1$ that

(3.33) $$k \sum_{n=1}^{k} \frac{a_n}{n^s} - \sum_{n=1}^{k} a_n \sum_{n=1}^{k} \frac{1}{n^s} = \frac{1}{2} \sum_{n=1}^{k} \sum_{m=1}^{k} (a_n - a_m) \left(\frac{1}{n^s} - \frac{1}{m^s} \right)$$

(i) If a_n is increasing, then by (3.33) we deduce that

(3.34) $$\sum_{n=1}^{k} \frac{a_n}{n^s} \leq \left(\frac{1}{k} \sum_{n=1}^{k} a_n \right) \sum_{n=1}^{k} \frac{1}{n^s} \leq M \sum_{n=1}^{k} \frac{1}{n^s}.$$

Taking the limit over $k \to \infty$ in (3.34) we deduce (3.31).

(ii) Goes likewise and we omit the details.

    □

4   Inequalities in Terms of the First and Second Derivatives

We consider the sequence

$$(4.1) \qquad S_k(s) := \frac{1}{2} \sum_{n=1}^{k} \sum_{m=1}^{k} \frac{(\ln n - \ln m)^2}{n^s m^s} a_n a_m, \quad s > 1,$$

where $k \in \mathbb{N}$, $k \geq 1$.

The following representation holds [2]:

Proposition 4.1. *Consider the Dirichlet series* $\psi(s) := \sum_{n=1}^{\infty} \frac{a_n}{n^s}$ *with* $a_n \geq 0$ *and assumed to be uniformly convergent on* $(1, \infty)$. *Then*

$$(4.2) \qquad S(s) := \lim_{k \to \infty} S_k(s) = \psi''(s)\psi(s) - [\psi'(s)]^2 \,(\geq 0),$$

for $s \in (1, \infty)$.

Proof. It is obvious that

$$\psi'(s) = -\sum_{n=1}^{\infty} \frac{a_n}{n^s} \cdot \ln n$$

and

$$\psi''(s) = \sum_{n=1}^{\infty} \frac{a_n}{n^s} \cdot (\ln n)^2$$

for $s > 1$.

Now, observe that for $k \geq 1$

$$S_k(s) = \frac{1}{2} \sum_{n=1}^{k} \sum_{m=1}^{k} \left[\frac{(\ln n)^2 + (\ln m)^2 - 2\ln n \cdot \ln m}{n^s m^s} \right] a_n a_m$$

$$= \sum_{n=1}^{k} \frac{a_n}{n^s} \cdot (\ln n)^2 \sum_{n=1}^{k} \frac{a_n}{n^s} - \left(\sum_{n=1}^{\infty} \frac{a_n}{n^s} \cdot \ln n \right)^2,$$

and since

$$\lim_{k \to \infty} \sum_{n=1}^{k} \frac{a_n}{n^s} \cdot (\ln n)^2 = \psi''(s) \quad \text{and} \quad \lim_{k \to \infty} \sum_{n=1}^{\infty} \frac{a_n}{n^s} \cdot \ln n = \psi'(s)$$

then (4.2) holds. □

The following result concerning the convexity property of $S(s)$ may be stated [2].

Proposition 4.2. *The function* $S(s) = \psi''(s)\psi(s) - [\psi'(s)]^2$ *is log-convex on* $(1, \infty)$.

The proof follows by making use of the representation (4.1) and utilising the Hölder inequality for double sums.

The details are omitted.

Theorem 4.3 ([2]). *We have the inequality:*

$$(4.3) \qquad (0 \leq)\, \psi''(s)\psi(s) - [\psi'(s)]^2 \leq \psi(s-1)\psi(s+1) - [\psi(s)]^2,$$

for any $s > 2$.

Proof. We use the following inequality between the geometric mean and the logarithmic mean of two positive numbers $a, b, a \neq b$,

$$\frac{b-a}{\ln b - \ln a} > \sqrt{ab},$$

to state that

$$\frac{\ln n - \ln m}{n - m} \leq \frac{1}{\sqrt{nm}} \quad \text{for } n, m \geq 1, \ n \neq m.$$

This obviously implies that

$$(\ln n - \ln m)^2 \leq \frac{(n-m)^2}{nm}$$

for each $n, m \geq 1$ and then from (4.1)

$$(4.4) \qquad S_k(s) \leq \frac{1}{2} \sum_{n=1}^{k} \sum_{m=1}^{k} \frac{(n-m)^2}{n^{s+1} m^{s+1}} a_n a_m = \sum_{n=1}^{k} \frac{1}{n^{s-1}} a_n \cdot \sum_{n=1}^{k} \frac{a_n}{n^{s+1}} - \left(\sum_{n=1}^{k} \frac{a_n}{n^s} \right)^2,$$

for each $k \in \mathbb{N}, \ k \geq 1$.

Since

$$\lim_{k \to \infty} \sum_{n=1}^{k} \frac{a_n}{n^s} = \psi(s)$$

for $s > 1$, hence by (4.4) we deduce the desired inequality (4.3). $\square$

In [7], F. Topsøe obtained amongst others, the following inequality for the logarithmic function:

$$(4.5) \qquad |\ln x| \leq \frac{1}{2} \left| x - \frac{1}{x} \right| \quad \text{for } x > 0.$$

We may state the following result based on (4.5) [2]:

Theorem 4.4. *We have the inequality:*

$$(4.6) \qquad (0 \leq) \psi''(s) \psi(s) - [\psi'(s)]^2 \leq \frac{1}{2} \left[\psi(s+2) \psi(s-2) - [\psi(s)]^2 \right],$$

for any $s > 3$.

Proof. On making use of (4.5), we have:

$$(\ln n - \ln m)^2 \leq \frac{1}{2} \left(\frac{n}{m} - \frac{m}{n} \right)^2 \quad \text{for } n, m \in \mathbb{N}, \ n \neq m; n, m \geq 1$$

which gives from (4.1):

$$S_k(s) \leq \frac{1}{4} \sum_{n=1}^{k} \sum_{m=1}^{k} \frac{n^4 - 2n^2 m^2 + m^4}{n^{s+2} m^{s+2}} a_n a_m = \frac{1}{2} \left[\sum_{n=1}^{k} \frac{a_n}{n^{s-2}} \sum_{n=1}^{k} \frac{a_n}{n^{s+2}} - \left(\sum_{n=1}^{k} \frac{a_n}{n^s} \right)^2 \right]$$

which implies the desired inequality (4.6). $\square$

Remark 4.1. *From (4.3) and (4.6), a computer comparison of the bounds*

$$B_1(s) := \psi(s-1)\,\psi(s+1) - [\psi(s)]^2, \quad s > 2$$

and

$$B_2(s) := \frac{1}{2}\left[\psi(s+2)\,\psi(s-2) - [\psi(s)]^2\right], \quad s > 3$$

for $s > 3$ and $\psi = \zeta$ (Zeta function) shows that

$$B_2(s) \le B_1(s) \text{ for all } s > 3.$$

However, we do not have an analytic proof for this inequality.

The following result may be stated as well [2]:

Theorem 4.5. *We have the inequality:*

(4.7) $$(0 \le)\,\psi(s+2)\,\psi(s) - [\psi(s+1)]^2 \le \psi''(s)\,\psi(s) - [\psi'(s)]^2$$

for any $s > 1$.

Proof. We use the following elementary inequality for the logarithmic mean:

$$\frac{b-a}{\ln b - \ln a} \le \frac{a+b}{2}, \quad a,b > 0 \ (a \ne b)$$

which implies:

$$\frac{\ln n - \ln m}{n - m} \ge \frac{2}{n+m} \quad \text{for} \ \ n,m \in \mathbb{N}, \ n \ne m; n,m \ge 1.$$

This obviously implies:

$$(\ln n - \ln m)^2 \ge \frac{4(n-m)^2}{(n+m)^2} \quad \text{for any} \ \ n,m \in \mathbb{N}, \ n,m \ge 1.$$

Consequently, with the above notation, we have from (4.1):

(4.8) $$S_k(s) \ge 2\sum_{n=1}^{k}\sum_{m=1}^{k}\frac{(n-m)^2}{(n+m)^2}\cdot\frac{1}{n^s m^s}a_n a_m$$

$$= 2\sum_{n=1}^{k}\sum_{m=1}^{k}\frac{(n-m)^2}{\left(\frac{1}{n}+\frac{1}{m}\right)^2}\cdot\frac{1}{n^{s+2}m^{s+2}}a_n a_m$$

$$\ge \frac{1}{2}\sum_{n=1}^{k}\sum_{m=1}^{k}\frac{(n-m)^2}{n^{s+2}m^{s+2}}\cdot a_n a_m$$

$$=: L_k(s),$$

where we have used the fact that $\frac{1}{n}+\frac{1}{m} \le 2$ for $n,m \ge 1$.
Observing that

(4.9) $$L_k(s) = \frac{1}{2}\sum_{n=1}^{k}\sum_{m=1}^{k}\frac{n^2 - 2nm + m^2}{n^{s+2}m^{s+2}}a_n a_m$$

$$= \sum_{n=1}^{k}\frac{a_n}{n^{s+2}}\sum_{n=1}^{k}\frac{a_n}{n^s} - \left(\sum_{n=1}^{k}\frac{a_n}{n^{s+1}}\right)^2$$

$$= M_k(s),$$

then, on making use of (4.8) and (4.9) we deduce:

$$(4.10) \qquad S_k(s) \geq M_k(s) \quad \text{for } k \geq 1 \text{ and } s > 1.$$

Further, since

$$\lim_{k \to \infty} S_k(s) = \psi''(s)\,\psi(s) - \left[\psi'(s)\right]^2$$

and

$$\lim_{k \to \infty} M_k(s) = \psi(s+2)\,\psi(s) - \left[\psi(s+1)\right]^2$$

uniformly for $s > 1$, then by (4.10) we conclude the desired result (4.7). $\qquad \square$

Remark 4.2. *Theorem 4.5 provides a lower bound for $\psi''(s)\,\psi(s) - \left[\psi'(s)\right]^2$ whereas Theorems 4.3 and 4.4 give upper bounds.*

4.1   Other Inequalities for the First Derivative

In this section we establish some bounds for the quantity

$$(4.11) \qquad Q(s) := \frac{\zeta'(s)}{\zeta(s)} - \frac{\psi'(s)}{\psi(s)}, \quad s > 1$$

provided ψ is defined by the Dirichlet series

$$(4.12) \qquad \psi(s) := \sum_{n=1}^{\infty} \frac{a_n}{n^s}, \quad s > 1$$

and ζ is the Zeta function.

We observe that if $(a_n)_{n \in \mathbb{N}}$ is nonnegative and monotonic nondecreasing (nonincreasing) then (see [1]):

$$(4.13) \qquad \frac{\zeta'(s)}{\zeta(s)} \geq (\leq) \frac{\psi'(s)}{\psi(s)} \quad \text{for} \quad s > 1.$$

The following result may be stated as well [2].

Theorem 4.6. *If $(a_n)_{n \in \mathbb{N}}$ is nonnegative and nondecreasing, then we have the reverse inequality:*

$$(4.14) \qquad (0 \leq)\, \frac{\zeta'(s)}{\zeta(s)} - \frac{\psi'(s)}{\psi(s)} \leq \frac{\psi\left(s - \frac{1}{2}\right)\zeta\left(s + \frac{1}{2}\right) - \psi\left(s + \frac{1}{2}\right)\zeta\left(s - \frac{1}{2}\right)}{\zeta(s)\,\psi(s)},$$

for any $s > \frac{3}{2}$.

Proof. Consider the sequence:

$$Q_k(s) := \frac{\sum_{n=1}^{k} \frac{a_n \ln n}{n^s} \cdot \sum_{n=1}^{k} \frac{1}{n^s} - \sum_{n=1}^{k} \frac{a_n}{n^s} \cdot \sum_{n=1}^{k} \frac{\ln n}{n^s}}{\zeta(s)\,\psi(s)}$$

for $k \geq 1$.

We observe that for $s > 1$ the sequence $Q_n(s)$ is uniformly convergent and

$$\lim_{n \to \infty} Q_n(s) = Q(s) = \frac{\zeta'(s)}{\zeta(s)} - \frac{\psi'(s)}{\psi(s)}, \quad s > 1.$$

Utilising Korkine's identity, we also have:

$$(4.15) \qquad Q_k(s) = \frac{1}{2} \cdot \frac{\sum_{n=1}^{k} \sum_{m=1}^{k} (a_n - a_m)(\ln n - \ln m) \frac{1}{n^s m^s}}{\sum_{n=1}^{k} \frac{1}{n^s} \cdot \sum_{n=1}^{k} \frac{a_n}{n^s}}$$

for $k \geq 1$, $s > 1$.

Utilising the fact that (a_n) is monotonic nondecreasing, the elementary inequality:

$$\frac{\ln n - \ln m}{n - m} \leq \frac{1}{\sqrt{nm}}, \quad n, m \geq 1, \ n \neq m,$$

we get

$$(4.16) \qquad Q_k(s) \leq \frac{1}{2} \cdot \frac{\sum_{n=1}^{k} \sum_{m=1}^{k} (a_n - a_m)(n - m) \frac{1}{n^{s+\frac{1}{2}} m^{s+\frac{1}{2}}}}{\sum_{n=1}^{k} \frac{1}{n^s} \cdot \sum_{n=1}^{k} \frac{a_n}{n^s}}$$

$$= \frac{\sum_{n=1}^{k} \frac{a_n \cdot n}{n^{s+\frac{1}{2}}} \cdot \sum_{n=1}^{k} \frac{1}{n^{s+\frac{1}{2}}} - \sum_{n=1}^{k} \frac{a_n}{n^{s+\frac{1}{2}}} \cdot \sum_{n=1}^{k} \frac{n}{n^{s+\frac{1}{2}}}}{\sum_{n=1}^{k} \frac{1}{n^s} \cdot \sum_{n=1}^{k} \frac{a_n}{n^s}}$$

$$=: V_k(s), \quad s > 1.$$

Since

$$\lim_{k \to \infty} V_k(s) = \frac{\psi\left(s - \frac{1}{2}\right) \zeta\left(s + \frac{1}{2}\right) - \psi\left(s + \frac{1}{2}\right) \zeta\left(s - \frac{1}{2}\right)}{\zeta(s) \psi(s)}$$

for $s > \frac{3}{2}$, then by (4.16) we deduce the desired result (4.14). $\qquad\square$

The following upper bound for $Q(s)$, $s > 1$, can be established as well [2]:

Theorem 4.7. *With the assumptions of Theorem 4.6, we have*

$$(4.17) \qquad (0 \leq) \frac{\zeta'(s)}{\zeta(s)} - \frac{\psi'(s)}{\psi(s)} \leq \frac{1}{2} \cdot \left[\frac{\psi(s-1)\zeta(s+1) - \psi(s+1)\zeta(s-1)}{\zeta(s)\psi(s)} \right]$$

for any $s > 2$.

Proof. From inequality (4.9) we have:

$$\frac{\ln n - \ln m}{n - m} \leq \frac{n + m}{2nm}, \quad \text{for any } n, m \geq 1, \ n \neq m,$$

which from (4.15) implies that

$$(4.18) \qquad Q_k(s) \leq \frac{1}{4} \cdot \frac{\sum_{n=1}^{k} \sum_{m=1}^{k} (a_n - a_m)(n - m) \frac{n+m}{n^{s+1} m^{s+1}}}{\sum_{n=1}^{k} \frac{1}{n^s} \cdot \sum_{n=1}^{k} \frac{a_n}{n^s}}$$

$$= \frac{1}{2} \cdot \frac{\sum_{n=1}^{k} \frac{a_n \cdot n^2}{n^{s+1}} \cdot \sum_{n=1}^{k} \frac{1}{n^{s+1}} - \sum_{n=1}^{k} \frac{a_n}{n^{s+1}} \cdot \sum_{n=1}^{k} \frac{n^2}{n^{s+1}}}{\sum_{n=1}^{k} \frac{1}{n^s} \cdot \sum_{n=1}^{k} \frac{a_n}{n^s}}$$

$$=: W_k(s), \quad s > 1.$$

Since

$$\lim_{k \to \infty} W_k(s) = \frac{1}{2} \cdot \frac{\psi(s-1)\zeta(s+1) - \psi(s+1)\zeta(s-1)}{\zeta(s)\psi(s)}$$

for $s > 1$, the inequality (4.18) produces the desired result (4.17). $\qquad\square$

Finally, the following refinement of the inequality (4.13) may be stated as well [2]:

Theorem 4.8. *With the assumptions of Theorem 4.6, we have the inequality:*

$$(4.19) \qquad 0 \le \frac{\zeta(s+1)}{\zeta(s)} - \frac{\psi(s+1)}{\psi(s)} \le \frac{\zeta'(s)}{\zeta(s)} - \frac{\psi'(s)}{\psi(s)},$$

for $s > 1$.

Proof. Utilising the inequality:

$$\frac{\ln n - \ln m}{n - m} \le \frac{2}{n + m}, \quad \text{for } n, m \in \mathbb{N}, \ n \ne m, \ n, m \ge 1,$$

we have

$$(4.20) \qquad Q_k(s) \ge \frac{1}{2} \cdot \frac{\sum_{n=1}^{k} \sum_{m=1}^{k} (a_n - a_m)(n - m) \cdot \frac{2}{n+m} \cdot \frac{1}{n^s m^s}}{\sum_{n=1}^{k} \frac{1}{n^s} \cdot \sum_{n=1}^{k} \frac{a_n}{n^s}}$$

$$\ge \frac{1}{2} \cdot \frac{\sum_{n=1}^{k} \sum_{m=1}^{k} (a_n - a_m)(n - m) \cdot \frac{1}{n^{s+1} m^{s+1}}}{\sum_{n=1}^{k} \frac{1}{n^s} \cdot \sum_{n=1}^{k} \frac{a_n}{n^s}}$$

$$= Z_k(s)$$

since for $n, m > 1$,

$$\frac{2}{n+m} = \frac{2}{nm\left(\frac{1}{n} + \frac{1}{m}\right)} \ge \frac{1}{nm}.$$

Observing that:

$$Z_k(s) = \frac{\sum_{n=1}^{k} \frac{a_n \cdot n}{n^{s+1}} \cdot \sum_{n=1}^{k} \frac{1}{n^{s+1}} - \sum_{n=1}^{k} \frac{a_n}{n^{s+1}} \cdot \sum_{n=1}^{k} \frac{n}{n^{s+1}}}{\sum_{n=1}^{k} \frac{1}{n^s} \cdot \sum_{n=1}^{k} \frac{a_n}{n^s}}$$

$$= \frac{\sum_{n=1}^{k} \frac{a_n}{n^s} \cdot \sum_{n=1}^{k} \frac{1}{n^{s+1}} - \sum_{n=1}^{k} \frac{a_n}{n^{s+1}} \cdot \sum_{n=1}^{k} \frac{n}{n^{s+1}}}{\sum_{n=1}^{k} \frac{1}{n^s} \cdot \sum_{n=1}^{k} \frac{a_n}{n^s}}$$

for $k \ge 1$, and

$$\lim_{k \to \infty} Z_k(s) = \frac{\zeta(s+1)\psi(s) - \psi(s+1)\zeta(s)}{\psi(s)\zeta(s)} = \frac{\zeta(s+1)}{\zeta(s)} - \frac{\psi(s+1)}{\psi(s)},$$

then by (4.20) we deduce the desired result (4.19). $\qquad \square$

Remark 4.3. *The inequalities (4.14), (4.17) and (4.19) are obviously equivalent to:*

$$(4.21) \qquad (0 \le)\zeta'(s)\psi(s) - \psi'(s)\zeta(s)$$

$$\le \psi\left(s - \frac{1}{2}\right)\zeta\left(s + \frac{1}{2}\right) - \psi\left(s + \frac{1}{2}\right)\zeta\left(s - \frac{1}{2}\right), \quad s > \frac{3}{2}$$

$$(4.22) \qquad (0 \le)\zeta'(s)\psi(s) - \psi'(s)\zeta(s)$$

$$\le \frac{1}{2}\left[\psi(s-1)\zeta(s+1) - \psi(s+1)\zeta(s-1)\right], \quad s > 2$$

and

$$(4.23) \qquad (0 \le)\zeta(s+1)\psi(s) - \psi(s+1)\zeta(s)$$

$$\le \zeta'(s)\psi(s) - \psi'(s)\zeta(s), \quad s > 1$$

respectively.

Now, consider $\psi(s) := \sum_{n=1}^{\infty} \frac{\ln n}{h^s}$, $s > 1$. We observe that this Dirichlet series satisfies the assumptions of Theorem 4.6. Also $\psi(s) = -\zeta(s)$, $s > 1$. Therefore, by (4.21), (4.22) and (4.23) we have the inequalities:

(4.24)
$$(0 \le)\zeta''(s)\,\zeta(s) - \left[\zeta'(s)\right]^2$$
$$\le \zeta'\left(s + \frac{1}{2}\right)\zeta\left(s - \frac{1}{2}\right) - \zeta'\left(s - \frac{1}{2}\right)\zeta\left(s + \frac{1}{2}\right), \quad s > \frac{3}{2}$$

(4.25)
$$(0 \le)\zeta''(s)\,\zeta(s) - \left[\zeta'(s)\right]^2$$
$$\le \frac{1}{2}\left[\zeta'(s+1)\,\zeta(s-1) - \zeta'(s-1)\,\zeta(s+1)\right], \quad s > 2$$

and

(4.26)
$$(0 \le)\zeta'(s+1)\,\zeta(s) - \zeta(s+1)\,\zeta'(s)$$
$$\le \zeta''(s)\,\zeta(s) - \left[\zeta'(s)\right]^2, \quad s > 2$$

respectively.

REFERENCES

[1] P. Cerone and S.S. Dragomir, Some inequalities for Dirichlet series via logarithmic convexity, *RGMIA Res. Rep. Coll.* **8**(2005), No. 4, Article 14 [ONLINE http://rgmia.vu.edu.au/v8n4.html].

[2] P. Cerone and S.S. Dragomir, Inequalities for Dirichlet series with positive terms, *RGMIA Res. Rep. Coll.* **9**(2006), No. 1, Article 8 [ONLINE http://rgmia.vu.edu.au/v9n1.html].

[3] A. Gut, Some remarks on the Riemann zeta distribution. *Rev. Roumaine Math. Pures et Appl.* **51** (2006), 205-217. Preprint, U.U.D.M. Report 2005:6, ISSN 1101-3591, Department of Mathematics, Uppsala University.

[4] A. Ivić, *The Riemann Zeta-Function, Theory and Applications*, Dover Publications, Inc., Mineola, New York, 1985, 517 pp.

[5] A. Laforgia and P. Natalini, Turán-type inequalities for some special functions, *J. Inequal. Pure & Appl. Math.*, **7**(1) (2006), Art. 22, [ONLINE http://jipam.vu.edu.au/article.php?sid=638].

[6] J.E. Pečarić, F. Proschan and Y. L. Tong, *Convex Functions, Partial Orderings, and Statistical Applications,* Mathematics in Science and Engineering, 187. Academic Press, Inc., Boston, MA, 1992. xiv+467 pp.

[7] F. Topsøe, Some bounds for the logarithmic function, *RGMIA Res. Rep. Coll.*, **7**(2004), No. 2. Article 6, [ONLINE http://rgmia.vu.edu.au/v7n2.html].

In: Advances in Inequalities for Special Functions   ISBN 978-1-60021-919-1
Editors: P. Cerone and S. S. Dragomir, pp. 67–72   © 2008 Nova Science Publishers, Inc.

Monotonicity of the Mean Value Function of Normalized Bessel Functions of First Kind

Stamatis Koumandos

Department of Mathematics and Statistics
University of Cyprus, P. O. Box 20537
1678 Nicosia, Cyprus
E-mail address: skoumand@ucy.ac.cy

ABSTRACT. We determine all the values of the parameters α, β for which $\frac{d}{dx}\left\{ \frac{1}{x}\int_0^x t^{-\beta} J_\alpha(t)\, dt \right\} < 0$, for all $x > 0$, where $J_\alpha(t)$ is the Bessel function of the first kind and order α. As an application we give some new examples of subadditive functions on $[0, \infty)$. These generalize corresponding results for the sine integral function $\mathrm{Si}(x) = \int_0^x \frac{\sin t}{t}\, dt$.

1991 Mathematics Subject Classification: Primary 33C10; Secondary 33C20; 26D15

Key words and phrases: Subadditive functions, integrals of Bessel functions, hypergeometric functions

1   INTRODUCTION

Let $\mathbf{I}$ be an interval on the real line $\mathbb{R}$. A function $f : \mathbf{I} \to \mathbb{R}$ is called subadditive on $\mathbf{I}$, if

$$f(x + y) \le f(x) + f(y) \quad \text{for all} \quad x, y \in \mathbf{I} \quad \text{with} \quad x + y \in \mathbf{I}.$$

Subadditive functions are of importance in several branches of mathematics, such as semigroup theory, number theory and the theory of special functions; see [1], [2], [10] and the references given therein.

It is shown in [9] that if a function $f : [0, \infty) \to \mathbb{R}$ has a continuous derivative and satisfies the conditions $f(0) = 0$ and $\left(\frac{f(x)}{x} \right)' < 0$, for all $x > 0$, then f is subadditive on $[0, \infty)$. Using this result several examples of subadditive functions can be obtained. More specifically, let ϕ be a continuous function on $[0, \infty)$. In view of the above, when the meanvalue function $\frac{1}{x} \int_0^x \phi(t)\, dt$ satisfies the inequality $\frac{d}{dx}\left(\frac{1}{x} \int_0^x \phi(t)\, dt \right) < 0$, for all $x > 0$, then $f(x) = \int_0^x \phi(t)\, dt$, is subadditive on $[0, \infty)$.

Let $\mathrm{Si}(x) = \int_0^x \frac{\sin t}{t}\, dt$ be the sine integral. This function is subadditive on $[0, \infty)$ because

$$(1.1) \qquad \frac{d}{dx}\left(\frac{1}{x} \int_0^x \frac{\sin t}{t}\, dt \right) < 0, \quad \text{for all} \quad x > 0.$$

This inequality has been established in [9]. The aim of this article is to present some generalizations of (1.1). In particular, we show that

$$(1.2) \qquad \frac{d}{dx}\left(\frac{1}{x} \int_0^x \frac{\sin t}{t^a}\, dt \right) < 0, \quad \text{for all} \quad x > 0,$$

precisely when $1 \leq a < 2$. Inequality (1.2), in turn, is a special case of a more general inequality involving Bessel functions. Let $J_\alpha(t)$ be the Bessel function of the first kind and order α defined by

$$J_\alpha(t) = \sum_{k=0}^{\infty} \frac{(-1)^k \, (t/2)^{2k+\alpha}}{k! \, \Gamma(k+\alpha+1)},$$

for $\alpha > -1$.

The main result we prove here is the following.

Theorem 1.1. *For all $x > 0$ we have*

$$(1.3) \qquad \frac{d}{dx}\left\{ \frac{1}{x} \int_0^x t^{-\beta} J_\alpha(t)\, dt \right\} < 0,$$

when $0 < \beta - \alpha < 1$, $\beta \geq \frac{1}{2}$ and $\alpha > -\frac{1}{2}$ or $\beta = \alpha \geq \frac{1}{2}$. This result is best possible with respect to α, β.

It should first be noted that the condition $\beta - \alpha < 1$, is necessary for the convergence of the integral in (1.3) at zero.

Recalling that $J_{\frac{1}{2}}(t) = \left(\frac{2}{\pi t}\right)^{\frac{1}{2}} \sin t$, we see that (1.2) is the special case $\alpha = \frac{1}{2}$ and $\beta = a - \frac{1}{2}$ of (1.3). The case $\alpha = \beta = 1/2$ is the inequality (1.1).

Using Theorem 1.1 we deduce the following.

Corollary 1.2. *If α, β satisfy the conditions of Theorem 1.1, then the function*

$$f(x) := \int_0^x t^{-\beta} J_\alpha(t)\, dt,$$

is subadditive on $[0, \infty)$.

2   Proof of the Main Result

Proof. We set $c := \frac{\alpha - \beta}{2}$ and assume that $c > -\frac{1}{2}$. When $c \neq 0$ it is easy to see that

$$(2.1) \qquad \frac{d}{dx}\left\{ \frac{1}{x} \int_0^x t^{-\beta} J_\alpha(t)\, dt \right\} = \frac{x^{2c-1}}{2^\alpha \, \Gamma(\alpha+1)} \, \frac{c}{c+\frac{1}{2}} \, {}_2F_3\left(\begin{array}{c} c+1, c+\frac{1}{2} \\ c, c+\frac{3}{2}, \alpha+1 \end{array} ; -z^2 \right),$$

where $z = x/2$ and ${}_pF_q$ denotes the generalized hypergeometric function with p numerator and q denominator parameters defined by

$${}_pF_q\left(\begin{array}{c} a_1, a_2, \ldots, a_p \\ b_1, b_2, \ldots, b_q \end{array} ; y \right) = 1 + \sum_{k=1}^{\infty} \frac{(a_1)_k (a_2)_k \cdots (a_p)_k}{(b_1)_k (b_2)_k \cdots (b_q)_k} \frac{y^k}{k!}.$$

As usual, $(a)_k$ denotes the Pochhammer symbol, defined by $(a)_0 = 1$ and

$$(a)_k = a(a+1) \cdots (a+k-1) = \frac{\Gamma(k+a)}{\Gamma(a)}.$$

for $k = 1, 2, \ldots$.

By an elementary calculation we then find that

$$(2.2) \quad \frac{c}{c + \frac{1}{2}} \, {}_2F_3 \left(\begin{array}{c} c + 1, \, c + \frac{1}{2} \\ c, \, c + \frac{3}{2}, \, \alpha + 1 \end{array} ; -z^2 \right)$$

$$= -\frac{z^2}{(\alpha + 1)(c + \frac{3}{2})} \, {}_1F_2 \left(\begin{array}{c} c + \frac{3}{2} \\ c + \frac{5}{2}, \, \alpha + 2 \end{array} ; -z^2 \right)$$

$$+ \frac{c}{c + \frac{1}{2}} \, {}_1F_2 \left(\begin{array}{c} c + \frac{1}{2} \\ c + \frac{3}{2}, \, \alpha + 1 \end{array} ; -z^2 \right).$$

From (2.2) and (2.1) we see that it is sufficient to prove that

$$(2.3) \qquad {}_1F_2 \left(\begin{array}{c} c + \frac{1}{2} \\ c + \frac{3}{2}, \, \alpha + 1 \end{array} ; -z^2 \right) > 0, \quad z > 0$$

and

$$(2.4) \qquad {}_1F_2 \left(\begin{array}{c} c + \frac{3}{2} \\ c + \frac{5}{2}, \, \alpha + 2 \end{array} ; -z^2 \right) > 0, \quad z > 0$$

when $-1/2 < c < 0$, $\beta \geq 1/2$ and $\alpha > -1/2$.

In the case where $c = 0$ we similarly have

$$(2.5) \qquad \frac{d}{dx} \left\{ \frac{1}{x} \int_0^x t^{-\alpha} J_\alpha(t) \, dt \right\} = -\frac{1}{3} \frac{z}{2^\alpha \, \Gamma(\alpha + 2)} \, {}_1F_2 \left(\begin{array}{c} \frac{3}{2} \\ \frac{5}{2}, \, \alpha + 2 \end{array} ; -z^2 \right),$$

where $z = x/2$, so that in this case we need only to verify that (2.4) holds for $c = 0$ and $\alpha \geq 1/2$.

We observe that for $c > -1/2$ we have

$$\int_0^x t^{-\beta} J_\alpha(t) \, dt = \frac{x^{2c+1}}{2^{\alpha+1} \, \Gamma(\alpha + 1)(c + \frac{1}{2})} \, {}_1F_2 \left(\begin{array}{c} c + \frac{1}{2} \\ c + \frac{3}{2}, \, \alpha + 1 \end{array} ; -z^2 \right).$$

The desired inequality (2.3) follows from this and the inequality

$$(2.6) \qquad \int_0^x t^{-\beta} J_\alpha(t) \, dt > 0, \quad \text{for all } x > 0$$

which holds for all $\beta \geq 0$ when $\beta - \alpha < 1$. See [4] and also [3, p. 390].

In order to prove (2.4), we shall show that the generalized hypergeometric series ${}_1F_2$ on the left hand side can be written as a sum of squares of Bessel functions with positive coefficients. This method was introduced in [6], and also used in [7] and [8], to prove the positivity of certain integrals involving the Bessel functions. Indeed, using the formula

$$z^{2\nu} = \frac{\Gamma^2(\nu + 1)2^{2\nu+1}}{\Gamma(2\nu + 1)} \sum_{n=0}^{\infty} \frac{(n + \nu)\Gamma(n + 2\nu)}{n!} J^2_{n+\nu}(z)$$

(see [11, (5.5)(1)]), it can be shown that

$$(2.7) \quad {}_1F_2 \left(\begin{array}{c} a_1 \\ b_1, \, b_2 \end{array} ; -z^2 \right) = \Gamma^2(\nu + 1) 2^{2\nu} z^{-2\nu}$$

$$\times \sum_{n=0}^{\infty} \frac{(2\nu + 1)_n}{n!} \frac{2n + 2\nu}{n + 2\nu} J^2_{n+\nu}(z) \, {}_4F_3 \left(\begin{array}{c} -n, \, n + 2\nu, \, \nu + 1, \, a_1 \\ \nu + \frac{1}{2}, \, b_1, \, b_2 \end{array} ; 1 \right),$$

where 2ν is not a negative integer and the factor $(2n + 2\nu)/(n + 2\nu)$ is replaced by 1 at $n = 0$ (cf. [6, (3.1)]). On account of (2.7), it suffices to show that

$$
{}_4F_3\left(\begin{array}{c} -n,\, n + 2\nu,\, \nu + 1,\, c + \frac{3}{2} \\ \nu + \frac{1}{2},\, c + \frac{5}{2},\, \alpha + 2 \end{array}; 1\right) > 0, \quad \text{for } n = 0, 1, 2, \ldots.
$$

We set $\nu = \frac{\alpha}{2} + \frac{3}{4}$ and see that this ${}_4F_3$ is a balanced (or Saalschützian) hypergeometric series which can be transformed into another balanced ${}_4F_3$ by Whipple's transformation formula, viz.,

$$
{}_4F_3\left(\begin{array}{c} -n,\, x,\, y,\, z \\ u,\, v,\, w \end{array}; 1\right) = \frac{(v - z)_n (w - z)_n}{(v)_n (w)_n} {}_4F_3\left(\begin{array}{c} -n,\, u - x,\, u - y,\, z \\ 1 - v + z - n,\, 1 - w + z - n,\, u \end{array}; 1\right),
$$

where it is assumed that $u + v + w - x - y - z + n = 1$, (see [3, p. 140]). We have, in fact,

$$
(2.8) \quad {}_4F_3\left(\begin{array}{c} -n,\, n + \alpha + \frac{3}{2},\, \frac{\alpha}{2} + \frac{7}{4},\, c + \frac{3}{2} \\ \frac{\alpha}{2} + \frac{5}{4},\, c + \frac{5}{2},\, \alpha + 2 \end{array}; 1\right)
$$

$$
= \frac{\left(\frac{\alpha}{2} - \frac{1}{4} - c\right)_n n!}{\left(\frac{\alpha}{2} + \frac{5}{4}\right)_n \left(c + \frac{5}{2}\right)_n} {}_4F_3\left(\begin{array}{c} -n,\, -n + \frac{1}{2},\, \frac{\alpha}{2} + \frac{1}{4},\, c + \frac{3}{2} \\ -n - \frac{\alpha}{2} + \frac{5}{4} + c,\, -n,\, \alpha + 2 \end{array}; 1\right) > 0,
$$

when $c > -1/2$, $\beta > 1/2$ and $\alpha > -1/2$. In particular, when $c = 0$, the above inequality is valid for $\alpha > 1/2$. We have used the formula

$$
(2.9) \qquad\qquad (-n + A)_k = (-1)^k \frac{(1 - A)_n}{(1 - A)_{n-k}}, \quad 1 \le k \le n.
$$

When $\beta = 1/2$, the ${}_4F_3$ series of the first part of (2.8) reduces to a balanced ${}_3F_2$ series which can be summed by the Pfaff-Saalschütz formula, viz.,

$$
{}_3F_2\left(\begin{array}{c} -n,\, a,\, b \\ c,\, 1 + a + b - c - n \end{array}; 1\right) = \frac{(c - a)_n (c - b)_n}{(c)_n (c - a - b)_n}
$$

(cf. [3, p. 69]). Using this and (2.9) we obtain

$$
{}_3F_2\left(\begin{array}{c} -n,\, n + \alpha + \frac{3}{2},\, \frac{\alpha}{2} + \frac{7}{4} \\ \frac{\alpha}{2} + \frac{9}{4},\, \alpha + 2 \end{array}; 1\right) = \frac{\left(\frac{1}{2}\right)_n \left(\frac{\alpha}{2} + \frac{1}{4}\right)_n}{(\alpha + 2)_n \left(\frac{\alpha}{2} + \frac{9}{4}\right)_n} > 0,
$$

for $\alpha > -1/2$ and the proof of (2.4) is now complete.

Next we shall show that inequality (1.3) holds for no other values of α and β than the ones given in Theorem 1.1.

It follows from (2.1) that inequality (1.3) fails to hold for some $x > 0$ when $\alpha - \beta > 0$.

We observe that inequality (1.3) is also equivalent to

$$
(2.10) \qquad\qquad \int_0^x t^{-\beta} J_\alpha(t)\, dt - x^{1-\beta} J_\alpha(x) > 0.
$$

When $-1 < \alpha \le \beta \le -1/2$, we set $x = j_{\alpha,2}$ in (2.10), where $j_{\alpha,2}$ is the second positive root of the Bessel function $J_\alpha(x)$. In this case we have

$$
\int_0^{j_{\alpha,2}} t^{-\beta} J_\alpha(t)\, dt < 0,
$$

see [4] and compare also the paper [5] in the case where $\alpha = \beta$.

Since $J_{-\frac{1}{2}}(t) = \left(\frac{2}{\pi t}\right)^{\frac{1}{2}} \cos t$, in the case where $\alpha = \beta = -1/2$, the left hand side of (2.10) equals $\left(\frac{2}{\pi}\right)^{\frac{1}{2}} (\sin x - x \cos x)$, which assumes negative values for appropriate x.

In the case where $-1 < \alpha < -1/2$ and $-1/2 < \beta < 0$ there exists a unique solution $\beta(\alpha)$ of the equation

$$\int_0^{j_{\alpha,2}} t^{-\beta(\alpha)} J_\alpha(t) \, dt = 0$$

and the integral in (2.10) is positive for $\beta(\alpha) < \beta < \alpha + 1$ but not for $\beta < \beta(\alpha)$. Also in this case we have $-1/2 < -1 - \alpha < \beta(\alpha) < 0$ (see [4, p. 306]). In the cases where the integral in (2.10) is positive we follow a different method in order to show that this inequality fails to hold when α, β do not satisfy the conditions of Theorem 1.1.

For $-1/2 < \alpha \leq \beta < 1/2$, we study the asymptotic behavior of the left-hand side of (2.10) as $x \to \infty$. Since

$$\int_0^\infty t^{-\beta} J_\alpha(t) \, dt = \frac{\Gamma\left(\frac{\alpha-\beta+1}{2}\right)}{2^\beta \Gamma\left(\frac{\alpha+\beta+1}{2}\right)},$$

(see [11, p. 391]) and

$$J_\alpha(x) = \left(\frac{2}{\pi x}\right)^{\frac{1}{2}} \cos\left(x - \left(\alpha + \frac{1}{2}\right)\frac{\pi}{2}\right) + O(x^{-3/2}), \quad \text{as } x \to \infty,$$

(cf. [3, p. 209]), we see that the left-hand side of (2.10) as $x \to \infty$ is asymptotically equal to

$$\frac{\Gamma\left(\frac{\alpha-\beta+1}{2}\right)}{2^\beta \Gamma\left(\frac{\alpha+\beta+1}{2}\right)} - \left(\frac{2}{\pi}\right)^{\frac{1}{2}} x^{\frac{1}{2}-\beta} \cos\left(x - \left(\alpha + \frac{1}{2}\right)\frac{\pi}{2}\right) + O\left(\frac{1}{x^{\beta+\frac{1}{2}}}\right)$$

which changes sign infinitely often for $-1/2 < \alpha \leq \beta < 1/2$.

In the same way it can be shown that (2.10) fails to hold for appropriate x when $-1 < \alpha \leq -1/2$, $0 \leq \beta < 1/2$, $\beta - \alpha < 1$. Also in the case where $-1 < \alpha < -1/2$ and $\beta(\alpha) \leq \beta < 1/2$, $\beta - \alpha < 1$, because $\alpha + 1 + \beta(\alpha) > 0$.

When $\alpha = -1/2$ and $-1/2 < \beta < 1/2$ the above argument simplifies as follows. In this case inequality (2.10) is equivalent to

$$(2.11) \qquad \int_0^x \frac{\cos t}{t^{\beta+\frac{1}{2}}} \, dt - x^{\frac{1}{2}-\beta} \cos x > 0.$$

For $0 < a < 1$ we have

$$\int_0^\infty \frac{\cos t}{t^a} \, dt = \Gamma(1-a) \sin\frac{\pi a}{2},$$

see for example [3, p. 50]. It is clear that inequality (2.11) cannot hold for x sufficiently large when $-1/2 < \beta < 1/2$.

We conclude from the above that inequality (1.3) fails to hold for appropriate x when $\beta < 1/2$. Finally, we observe that when $\alpha < -1/2$ the convergence condition $\beta < \alpha + 1$ forces $\beta < 1/2$. Therefore inequality (1.3) holds only when α, β satisfy the conditions of Theorem 1.1.

The proof of Theorem 1.1 is complete. $\qquad\qquad\qquad\qquad\qquad\qquad\qquad\quad \square$

Remark 2.1. *By observing that (1.2) is equivalent to*

$$(2.12) \qquad \int_0^x \frac{\sin t}{t^a}\, dt - x^{1-a} \sin x > 0$$

and that for $0 < a < 1$ we have

$$\int_0^\infty \frac{\sin t}{t^a}\, dt = \Gamma(1 - a) \cos \frac{\pi a}{2},$$

(cf. [3, p. 50]), it can be easily verified that this inequality fails to hold for appropriate x when $0 < a < 1$. Evidently, the left hand side of (2.12) assumes negative values for some x when $a < 0$.

References

[1] H. Alzer and S. Koumandos, Sub- and superadditive properties of Fejér's sine polynomial, *Bull. London Math. Soc.*, **38**(2) (2006), 261–268.

[2] H. Alzer and S. Ruscheweyh, A subadditive property of the gamma function, *J. Math. Anal. Appl.*, **285** (2003), 564-577.

[3] G.E. Andrews, R. Askey and R. Roy, Special functions, *Encyclopedia of Mathematics and its Applications*, 71. Cambridge University Press, Cambridge, 1999.

[4] R. Askey and J. Steinig, Some positive trigonometric sums, *Trans. Amer. Math. Soc.*, **187** (1974), 295–307.

[5] E. Feldheim, On the positivity of certain sums of ultraspherical polynomials, *J. Analyse Math.*, **11** (1963), 275-284 (edited with additional notes by G. Szegő), also in G. Szegő collected papers Vol.3, Birkhäuser Boston, 1982, 821-830.

[6] G. Gasper, Positive integrals of Bessel functions, *SIAM J. Math. Anal.*, **6** (1975), 868-881.

[7] G. Gasper, Positive sums of the classical orthogonal polynomials, *SIAM J. Math. Anal.*, **8** (1977), 423-447.

[8] S. Koumandos, Some positive integrals of products of Bessel functions, *Analysis* (Munich), **23**(3) (2003), 277-286.

[9] S. Koumandos, Some inequalities for the sine integral, *J. Inequal. Pure Appl. Math.*, **6**(1) (2005), Art. 25, 5 pp. (electronic).

[10] R.A. Rosenbaum, Sub-additive functions, *Duke Math. J.*, **17** (1950), 227-247.

[11] G.N. Watson, *A Treatise on the Theory of Bessel Functions*, 2nd ed. Cambridge University Press, 1944.

In: Advances in Inequalities for Special Functions
Editors: P. Cerone and S. S. Dragomir, pp. 73–80

ISBN 978-1-60021-919-1
© 2008 Nova Science Publishers, Inc.

Sturm Theory for Some Classes of Sturm-Liouville Equations and Inequalities and Monotonicity Properties for the Zeros of Bessel Functions

Andrea Laforgia and Pierpaolo Natalini

Dedicated to Carlo Bernardini on his seventy-fifth birthday

Department of Mathematics
Roma Tre University, Largo San Leonardo Murialdo, 1
00146, Rome, Italy
E-mail addresses: {laforgia,natalini}@mat.uniroma3.it

ABSTRACT. It has been more than 150 years since the first formulation of the Sturm comparison theorem concerning solutions of second order linear differential equations. In these years the theorem has been extended to higher order differential equations, to partial differential equations and to difference equations. The aim of this paper is to present a survey of the most important inequalities and monotonicity properties of the zeros of Bessel functions. The results are obtained as a consequence of the Sturm comparison theorem.

1991 Mathematics Subject Classification: Primary 34C10, 33C10; Secondary 26D07, 26A48, 26A51.

Key words and phrases: Sturm comparison theorem, zeros of Bessel functions, inequalities, monotonicity, concavity (convexity) properties.

1 THE STURM COMPARISON THEOREM

There are many formulations of the Sturm comparison theorem concerning solutions of the second order linear differential equations. One of these which is very useful for applications to the zeros of Bessel functions and classical orthogonal polynomials is the following due to G. Szegö [27, p. 19].

Lemma 1.1 (Sturm comparison theorem in Szegö's form). *Let the functions y and Y be nontrivial solutions of the differential equations*

$$(1.1) \qquad y'' + f(x)\, y = 0, \qquad Y'' + F(x)\, Y = 0$$

and let them have consecutive zeros at $x_1, x_2, \ldots, x_m$ and $X_1, X_2, \ldots, X_m$, respectively, on an interval (a, b). Suppose that f and F are continuous on (a, b), that

$$(1.2) \qquad f(x) < F(x), \qquad a < x < x_m$$

and that

$$(1.3) \qquad \lim_{x \to a^+} [y'(x)\, Y(x) - y(x)\, Y'(x)] = 0.$$

Research supported by MIUR, Ministero dell'Istruzione, Università e Ricerca of Italy.

Then

(1.4) $$X_k < x_k, \qquad k = 1, 2, \ldots, m.$$

Remark 1.1. *It has been pointed out in [2] that the condition (1.2) can be replaced by the less restrictive*

(1.5) $$f(x) < F(x), \qquad a < x < X_m.$$

We shall need this condition to prove some monotonicity results and inequalities.

2   ZEROS OF BESSEL FUNCTIONS

The general Bessel (cylinder) function of order ν can be considered in the form

$$C_\nu(x; \alpha) = C_\nu(x) = J_\nu(x) \cos \alpha - Y_\nu(x) \sin \alpha, \qquad 0 \le \alpha < \pi,$$

where $J_\nu(x)$ and $Y_\nu(x)$ denote the Bessel functions of the first and second kind, respectively. Here, α is independent of ν and x. We denote by $c_{\nu k}$, $j_{\nu k}$ and $y_{\nu k}$ $(k = 1, 2, \ldots)$ the positive zeros of $C_\nu(x)$, $J_\nu(x)$ and $Y_\nu(x)$, respectively. The corresponding zeros of the derivatives $\dfrac{d}{dx} C_\nu(x)$, $\dfrac{d}{dx} J_\nu(x)$ and $\dfrac{d}{dx} Y_\nu(x)$ are denoted by $c'_{\nu k}$, $j'_{\nu k}$ and $y'_{\nu k}$, respectively.

The definition of $c_{\nu k}$, may be extended to negative values of ν in such a way that $c_{\nu k}$ varies continuously with ν, $c_{\nu k} \to 0$ when $\nu \to \dfrac{\alpha}{\pi} - k$ and on the interval

$$\frac{\alpha}{\pi} - k < \nu < \frac{\alpha}{\pi} - k + 1$$

$c_{\nu k}$ is the first positive zero of $C_\nu(x)$ [27, pp. 508–509].

In [8] Elbert and Laforgia defined the function $j_{\nu\kappa}$ for all fixed $\kappa > 0$ as the solution of the differential equation

(2.1) $$\frac{d}{d\nu} j = 2j \int_0^\infty K_0 \left(2j \sinh t\right) e^{-2\nu t} dt$$

with the boundary condition

(2.2) $$\lim_{\nu \to -\kappa + 0} j_{\nu\kappa} = 0,$$

where $K_0(x)$ denotes the modified Bessel function of order zero.

For $\kappa = 1, 2, \ldots$ we have the zeros $j_{\nu k}$ of $J_\nu(x)$. If $k - 1 < \kappa < k$ we get $c_{\nu k} = j_{\nu \kappa}$, with $\alpha = (k - \kappa)\pi$. The uniqueness of the solutions of (2.1) for any initial value problem, has been shown in [6]. This definition is very useful for investigating the properties of $c_{\nu k}$.

There are several proofs that each $j_{\nu k}$ increases as ν increases, $\nu \ge 0$. One of these is due to M.B. Porter and M. Bôcher [3] and is based on the Sturm comparison theorem. By (2.1) we find immediately that the zeros $j_{\nu\kappa}$ of any cylinder function increase with ν, for $\nu > -\kappa$. Formula (2.1) is the main tool in the investigation of concavity (convexity) properties of $j_{\nu\kappa}$, with respect to $\nu \ge 0$. We observe that the study of the concavity (convexity) properties of $c_{\nu k}$ ($j_{\nu\kappa}$ with our notation), was originated by the paper [25] by Putterman, Kac and Uhlenbeck. They proposed a quantum mechanical explanation for the origin of the vortex lines produced in superfluid Helium when its container is rotated. They conjectured that for $k = 1, 2, \ldots$, $n = 1, 2, \ldots$, $j_{n,k}$ is concave with respect to n, while $j_{n,k}^2$ is convex.

J.T. Lewis and M.E. Muldoon [19] have established some monotonicity results using the Hellmann-Feynmann theorem of quantum chemistry. In [4] Á. Elbert proved that the functions $j_{\nu,1}, j_{\nu,2}, \ldots$ are concave not only for $\nu = 1, 2, \ldots$, but on the whole domain of existence. This result was extended by M.E. Muldoon and A. Laforgia [17] to $j_{\nu\kappa}$. Precisely they proved that $j_{\nu\kappa}$ is concave for $\kappa \geq \dfrac{1}{2}$ as a function of $\nu \geq 0$. The question aries naturally whether the concavity of $j_{\nu\kappa}$ holds for every $\kappa > 0$. The answer is in the negative. Indeed Elbert and Laforgia [7] proved that for sufficiently small κ the function $j_{\nu\kappa}$ is convex at least on $\nu \geq \dfrac{1}{2}$. In the proof of concavity of $j_{\nu k}$, $\nu > 0$, the following result on the monotonicity of $\dfrac{j_{\nu k}}{\nu}$ was essential. The proof, due to Makai [23], is based on the Sturm theorem.

Theorem 2.1. *For $k = 1, 2, \ldots$ and $\nu > 0$ let $j_{\nu k}$ denote the k-th zero of the Bessel function $J_\nu(x)$ of the first kind. Then*

$$\frac{j_{\nu k}}{\nu} \qquad \text{decreases as } \nu \text{ increases, } \nu > 0, \ k = 1, 2, \ldots.$$

Proof. We use the fact that the function

$$y_\nu(x) = x^{1/2} \, J_\nu\left(j_{\nu k} \, x^{1/(2\nu)}\right)$$

satisfies

$$y_\nu'' + p_\nu(x) \, y_\nu = 0,$$

where

$$p_\nu(x) = \left\{ \frac{j_{\nu k}}{2\nu} \, x^{\frac{1}{2\nu} - 1} \right\}^2.$$

This follows from the differential equation [30]

$$x^2 \, y'' + x \, y' + \left(x^2 - \nu^2\right) \, y = 0$$

by suitable changes of variables.

Now suppose that for some μ and ν, with $0 < \mu < \nu$, we have

$$(2.3) \qquad \frac{j_{\mu k}}{\mu} \leq \frac{j_{\nu k}}{\nu}.$$

The functions $y_\mu(x)$ and $y_\nu(x)$ both vanish at $x = 0$ and both have their k-th positive zero at $x = 1$. Moreover, they satisfy the condition (1.3) of the Sturm theorem and by (2.3) $p_\mu(x) < p_\nu(x)$, $0 < x < 1$. Thus an application of the Sturm comparison theorem shows that the k-th zero of $y_\nu(x)$ occurs before the k-th zero of $y_\mu(x)$. This contradiction shows that (2.3) cannot hold and so $j_{\nu k}/\nu$ decreases as ν increases, $0 < \nu < \infty$. $\square$

Remark 2.1. *The reader should observe that Makai used the Sturm theorem not in the usual way, but in an indirect way. In the proof of Theorem 2.1 we know that the k-th zero is exactly at $x = 1$ and we use this fact to prove that the function is monotonic. This is the only indirect application of the Sturm theorem that we know of.*

Remark 2.2. *The most obvious direct approach of scaling the independent variable, i.e. considering the equation*

$$y'' + \left[\nu^2 + \left(\frac{1}{4} - \nu^2\right) x^{-2}\right] y = 0$$

satisfied by $x^{1/2} \, J_\nu(\nu x)$ is ineffective here, since the Sturm theorem cannot be applied. Nevertheless the idea of scaling is sometimes useful. The first author used the idea of scaling to show that $\lambda \, x_{nk}^{(\lambda)}$ increases with λ, $0 < \lambda < 1$, $k = 1, 2, \ldots, \left[\frac{n}{2}\right]$, where $x_{nk}^{(\lambda)}$ denotes the k-th positive zero of the ultraspherical polynomial.

The second application of Sturm theorem that we now present is concerned with a determinantal inequality whose elements are the zeros of cylinder functions. L. Lorch proved the determinantal inequality

$$(2.4) \qquad \begin{vmatrix} c_{\nu k} & c_{\nu,k+1} \\ c_{\nu,k+1} & c_{\nu,k+2} \end{vmatrix} < 0 \qquad \text{for } \nu \geq 0, \ k = 1, 2, \ldots .$$

It is possible to obtain a more general result using only the Sturm comparison theorem. This is as follows.

Theorem 2.2. *For* $\nu \geq 0$, $k = 1, 2, \ldots$ *and* $m = 1, 2, \ldots$ *let* $a_{\nu m}$ *and* $b_{\nu k}$ *be the zeros of the cylinder functions* $C_\nu(x)$ *and* $Z_\nu(x)$, *respectively. Suppose that for some* $\varepsilon \geq 0$ *and for some* k *and* m, $b_{\nu+\varepsilon,k} < a_{\nu m}$. *Then*

$$(2.5) \qquad \begin{vmatrix} b_{\nu+\varepsilon,k} & b_{\nu+\varepsilon,k+1} \\ a_{\nu m} & a_{\nu,m+1} \end{vmatrix} < 0.$$

Proof. The functions $C_\nu(e^x)$ and $Z_\nu(e^x)$ are the solutions of the differential equation

$$(2.6) \qquad\qquad y'' + p(x; \nu)\, y = 0,$$

where

$$p(x; \nu) = e^{2x} - \nu^2.$$

Let

$$h = \log a_{\nu m} - \log b_{\nu+\varepsilon,k} > 0.$$

It is immediate to see that

$$p(x - h, \nu + \varepsilon) < p(x, \nu), \qquad \varepsilon \geq 0, \quad h > 0, \quad \nu \geq 0$$

and that $Z_{\nu+\varepsilon}(x - h)$ is a solution of

$$(2.7) \qquad\qquad z'' + p(x - h, \nu + \varepsilon)\, z = 0.$$

Both the functions $C_\nu(e^x)$ and $Z_{\nu+\varepsilon}(x - h)$ are zero at $x = \log a_{\nu m} = \log b_{\nu+\varepsilon,k} + h$. Thus we can apply the Sturm comparison theorem. Its application to equations (2.6) and (2.7) shows that $\log a_{\nu,m+1} < \log b_{\nu+\varepsilon,k+1} + h$ and recalling the value of h, we get

$$\frac{a_{\nu,m+1}}{a_{\nu m}} < \frac{b_{\nu+\varepsilon,k+1}}{b_{\nu+\varepsilon,k}}$$

which is equivalent to (2.5). The proof is complete. $\qquad\qquad\qquad\qquad\qquad \square$

Remark 2.3. *We observe that in the proof of Theorem 2.2 it is not necessary to specify if the functions* $C_\nu(e^x)$ *and* $Z_\nu(x)$ *are linearly independent or not.*

Remark 2.4. *By (2.5) we can deduce some interesting particular cases. For example with* $\varepsilon = 0$, $a_{\nu k} = c_{\nu k}$, $b_{\nu m} = c_{\nu m}$, $m = k + 1$, *the restriction* $b_{\nu+\varepsilon,k} < a_{\nu m}$ *becomes* $c_{\nu k} < c_{\nu,k+1}$ *which is clearly true. In this case by (2.5) we find*

$$\frac{c_{\nu,k+2}}{c_{\nu,k+1}} < \frac{c_{\nu,k+1}}{c_{\nu k}} \qquad k = 1, 2, \ldots, \ \nu \geq 0$$

which is the Lorch's inequalities (2.4).

A more general result has been established by Á. Elbert and A. Laforgia in [6]. Specifically, using the notation $j_{\nu\kappa}$ introduced above to denote the zeros of the cylinder function, they proved the following theorem.

Theorem 2.3. *For* ε, δ, h, $r \geq 0$, *let* T *be the determinant defined by*

$$T = \begin{vmatrix} j_{\nu\kappa} & j_{\nu+\delta,\kappa+h} \\ j_{\nu+\varepsilon,\kappa+r} & j_{\nu+\delta+\varepsilon,\kappa+h+r} \end{vmatrix}.$$

If $\varepsilon + r > 0$ *and* $h + \delta > 0$, *then* $T < 0$.

We shall not give the proof of this theorem. We say only that this is not based on the Sturm theorem, but on the integral formula (2.1). By (2.1) it is possible to derive several monotonicity, concavity (convexity) properties and as a consequence of these, Theorem 2.3. We mention here just one of these results.

Theorem 2.4. *The function* $j_{\nu\kappa}$ *is concave with respect to* κ *if* $\nu \geq \frac{1}{2}$ *and convex if* $0 \leq \nu \leq \frac{1}{2}$.

We conclude this section with the following remark. The determinants considered in this section are called *Turánians*. In fact P. Turán proved the inequality

$$\begin{vmatrix} P_n(x) & P_{n+1}(x) \\ P_{n+1}(x) & P_{n+2}(x) \end{vmatrix} \leq 0, \qquad -1 \leq x \leq 1,,$$

where $P_n(x)$ denotes the Legendre polynomial of degree n and where equality holds if and only if $x = \pm 1$. Similar properties have been proved by many authors, for many other special functions. Thus, Karlin and Szegö named these inequalities *Turánians*.

3 A General Consequence of the Sturm Comparison Theorem

In this section we are concerned with some monotonicity properties, with respect to n, of quantities of the type

$$(3.1) \qquad\qquad x_{n,k+1} - x_{nk}$$

where x_{nk} is the k-th zero of particular solutions of linear second order differential equations. The main applications are to the zeros of classical orthogonal polynomials. In [2] the reader can find several applications of Theorem 3.1, to the zeros of Jacobi polynomials.

Theorem 3.1. *Let the hypotheses of the Sturm comparison theorem hold and let* f *in* (1.1) *be non-increasing on* $a < x < x_m$. *Then*

$$X_{k+1} - X_k < x_{k+1} - x_k \qquad k = 1, 2, \ldots, m-1.$$

Proof. The function $y(x + \delta)$ satisfies the equation

$$y'' + f(x + \delta)\, y = 0, \qquad a - \delta < x < x_m - \delta$$

and its zeros occur at $x_1 - \delta$, $x_2 - \delta$, ..., $x_m - \delta$. For a fixed $k = 1, 2, \ldots, m-1$ we choose $\delta = x_k - X_k$ and observe that $\delta > 0$ on account of the Sturm theorem. Thus the k-th zero of $Y(x)$ coincides with the k-th zero of $y(x + \delta)$. Moreover,

$$f(x + \delta) \leq f(x) < F(x), \qquad 0 < x < x_m - \delta$$

and by the Sturm theorem applied on the interval $(X_k, x_{k+1} - \delta)$, the next larger zero of $Y_\nu(x)$ occurs before the next larger zero of $y(x + \delta)$, that is

$$x_{k+1} - \delta > X_{k+1}, \qquad \delta = x_k - X_k$$

leading to the desired result. $\qquad\qquad\qquad\qquad\qquad\qquad\qquad\qquad\qquad\square$

Remark 3.1. *In the theorem the hypothesis that f be non-increasing may be replaced by the hypothesis that F be non-increasing, on $a < x < x_m$. In this case we get*

$$f(x + \delta) < F(x + \delta) \leq F(x), \qquad a < x < x_m - \delta$$

and the conclusion of Theorem 3.1, follows as above.

4   ZEROS OF $K_{i\nu}(x)$

It is known that for real x the function $K_\mu(x)$ has no zeros if μ is real or complex. But, when μ is a pure imaginary number, i.e. $\mu = i\,\nu$, the function $K_\mu(x)$ vanishes at $+\infty$ and has infinitely many positive zeros whose only point of accumulation is $x = 0$, (see [10] and [11] for further information). These zeros occur in certain physical problems such as in the determination of the bound states for an inverse square potential with hard core in the Schrödinger equation.

For $k = 1, 2, \ldots$ we denote by $x_k(\nu)$ the positive zeros of the modified Bessel function $K_{i\nu}(x)$ in decreasing order:

$$x_1(\nu) > x_2(\nu) > \cdots > x_n(\nu) > x_{n+1}(\nu) > \cdots > 0$$

and prove the following result, [14].

Theorem 4.1. *For $\nu > 0$ let $x_k(\nu)$ be the k-th positive zero of the modified Bessel function $K_{i\nu}(x)$ of purely imaginary order. Then*

$$x_{k-1}(\nu) - x_k(\nu) < x_{k-2}(\nu) - x_{k-1}(\nu).$$

Proof. We consider the differential equation

$$y'' + P(x; \nu)\, y = 0,$$

where

$$P(x; \nu) = -1 + \frac{\frac{1}{4} + \nu^2}{x^2},$$

satisfied by $y_\nu(x) = x^{1/2}\, K_{i\nu}(x)$, [1, p. 377], and the equation

$$z'' + P(x - h; \nu)\, z = 0,$$

where $h = x_{k-1}(\nu) - x_k(\nu)$, satisfied by $y_\nu(x - h)$. It is immediate to check that $P(x; \nu) < P(x - h; \nu)$ and that $y_\nu(x)$ and $y_\nu(x - h)$ both are zero at $x_{k-1}(\nu)$. Thus an application of the Sturm theorem gives that the next zero $x_{k-1}(\nu)$ of $y_\nu(x - h)$ occurs before the next zero $x_{k-2}(\nu)$ of $y_\nu(x)$. Recalling the value of h, this shows that

$$x_{k-1}(\nu) - x_k(\nu) < x_{k-2}(\nu) - x_{k-1}(\nu).$$

The proof of Theorem 4.1 is complete. $\square$

REFERENCES

[1] M. Abramowitz and I.A. Stegun (Eds.), *Handbook of Mathematical Functions with Applications, Graphs and Mathematical Tables*, Dover, New York, 1970.

[2] S. Ahmed, A. Laforgia and M.E. Muldoon, On the spacing of the zeros of some classical orthogonal polynomials, *J. London Math. Soc.*, **25** (1982), 246–252.

[3] M. Bôcher, On certain methods of Sturm and their application to the roots of Bessel's functions, *Bull. Amer. Math. Soc.*, **3** (1897), 205–213.

[4] Á. Elbert, Concavity of the zeros of Bessel functions, *Studia Sci. Math. Hungar.*, **12** (1977), 81–88.

[5] Á. Elbert, L. Gatteschi and A. Laforgia, On the concavity of the zeros of Bessel functions, *Appl. Anal.*, **16** (1983), 261–278.

[6] Á. Elbert and A. Laforgia, Monotonicity properties of the zeros of the Bessel functions, *SIAM J. Math. Anal.*, **17** (1986), 1483–1488.

[7] Á. Elbert and A. Laforgia, On the convexity of the zeros of Bessel functions, *SIAM J. Math. Anal.*, **16** (1985), 614–619.

[8] Á. Elbert and A. Laforgia, On the square of the zeros of Bessel functions, *SIAM J. Math. Anal.*, **15** (1984), 206–212.

[9] Á. Elbert and A. Laforgia, Some monotonicity properties of the zeros of ultraspherical polynomials, *Acta Math. Hung.*, **48** (1986), 155–159.

[10] E.M. Ferreira and G. Sesma, Zeros of modified Hankel functions, *Numer. Math.*, **16** (1970), 278–284.

[11] A. Gray, G.B. Matthews and T.M. MacRobert, *A Treatise on Bessel functions and their Applications to Physics*, Macmillian, London, 1952.

[12] S. Karlin and G. Szegö, On certain determinants whose elements are orthogonal polynomials, *J. d'Analyse Math.*, **8** (1960), 1–157.

[13] A. Laforgia, A monotonicity property for the zeros of ultraspherical polynomials, *Proc. Am. Math. Soc.*, **4** (1981), 757–758.

[14] A. Laforgia, Inequalities and monotonicity results for zeros of modified Bessel functions of purely imaginary order, *Quarterly of Applied Math.*, **1** (1986), 91–96.

[15] A. Laforgia, Sturm theory for certain classes of Sturm-Liouville equations and Turánians and Wronskians for the zeros of derivative of Bessel functions, *Indag. Math.*, **3** (1982), 295–301.

[16] A. Laforgia and M.E. Muldoon, Inequalities and appoximations for zeros of Bessel functions of small order, *SIAM J. Math. Anal.*, **14** (1983), 383–388.

[17] A. Laforgia and M.E. Muldoon, Monotonicity and concavity properties of zeros of Bessel functions, *J. Math. Anal. Appl.*, **98** (1984), 470–477.

[18] A. Laforgia and M.E. Muldoon, Some consequences of the Sturm comparison theorem, *Amer. Math. Monthly*, **93** (1986), 89–94.

[19] J.T. Lewis and M.E. Muldoon, Monotonicity and convexity properties of zeros of Bessel functions, *SIAM J. Math. Anal.*, **8** (1977), 171–178.

[20] L. Lorch, Elementary comparison techniques for certains classes of Sturm-Liouville equations, *Proc. Internat. Conference Uppsala 1977*, Sympos. Univ. Upsaliensis Ann. Quingentesimum Celebrantis 7 (Almqvist and Wiksill), Stockholm, (1977), 125–133.

[21] L. Lorch, Turánians and Wronskians for the zeros of Bessel functions, *SIAM J. Math. Anal.*, **2** (1980), 222–227.

[22] E. Makai, On a monotonic property of certain Sturm-Liouvile functions, *Acta Math. Acad. Sci. Hungar.*, **3** (1952), 165–172.

[23] E. Makai, On zeros of Bessel functions, *Univ. Beograd. Publ. Elektrotekn. Fak. Ser. Mat. Fiz.*, **602 − 633** (1978), 109–110.

[24] M.E. Muldoon, The variation with respect to order of zeros of Bessel functions, *Rend. Sem. Mat. Univ. Politec. Torino*, **39** (1981), 15–25.

[25] S.J. Putterman, M. Kac and G.E. Uhlenbeck, Possible origin of the quantized vortices in He, II, *Phys. Rev. Lett.*, **29** (1972), 546–549.

[26] O. Szász, Inequalities concerning ultraspherical polynomials and Bessel functions, *Proc. Amer. Math. Soc.*, **1** (1950), 256–267.

[27] G. Szegö, *Orthogonal Polynomials*, 4th ed., Amer. Math. Soc., Colloquium Publications, **23**, Amer. Math. Soc. Providence, RI, 1975.

[28] C. Sturm, Mémoire sur les équations différentialles du second ordre, *J. Math. Pures Appl.*, **1** (1936), 106–186.

[29] P. Turán, On the zeros of the polynomials of Legendre, *Casopis pro Pestováni Mat. a Fys*, **75** (1950), 113–122.

[30] G.N. Watson, *A Treatise on the Theory of Bessel functions*, 2nd ed. Cambridge University Press, Cambridge, 1958.

In: Advances in Inequalities for Special Functions   ISBN 978-1-60021-919-1
Editors: P. Cerone and S. S. Dragomir, pp. 81–100   © 2008 Nova Science Publishers, Inc.

Inequalities for the Gamma Function via Convexity

Milan Merkle

Računarski fakultet,
Knez Mihailova 6, 11000 Beograd, Serbia

Elektrotehnički fakultet,
P.P. Box 35-54, 11120 Beograd, Serbia

Universidade Federal do Rio de Janeiro,
Instituto de Mathematica,
Departamento de Métodos Estatisticos,
Rio de Janeiro, Brasil
E-mail address: emerkle@kondor.etf.bg.ac.yu

ABSTRACT. We review techniques based on convexity, logarithmic convexity and Schur-convexity, for producing inequalities and asymptotic expansions for ratios of Gamma functions. As an illustration, results for the Gautschi's and Gurland's ratio are presented, as well as asymptotic expansions for the Gamma function, along the lines of W. Krull's work. We argue that convexity-based techniques are advantageous over other methods, because they enable a comparison of inequalities, provide two transformations for their sharpening, and also yield two sided asymptotic expansions.

The Gamma function... is simple enough for juniors in college to meet, but deep enough to have called forth contributions from the finest mathematicians.

Philip Davis [7]

1991 Mathematics Subject Classification: 33B15, 39B62.

Key words and phrases: Gamma function, convexity, Gautschi's ratio, Gurland's ratio, Krull's functional equation.

1 INTRODUCTION

This paper is devoted to the Euler's Gamma function of a real positive argument:

$$(1.1) \qquad \Gamma(x) = \int_0^{+\infty} e^{-t} t^{x-1} dt, \qquad x > 0.$$

The importance of this function, which is classified as being *transcendentally transcendental* (Otto Hölder [13], Lee Rubel [33]) is enormous. It appears in almost every branch of Mathematics, and it is considered as an *almost elementary function*. Every mathematical or engineering software and even advanced calculators have a routine for calculation of $\Gamma(x)$.

The Gamma function first appeared in a letter of Leonard Euler to Goldbach in 1729, in the form of an infinite product:

$$(1.2) \qquad x\Gamma(x) = \prod_{k=1}^{+\infty} \frac{k^{1-x}(k+1)^x}{x+k}.$$

In this paper we give a survey of tools and techniques which can be used to produce inequalities for the Gamma function. We also present some examples of inequalities and asymptotic expansions.

By a famous theorem due to Bohr and Mollerup [3] and popularized by Emil Artin in his no less famous monograph [2] of 1931, Euler's gamma function is the unique solution to the functional equation $f(x + 1) = xf(x)$, under the condition that $\log f$ is convex on $(0, +\infty)$. Hence, the logarithmic convexity is an essential property of the gamma function, and this property is shared by many of its generalizations in various directions. In spite of this well known fact, there is a wide spectrum of techniques and methods that have been used in the literature for producing inequalities, chiefly of the following types:

- Inequalities for the ratio $Q(x, \beta) = \dfrac{\Gamma(x + \beta)}{\Gamma(x)}$ (*Gautschi type*)

- Inequalities for the ratio $T(x, y) = \dfrac{\Gamma(x)\Gamma(y)}{\Gamma^2((x + y)/2)}$ (*Gurland type*)

The names are after W. Gautschi [9] and J. Gurland [10]. Gautschi type could as well be named after J. Wendel [38].

Most of the well known inequalities for the gamma and digamma functions can be derived and improved by means of logarithmic convexity, or related properties. Using convexity, we can also produce asymptotic expansions, expressed in terms of infinitely sharp inequalities. Our method is founded on certain general convexity results, as well as on integral representations of error terms in some classical and related inequalities, which will also be discussed.

Let us introduce two useful transformations; I call them a β-transform and a π_n-transform.

1.1 β-transform for Gautschi Type

This transform has been known since Shanbhag [35]. The inequality

$$(1.3) \qquad\qquad A(x, \beta) \leq \frac{\Gamma(x + \beta)}{\Gamma(x)}$$

implies, replacing x by $x + \beta$ and β by $1 - \beta$,

$$A(x + \beta, 1 - \beta) \leq \frac{\Gamma(x + 1)}{\Gamma(x + \beta)},$$

and therefore

$$(1.4) \qquad\qquad \frac{\Gamma(x + \beta)}{\Gamma(x)} \leq \frac{x}{A(x + \beta, 1 - \beta)},$$

so, only the lower bound (1.3) is enough, or vice versa. We say that the inequality (1.4) is derived from (1.3) by a β-transform.

Two successive applications of the β-transform do not return the original bound; instead, it is equivalent to replacing x with $x + 1$ and applying the recurrence $\Gamma(x + 1) = x\Gamma(x)$. This leads us to another useful transform.

1.2 π_n-transform

This transform works for inequalities of both Gautcshi and Gurland type. It was firstly applied by B.R. Rao [30].

Let, for $n \geq 1$

$$\Pi(x, \beta, n) = \frac{x(x+1) \cdots (x+n-1)}{(x+\beta)(x+\beta+1) \cdots (x+\beta+n-1)}.$$

Start from the inequality of Gautschi type

$$(1.5) \qquad \frac{\Gamma(x+\beta)}{\Gamma(x)} \leq B(x, \beta),$$

write it for $x + n$ and β and then apply the recurrence relation for the Gamma function, to obtain

$$(1.6) \qquad \frac{\Gamma(x+\beta)}{\Gamma(x)} \leq B(x+n, \beta)\Pi(x, \beta, n).$$

Similarly, for an inequality of Gurland type

$$(1.7) \qquad \frac{\Gamma(x)\Gamma(y)}{\Gamma^2((x+y)/2)} \leq B(x, y)$$

one obtains

$$(1.8) \qquad \frac{\Gamma(x)\Gamma(y)}{\Gamma^2((x+y)/2)} \leq B(x+n, y+n)\rho(x, y, n),$$

where

$$(1.9) \qquad \rho(x, y, n) = \frac{(x+y)^2(x+y+2)^2 \cdots (x+y+2n-2)^2}{2^{2n}x(x+1) \cdots (x+n-1)y(y+1) \cdots (y+n-1)}.$$

It turns out that a π-transform sharpens inequalities; the reason will be obvious later. Note that a β-transform can be thought of as a "square root" of π_1 transform.

We proceed with a survey of basic tools: convexity, logarithmic convexity, Schur-convexity and complete monotonicity.

2 CONVEXITY

We begin with a survey of basic facts about convex functions. Throughout the text, I will denote an arbitrary real interval and $\bar{I}$ its closure.

A function f is convex on an interval I if

$$(2.1) \qquad f(\lambda x + (1-\lambda)y) \leq \lambda f(x) + (1-\lambda)f(y)$$

for all $x, y \in I$ and all $\lambda \in [0, 1]$. If the inequality in (2.1) is strict for all $\lambda \in (0, 1)$, then we say that f is strictly convex on I.

This definition can be easily extended to functions of more than one variable, if I is understood to be an arbitrary convex set, i.e., a set that together with x and y contains all points $\lambda x + (1-\lambda)y$ for $\lambda \in (0, 1)$.

Inequality (2.1) is known as Jensen's inequality.

There are several equivalent forms of (2.1). For example, a function f is convex on I if and only if

$$(2.2) \qquad \frac{f(x) - f(x_1)}{x - x_1} \leq \frac{f(x_2) - f(x)}{x_2 - x}$$

for all $x_1 < x < x_2$ in I [28, proof of Theorem 2 in 1.4.4]. Further, f is convex on I if and only if

$$(2.3) \qquad \frac{f(y_1) - f(x_1)}{y_1 - x_1} \leq \frac{f(y_2) - f(x_2)}{y_2 - x_2}$$

whenever $x_1 < y_1 \leq y_2$ and $x_1 \leq x_2 < y_2$ [21, 16B.3.a]. This condition means that the ratio $(f(v) - f(u))/(v - u)$ is increasing if the interval $[u, v]$ is being stretched to the right. It is sufficient to consider only a particular case $y_1 - x_1 = y_2 - x_2$ [21, 16B.3.a], i.e., a function f is convex on I if and only if

$$(2.4) \qquad f(x + h) - f(x) \leq f(y + h) - f(y)$$

for all $x < y$ in I and $h \geq 0$, such that $x + h, y + h \in I$. Even a further special case where $y = x + h$ is enough [21, 16B.3.a]: A function f is convex on I if and only if

$$(2.5) \qquad f(x + 2h) - 2f(x + h) + f(x) \geq 0$$

whenever $x, x + h \in I$ and $h > 0$.

If a function f is convex on $\bar{I}$, then it is continuous on I and there exist left and right derivatives in each point $x \in I$. Moreover, $f'_-(x) \leq f'_+(x)$ for each $x \in I$ [28, Theorem 1. in 1.4.4].

If a function f is differentiable on I, then from (2.4) it can be easily deduced that f is convex on I if and only if its derivative is an increasing function on I. If f is twice differentiable, then it is convex on I if and only if $f''(x) > 0$ on I.

If a function f satisfies

$$(2.6) \qquad f\left(\frac{x + y}{2}\right) \leq \frac{f(x) + f(y)}{2}$$

for all $x, y \in I$, we say that f is J-convex (or convex in the sense of Jensen) on I [28]. A J-convex function on $\bar{I}$ need not be continuous, but if it is, then it must be convex in the sense of definition (2.1) [28]. Therefore, a continuous function f is convex on I if and only if (2.6) holds.

A function f is said to be concave on I if $-f$ is convex on I. The above formulas remain valid for a concave function f upon replacing $\leq$ with $\geq$.

Sometimes it is convenient to consider functions that may take values $\pm\infty$ at some points of I. Then we apply the usual conventions, in particular $0 \cdot \pm\infty = 0$. Each finite valued function f, convex on $I \subset \mathbb{R}$ can be extended to a function $\hat{f}$, convex on $\mathbb{R}$ by

$$\hat{f}(x) = f(x) \quad \text{if } x \in I, \qquad \hat{f}(x) = +\infty \quad \text{otherwise.}$$

By [29, p.39] or [31, p.15], a continuous function g is convex on I if and only if

$$\frac{1}{y - x} \int_x^y g(t)\mathrm{d}t \leq \frac{g(x) + g(y)}{2}.$$

For a further study of convex functions see [31, 32, 36].

3   Logarithmic Convexity

A function f is said to be logarithmically convex (or log-convex) on I if $f(x) \geq 0$ for $x \in I$ and the function $x \mapsto \log f(x)$ is convex on I. Here we apply the convention $\log 0 = -\infty$.

Using the necessary and sufficient conditions for convexity given in the Introduction, it is easy to write the corresponding conditions for log-convexity. In particular, from (2.1) and (2.4) it follows that a nonnegative function f is log-convex if and only if

$$(3.1) \qquad f(\lambda x + (1 - \lambda)y) \leq (f(x))^{\lambda}(f(y))^{1-\lambda}, \qquad x, y \in I, \quad \lambda \in [0, 1],$$

and if and only if

$$(3.2) \qquad f(x + h)f(y) \leq f(x)f(y + h), \qquad x < y, \ x, y, x + h, y + h \in I, \ h \geq 0.$$

A nonnegative continuous function f is log-convex on I if and only if

$$(3.3) \qquad f\left(\frac{x + y}{2}\right) \leq \sqrt{f(x)f(y)}$$

for each $x, y \in I$.

A positive twice differentiable function f is log-convex on I if and only if

$$(3.4) \qquad f''(x)f(x) - f'(x)^2 \geq 0$$

for all $x \in I$.

A function f is said to be log-concave on I if $f(x) \geq 0$ for all $x \in I$ and if the function $x \mapsto \log f(x)$ is concave on I. Clearly, f is log-concave on I if and only if $1/f$ is log-convex on I.

If f is log-convex on I, it is convex on I. If f is nonnegative and concave on I, it is log-concave on I. These assertions follow upon noticing that $t \mapsto e^x$ is an increasing convex and $t \mapsto \log t$ is an increasing concave function. Therefore, log-convexity is a stronger property of plain convexity and log-concavity is a weaker property than concavity. To illustrate the point, note that the function $x \mapsto e^{-x^2}$ is strictly convex and log-concave on $(1/\sqrt{2}, +\infty)$.

Since a sum of convex (concave) functions is also convex (concave), it follows that a product of log-convex (log-concave) functions on I is also a log-convex (log-concave) function on I.

If f_1, f_2 are log-convex functions on I, then their sum $f_1 + f_2$ is also a log-convex function [2]. By induction, it can be proved that the class of log-convex functions is closed under finite sums; by an extension to integrals one concludes that the function

$$F(x) = \int_a^b g(x, t)\mathrm{d}t$$

is a log-convex function on $x \in I$ if for each fixed $t \in (a, b)$ the function $x \mapsto g(x, t)$ is log-convex on I. As a classical example, one can show that the Gamma function

$$\Gamma(x) = \int_0^{+\infty} e^{-t}t^{x-1}\mathrm{d}t$$

is log-convex on $(0, +\infty)$.

However, this property does not hold for log-concave functions. Indeed, the sum of two log-concave functions may not be log-concave. This lack of additivity often makes proofs of log-concavity much more involved.

Many frequently encountered probability distribution functions are log-concave on their domain. For a survey see [26].

4   Schur Convexity

Given two vectors of dimension n, $x = (x_1, x_2, \ldots, x_n)$ and $y = (y_1, y_2, \ldots, y_n)$, we say that x is majorized by y if

$$\sum_{i=1}^{k} x_{[i]} \le \sum_{i=1}^{k} y_{[i]} \quad \text{for } k = 1, 2, \ldots, n-1 \quad \text{and} \quad \sum_{i=1}^{n} x_i = \sum_{i=1}^{n} y_i,$$

where $(x_{[1]}, x_{[2]}, \ldots, x_{[n]})$ is a decreasing rearrangement of coordinates of x. If x is majorized by y, we write $x \prec y$. For example,

$$(\bar{x}, \bar{x}, \ldots, \bar{x}) \prec (x_1, x_2, \ldots, x_n), \quad \text{where} \quad \bar{x} = (x_1 + \cdots + x_n)/n.$$

The notation and terminology was introduced in [11]. The theory and applications of the concept of majorization is studied in [21].

A function f of n variables is said to be Schur-convex on $A \subset \mathbb{R}^n$ if

$$(4.1) \qquad\qquad x \prec y \implies f(x) \le f(y) \qquad \text{for each } x, y \in A.$$

A function f is said to be Schur-concave on $A \subset \mathbb{R}^n$ if

$$(4.2) \qquad\qquad x \prec y \implies f(x) \ge f(y) \qquad \text{for each } x, y \in A.$$

Note that the term "convex" apparently has not much in common with the usual notion of convexity. The name was introduced by Schur [34], as opposed to convexity in the sense of Jensen. There are, however, many results showing a connection between these two notions.

Suppose that y is a permutation of x. Then $x \prec y$ and also $y \prec x$ and if f is Schur-convex then $f(x) \le f(y)$ and $f(y) \le f(x)$, i.e. $f(x) = f(y)$. Therefore, only symmetric functions (invariant to permutations) may be Schur-convex or Schur-concave.

If $x \prec y$ implies $f(x) < f(y)$ whenever $x, y \in A$ and x is not a permutation of y, we say that f is a strictly Schur-convex function. Strict Schur-concavity is defined analogously.

In case $n = 2$, there is a simple interpretation of Schur-convexity. Let $u = (u_1, u_2)$, $v = (v_1, v_2)$ and suppose that $u_1 \ge u_2$ and $v_1 \ge v_2$. Then $u \prec v$ means, by the definition,

$$u_1 \le v_1, \qquad u_1 + u_2 = v_1 + v_2,$$

which may be possible if and only if

$$v_1 = u_1 + \varepsilon, \quad v_2 = u_2 - \varepsilon \qquad \text{for some } \varepsilon \ge 0.$$

Therefore, a function $f(x, y)$ is Schur-convex on A if and only if

$$(4.3) \qquad\qquad f(x, y) \le f(x - \varepsilon, y + \varepsilon)$$

for every $\varepsilon \ge 0$ and $x \le y$, where $x, y, x - \varepsilon, x + \varepsilon \in A$. In words, $f(x, y)$ increases when the interval $[x, y]$ expands by equal amounts at both ends.

In general, let $A \subset \mathbb{R}^n$ be a convex and symmetric set (that is, it contains every chord connecting its two points and if it contains a point x, then it contains every y whose coordinates are a permutation of coordinates of x), with a nonempty interior. Then [21, 3.A.4] a continuously differentiable function f of n variables is Schur-convex on A if and only if it is symmetric and

$$(4.4) \qquad\qquad (x_i - x_j)\left(\frac{\partial f(x)}{\partial x_i} - \frac{\partial f(x)}{\partial x_j}\right) \ge 0 \qquad \text{for all } x \in A.$$

Most often $A = I^n$, where I is an interval.

If a function g is convex on a real interval I, then [21, 3.C.1] the function

$$f(x) = \sum_{i=1}^{n} g(x_i)$$

is Schur-convex on I^n. For example, the function

$$f(x_1, \dots, x_n) = \sum_{i=1}^{n} x_i^2$$

is Schur-convex on $\mathbb{R}^n$. Moreover, the inequality

$$\sum_{i=1}^{n} g(x_i) \le \sum_{i=1}^{n} g(y_i)$$

holds for all continuous convex functions $g : \mathbb{R} \mapsto \mathbb{R}$ if and only if $x \prec y$. This result was obtained in [34] and is related to the much cited works of Tomić [37] and Weyl [39]; see also [21].

Let g be a continuous nonnegative function defined on an interval $I \subset \mathbb{R}$. Then

$$f(x) = \prod_{i=1}^{n} g(x_i), \qquad x \in I^n$$

is Schur-convex (strictly Schur-convex, Schur-concave, strictly Schur-concave) on I^n if and only if g is log-convex (strictly log-convex, log-concave, strictly log-concave) on I. For $n = 2$ it can be easily seen by comparing (4.3) for $f(x, y) = g(x)g(y)$ and the condition (3.2) for the function g.

In Section 7 it will be shown that the function

$$F(x, y) = \frac{\log \Gamma(y) - \log \Gamma(x)}{y - x}, \quad F(x, x) = (\log \Gamma(x))'$$

is Schur-concave on $\mathbb{R}^2$.

5 COMPLETE MONOTONICITY

A function f on $(0, +\infty)$ is completely monotone if it has derivatives of all orders and

$$(-1)^k f^{(k)}(t) \ge 0, \qquad t \in (0, +\infty), \ k = 0, 1, 2, \dots$$

In particular, this implies $f \ge 0, f' \le 0, f'' \ge 0$ and hence by (3.4), each completely monotone function on $(0, +\infty)$ is convex.

The function f is completely monotone on $(0, +\infty)$ if and only if [42]

$$f(x) = \int_0^{+\infty} e^{-xt} d\mu(t),$$

where $\mu(t)$ is nondecreasing and the integral converges for $0 < x < +\infty$.

The following result is proved in [14]: If $t \mapsto f(t)$ is completely monotone on $I = (0, +\infty)$, if $g(I) \subset I$ and if $x \mapsto g'(x)$ is completely monotone on I, then $x \mapsto f(g(x))$ is completely monotone on I.

In [8], a connection between complete monotonicity and majorization in the sense of Section 2 is discovered: Let α and β be vectors of dimension r with integer coordinates, and let f be completely monotone on $(0, +\infty)$. If $\beta \prec \alpha$, then for all $x \geq 0$

$$(-1)^{\alpha_1} f^{(\alpha_1)}(x)(-1)^{\alpha_2} f^{(\alpha_2)}(x) \cdots (-1)^{\alpha_r} f^{(\alpha_r)}(x)$$
$$\geq (-1)^{\beta_1} f^{(\beta_1)}(x)(-1)^{\beta_2} f^{(\beta_2)}(x) \cdots (-1)^{\beta_r} f^{(\beta_r)}(x).$$

By letting here $\alpha = (0, 2)$ and $\beta = (1, 1)$, we discover that every completely monotone function on $(0, +\infty)$ is log-convex.

As an example related to the Gamma function, let us examine the Digamma function

$$\Psi(x) = (\log \Gamma(x))'.$$

The explicit expression for the second derivative of $\log \Gamma$ reads [1]:

$$\Psi'(x) = (\log \Gamma(x))'' = \sum_{k=0}^{+\infty} \frac{1}{(x+k)^2}, \quad x \in \mathbb{R} \setminus \{0, -1, -2, \ldots\}$$

and therefore

(5.1) $$\Psi^{(n)}(x) = (-1)^{n+1} n! \sum_{k=0}^{+\infty} \frac{1}{(x+k)^{n+1}}.$$

From (5.1) it follows that the function ψ' is completely monotone on $(0, +\infty)$. Several monotonicity results for functions related to the Gamma function are given in [14].

6   CHARACTERIZATIONS OF THE GAMMA FUNCTION AND KRULL'S THEORY

The best known characterization of the Gamma function in terms of a functional equation, is due to Bohr and Mollerup:

Theorem 6.1 (Bohr-Mollerup ([3, 1922])). *If a function G is defined on $(0, +\infty)$, and satisfies:*

(1) $G(x+1) = xG(x)$, for all $x > 0$;

(2) $G(x)$ is log-convex;

(3) $G(1) = 1$,

   then $G(x) \equiv \Gamma(x)$ for $x > 0$.

A parallel characterization of the Digamma function $\Psi(x) = (\log \Gamma(x))'$ is given in the next theorem.

Theorem 6.2 (Kairies ([15])). *If g is defined on $(0, +\infty)$ and*

(1) $g(x+1) - g(x) = 1/x$;

(2) $g(x)$ is concave on $(0, +\infty)$;

(3) $g(1) = -\gamma$,

then $g(x) \equiv \Psi(x)$ for $x > 0$.

Krull ([18], see also [19]) investigates the functional equation

(6.1) $$f(x+1) - f(x) = g(x), \qquad x \geq a,$$

where f is an unknown function and g is given, such that

(6.2) g is either convex or concave, or:

g is the sum of a convex and a concave function, for $x \geq a$

and

(6.3) $$\lim_{x \to +\infty} \big(g(x+1) - g(x)\big) = 0.$$

By refining and complementing Krull's work, Bohr-Mollerup's theorem can be obtained as a special case.

Theorem 6.3. *Suppose that the equation (6.1) has a solution f that satisfies condition*

(6.4) $$\lim_{x \to +\infty} \left(\frac{f(x+h_2) - f(x)}{h_2} - \frac{f(x) - f(x-h_1)}{h_1} \right) = 0, \quad h_1, h_2 < \delta$$

(without any other assumptions). Then all solutions that satisfy the condition (6.4) are of the form $f + C$, where C is an arbitrary constant.

Proof. Suppose that f_1 is another solution of (6.1) that satisfies condition (6.4) and let $\rho(x) = f_1(x) - f(x)$. Then ρ also satisfies the condition (6.4) and $\rho(x+1) = \rho(x)$ for $x \geq a$. Further, we have that

$$\frac{\rho(x_0 + h_2) - \rho(x_0)}{h_2} - \frac{\rho(x_0) - \rho(x_0 - h_1)}{h_1}$$
$$= \frac{\rho(x_0 + n + h_2) - \rho(x_0 + n)}{h_2} - \frac{\rho(x_0 + n) - \rho(x_0 + n - h_1)}{h_1} \to 0$$

as $n \to +\infty$, and we conclude that

$$\frac{\rho(x_0 + h_2) - \rho(x_0)}{h_2} - \frac{\rho(x_0) - \rho(x_0 - h_1)}{h_1} = 0$$

for any h_1, h_2 as specified above. Then by Section 2, we find that ρ is both convex and concave, and hence $\rho(x)$ is an affine function in a neighborhood of x_0; since x_0 is arbitrary, it follows that $\rho(x)$ is affine for $x > a$, and since ρ is periodic, it must be a constant. $\qquad \square$

Corollary 6.4. *If a function f is defined on $(0, +\infty)$ and*

(1) $f(x+1) - f(x) = \log x$;

(2) $\lim_{x \to +\infty} f''(x) = 0$;

(3) $f(1) = 0$.

then $f(x) \equiv \log \Gamma(x)$ for $x > 0$.

Proof. It is easy to show that condition (6.4) is implied by the condition that $f''(x) \to 0$ as $x \to +\infty$. The rest follows from Theorem 6.3. $\qquad \square$

7 Equivalent Conditions for Convexity of a Derivative

Theorem 7.1 (M. Merkle [24]). *Let f be defined on an interval I, with a continuous derivative f'. Define*

(7.1) $$F(x,y) = \frac{f(y) - f(x)}{y - x} \quad (x \neq y), \qquad F(x,x) = f'(x).$$

Then the following are equivalent:

(A) f' *is convex on I.*

(B) $f'\left(\dfrac{x+y}{2}\right) \leq F(x,y)$ *for all $x, y \in I$,*

(C) $F(x,y) \leq \dfrac{f'(x) + f'(y)}{2}$ *for all $x, y \in I$,*

(D) F *is convex on I^2,*

(E) F *is Schur-convex on I^2.*

Also the following are equivalent:

(A') f' *is concave on I.*

(B') $f'\left(\dfrac{x+y}{2}\right) \geq F(x,y)$ *for all $x, y \in I$,*

(C') $F(x,y) \geq \dfrac{f'(x) + f'(y)}{2}$ *for all $x, y \in I$,*

(D') F *is concave on I^2,*

(E') F *is Schur-concave on I^2.*

From the above result, among other things, we may get another characterization of the Gamma function, as in the following theorem.

Theorem 7.2. *Suppose that f is a continuously differentiable real function defined on $(0, +\infty)$. If any of the conditions $(A') - (E')$ is satisfied with f on $(0, +\infty)$ and*

$$f(x+1) - f(x) = \log x \quad (x > 0),$$

then $f(x) = \log \Gamma(x) + C$, where C is an arbitrary real constant.

8 Some Inequalities

From the expression (5.1) of Section 5, it follows that Ψ is concave for $x > 0$ and therefore, conditions $(A') - (E')$ of the previous section hold with $f = \log \Gamma$ on $I = (0, +\infty)$. In this and the next section we investigate some consequences of this fact.

8.1   From (B') and (C') it follows that

(8.1) $$\frac{1}{2}(\Psi(x) + \Psi(y)) \leq \frac{\log \Gamma(y) - \log \Gamma(x)}{y - x} \leq \Psi\left(\frac{x+y}{2}\right).$$

Letting $y = x + \beta$, $\beta > 0$, we get

$$(8.2) \qquad \exp\left(\beta \frac{\Psi(x) + \Psi(x+\beta)}{2}\right) \leq Q(x,\beta) \leq \exp(\beta\Psi(x+\beta/2)).$$

The upper bound in (8.2) was also obtained in [17] by other means. In [27] we showed that the lower bound in (8.2) is closer than a lower bound in [17].

8.2 Since

$$(x, x+1+\beta) = (1-\beta)(x, x+1) + \beta(x, x+2),$$

(D') yields

$$F(x, x+1+\beta) \geq (1-\beta)F(x, x+1) + \beta F(x, x+2) \qquad x > 0, \beta \in [0,1].$$

After an application of the recurrence relation $\Gamma(z+1) = z\Gamma(z)$ we get

$$(8.3) \qquad Q(x,\beta) \geq \frac{x^{(1+\beta)(2-\beta)/2}(x+1)^{\beta(1+\beta)/2}}{x+\beta}.$$

Note the equality in (8.3) for $\beta = 0$ and $\beta = 1$.

8.3 From

$$(x, x+\beta) = (1-\beta)(x, x) + \beta(x, x+1)$$

and applying (D') we obtain

$$(8.4) \qquad Q(x,\beta) \geq x^{\beta^2} \exp\left(\beta(1-\beta)\Psi(x)\right), \qquad x > 0, \beta \in [0,1].$$

Using the concavity of Ψ and inequality (8.7) below, it can be proved that this bound is closer than the lower bound in (8.2).

8.4 In a similar way, starting from

$$(x+\beta, x+\beta) = (1-\beta)(x+\beta, x) + \beta(x+\beta, x+1)$$

and applying (D'), we get

$$(8.5) \qquad Q(x,\beta) \leq x^{-\beta^2/(1-2\beta)} \exp\left(\frac{\beta(1-\beta)}{1-2\beta}\Psi(x+\beta)\right), \qquad x > 0, \beta < 1/2.$$

8.5 The condition (E') implies

$$\frac{\log\Gamma(y) - \log\Gamma(x)}{y-x} \geq \frac{\log\Gamma(y+\varepsilon) - \log\Gamma(x-\varepsilon)}{y-x+2\varepsilon}$$

for $0 < x < y$ and $0 < \varepsilon < x$. In particular, replacing x by $x+\beta$ and letting $y = x+2\beta$ and $\varepsilon = \beta$, we obtain

$$(8.6) \qquad \frac{\Gamma(x+3\beta)}{\Gamma(x)} \leq \left(\frac{\Gamma(x+2\beta)}{\Gamma(x+\beta)}\right)^2, \qquad x > 0, \beta > 0.$$

8.6 Let us now derive some bounds for the function Ψ. Letting $y = x+1$ in (8.1), we get

$$\Psi(x) + \frac{1}{2x} \leq \log x \leq \Psi\left(x + \frac{1}{2}\right),$$

where from it follows

$$(8.7) \qquad \log\left(x - \frac{1}{2}\right) \leq \Psi(x) \leq \log x - \frac{1}{2x}, \qquad x > 0.$$

9   "Error Terms" in Inequalities

In [23], we obtained the following integral representation related to Jensen's inequality:

Theorem 9.1. *Let f be a twice continuously differentiable function on an interval I. Then for all $\lambda \in [0,1]$ and all $(x,y) \in I^2$ we have*

$$\lambda f(x) + (1-\lambda)f(y) - f(\lambda x + (1-\lambda)y) = (y-x)^2 \int_0^1 K_0(\lambda,t) f''((1-t)x + ty)\mathrm{d}t,$$

where

$$K_0(\lambda,t) = \lambda t I_{[0,1-\lambda]}(t) + (1-\lambda)(1-t)I_{[1-\lambda,1]}(t),$$

Since the kernel K_0 is positive, this representation yields three important tools, that are expressed in following corollaries.

Corollary 9.2. *If $0 < f_1'' < f_2''$ on (x,y) then Jensen's inequality obtained with f_1 is sharper than the one with f_2.*

Corollary 9.3. *If $0 < f''(x) \to 0$ as $x \to +\infty$, then Jensen's inequality becomes infinitely sharp as $x \to +\infty$.*

Corollary 9.4. *Let $\{f_n\}$ be a sequence of twice continuously differentiable functions defined on an interval I and suppose that $\lim_{n \to +\infty} f_n''(x) = 0$ for all $x \in I$. Then*

$$\lim_{n \to +\infty} (\lambda f_n(x) + (1-\lambda)f_n(y) - f_n(\lambda x + (1-\lambda)y)) = 0$$

for all $x, y \in I$ and $\lambda \in \mathbb{R}$ such that $\lambda x + (1-\lambda)y \in I$.

Corollary 9.2 enables comparison of inequalities that are derived from convexity, whereas Corollary 9.3 gives a way of producing asymptotically infinitely sharp inequalites, as we will demonstrate in the next section. Corollary 9.4 also provides asymptotic expansions, but without additional information of the sign of the error. Results analogous to Theorem 9.1, for remainders of expressions in $(A) - (E)$, and $(A') - (E')$ of Section 7, can be found in [23], in terms of the magnitude of f'''.

10   Back to Krull's Theory

If a_n and b_n are two sequences, let $a_n \underset{\sim}{\leq} b_n$ stand for

$$a_n \leq b_n \quad \text{for all } n \quad \text{and} \quad \lim_{n \to +\infty} (a_n - b_n) = 0.$$

The notation $a_n \underset{\sim}{\geq} b_n$ is equivalent to $b_n \underset{\sim}{\leq} a_n$.

Let f be a convex solution of Krull's equation (6.1) on $x \geq a$ and suppose that $f''(x) \to 0$ as $x \to +\infty$.

Starting from

$$x + \beta = (1-\beta)x + \beta(x+1), \qquad x \geq a, \ \beta \in [0,1]$$

and applying Jensen's inequality, we get

$$(10.1) \qquad \begin{aligned} f(x+\beta) &\leq (1-\beta)f(x) + \beta f(x+1) \\ &= (1-\beta)f(x) + \beta(g(x) + f(x)) \\ &= f(x) + \beta g(x) \end{aligned}$$

Replacing x with $x + n$, we get an inequality which, by Corollary 9.3, becomes infinitely sharp as $n \to +\infty$, i.e.,

$$(10.2) \qquad f(x + n + \beta) - f(x + n) \underset{\sim}{\leq} \beta g(x + n).$$

However, since f satisfies (6.1), then

$$f(x + n) = f(x) + \sum_{k=0}^{n-1} g(x + k)$$

and (10.2) becomes

$$(10.3) \qquad f(x + \beta) - f(x) \underset{\sim}{\leq} \sum_{k=0}^{n-1} \big(g(x + k) - g(x + k + \beta)\big) + \beta g(x + n).$$

In the same way, starting from

$$x = \beta(x - 1 + \beta) + (1 - \beta)(x + \beta), \qquad x \geq a + 1 - \beta, \ \beta \in [0, 1]$$

we obtain

$$(10.4) \qquad f(x + \beta) \geq f(x) + \beta g(x - 1 + \beta)$$

and further

$$(10.5) \qquad f(x + \beta) - f(x) \underset{\sim}{\geq} \sum_{k=0}^{n-1} \big(g(x + k) - g(x + k + \beta)\big) + \beta g(x + n - 1 + \beta).$$

The pair of expressions (10.3)–(10.5) give sharp bounds for the difference $f(x+\beta)-f(x)$ when $\beta \in [0, 1]$ and for a large n. By Corollary 9.4, the asymptotics (with no knowledge of the sign of the error) holds regardless of convexity of f and for all meaningful β. For instance, the following version of (10.3) holds for any twice continuously differentiable solution of (6.1) with $\lim_{x \to +\infty} f''(x) = 0$

$$f(x + \beta) - f(x) = \lim_{n \to +\infty} \left(\sum_{k=0}^{n-1} \big(g(x + k) - g(x + k + \beta)\big) + \beta g(x + n) \right),$$

for all $x \geq a$ and all real β such that $x + \beta \geq a$ and also $x \geq a$. Replacing x by x_0 and $x + \beta$ by x, we get the following expansion:

$$f(x) = f(x_0) + \lim_{n \to +\infty} \left(\sum_{k=0}^{n-1} \big(g(x_0 + k) - g(x + k)\big) + (x - x_0)g(x_0 + n) \right),$$

which is also derived in [18] by other means.

As an example related to the Gamma function, let $f(x) = \log \Gamma(x)$. This is a convex solution of Krull's equation with $g(x) = \log x$, and with $f''(x)$ monotonically decreasing to zero.

Then (10.1) gives

$$(10.6) \qquad Q(x, \beta) = \frac{\Gamma(x + \beta)}{\Gamma(x)} \leq x^\beta,$$

which is Wendel's inequality [38]. Its improvement, by means of (10.3), reads:

$$Q(x, \beta) \underset{\sim}{\leq} (x + n)^\beta \Pi(x, \beta, n),$$

which is, in fact, a π_n-transform of (10.6).

11   How to Choose the Initial Function

In this section, we give a supply of convex and concave functions, to produce inequalities that involve the Gamma function.

Theorem 11.1 (M. Merkle, [25]). *Let B_{2k} be Bernoulli numbers and let L and R be generic notations for the following sums:*

$$L(x) = L_N(x) = - \sum_{k=1}^{2N} \frac{B_{2k}}{2k(2k-1)x^{2k-1}} \ , \quad (N = 1, 2, \ldots) \ , \quad L_0(x) = 0 \ .$$

$$R(x) = R_N(x) = - \sum_{k=1}^{2N+1} \frac{B_{2k}}{2k(2k-1)x^{2k-1}} \ , \quad (N = 0, 1, 2, \ldots)$$

(i) The functions

$$F_1(x) = \log \Gamma(x),$$

$$F_2(x) = \log \Gamma(x) - x \log x,$$

$$F_3(x) = \log \Gamma(x) - \left(x - \frac{1}{2} \right) \log x,$$

$$F_4(x) = \log \Gamma(x) - \left(x - \frac{1}{2} \right) \log x - \frac{1}{12x} + \frac{1}{360x^3}$$

and

$$F(x) = \log \Gamma(x) - \left(x - \frac{1}{2} \right) \log x + L(x)$$

are convex on $x > 0$.
(ii) The functions

$$G_1(x) = \log \Gamma(x) - \left(x - \frac{1}{2} \right) \log x - \frac{1}{12x},$$

$$G_2(x) = \log \Gamma(x) - \left(x - \frac{1}{2} \right) \log x - \frac{1}{12x} + \frac{1}{360x^3} - \frac{1}{1260x^5}$$

and

$$G(x) = \log \Gamma(x) - \left(x - \frac{1}{2} \right) \log x + R(x)$$

are concave on $x > 0$.

Including more terms has the effect of decreasing the absolute value of the second derivative, and hence, yields a sharper inequality (but, more complicated). In the limit, functions F and G become $(\log 2\pi)/2 - x$, in accordance with a well known asymptotic expansion:

$$\log \Gamma(x) \sim \left(x - \frac{1}{2} \right) \log x - x + \frac{1}{2} \log 2\pi + \sum_{k=1}^{+\infty} \frac{B_{2k}}{2k(2k-1)x^{2k-1}}.$$

12 INEQUALITIES FOR GAUTSCHI'S RATIO

As a starting point, let us see what one can obtain from the plain log-convexity of the Gamma function. By Jensen's inequality with $\varphi(x) = \log \Gamma(x)$, we find

$$(12.1) \qquad \varphi(x) \le \beta \varphi(x - 1 + \beta) + (1 - \beta)\varphi(x + \beta) \qquad (0 \le \beta \le 1) .$$

That is,

$$\Gamma(x) \le \Gamma^{\beta}(x - 1 + \beta)\Gamma^{1-\beta}(x + \beta) = \frac{\Gamma^{\beta}(x + \beta)}{(x - 1 + \beta)^{\beta}}\Gamma^{1-\beta}(x + \beta)$$

and this gives the well known Gautschi inequality

$$(12.2) \qquad Q(x, \beta) = \frac{\Gamma(x + \beta)}{\Gamma(x)} \ge (x - 1 + \beta)^{\beta} .$$

Eleven years before Gautschi, J.G.Wendel published a note [38] on the Gamma function, containing inequalities ($x \ge 1, \beta \in [0, 1]$)

$$(12.3) \qquad \frac{x}{(x + \beta)^{1-\beta}} \le Q(x, \beta)$$

and

$$(12.4) \qquad Q(x, \beta) \le x^{\beta}$$

J.T. Chu in the article [6], published in 1962, gives the following result:

$$(12.5) \qquad \sqrt{\frac{n-1}{2}}\sqrt{\frac{2n-3}{2n-2}} < \frac{\Gamma(\frac{n}{2})}{\Gamma\left(\frac{n}{2} - \frac{1}{2}\right)} < \sqrt{\frac{n-1}{2}}\sqrt{\frac{2n-2}{2n-1}},$$

($n = 2, 3, \ldots$), which, after letting $x = \frac{n-1}{2}$, becomes

$$(12.6) \qquad \sqrt{x - \frac{1}{4}} < \frac{\Gamma\left(x + \frac{1}{2}\right)}{\Gamma(x)} < \frac{x}{\sqrt{x + \frac{1}{4}}}.$$

Note that the upper bound may be obtained from the lower one by the $\beta-$ transform. Chu indicates that, for $x = 1, 2, \ldots$, there is an improvement in the lower bound, which we will write as

$$(12.7) \qquad \sqrt{x - \frac{1}{4} + \frac{1}{(4x + 2)^2}} < \frac{\Gamma\left(x + \frac{1}{2}\right)}{\Gamma(x)}.$$

In 1967, Boyd [5] gives inequalities in the same spirit. The lower bound in our notation reads

$$(12.8) \qquad \sqrt{x - \frac{1}{4} + \frac{1}{32x + 16}} < \frac{\Gamma\left(x + \frac{1}{2}\right)}{\Gamma(x)},$$

for $x = m + \frac{1}{2}$, $m = 1, 2, \ldots$, and an upper bound can be found from (12.8) and the $\beta-$ transform.

Finally, Lazarević and Lupaş' result [20] from 1979 reads:

$$(12.9) \qquad \left(x - \frac{1 - \beta}{2}\right)^{\beta} \le \frac{\Gamma(x + \beta)}{\Gamma(x)} ,$$

for $x > \frac{1-\beta}{2}$ and $\beta \in [0,1]$. This inequality was rediscovered by Kershaw [17] in 1983.

Applying the $\beta-$ transform, we can find the corresponding upper bound:

$$(12.10) \qquad \frac{\Gamma(x+\beta)}{\Gamma(x)} \leq \frac{x}{(x+\frac{\beta}{2})^{1-\beta}}.$$

Lazarević-Lupaş' inequality (12.9) is, for $x > (\beta^2 + 3)/4$ (and therefore, for $x \geq 1$ and every $\beta \in (0,1)$) sharper than Wendel's inequality (12.3), which is sharper than Gautschi's (12.2).

As we can see, (12.9) concides with (12.6) where the latter holds, but it is much more general than (12.6). On the other hand, (12.8) is sharper than (12.9) for a particular choice of x and β. An inequality which generalizes and sharpens all the mentioned inequalities is proved in [26]:

For any $x \geq (1-\beta)/2$ and $\beta \in [0,1]$,

$$(12.11) \qquad Q(x,\beta) \geq \left(x - \frac{1-\beta}{2} + \frac{1-\beta^2}{24x+12} \right)^\beta,$$

with equality if and only if $\beta = 0$ or $\beta = 1$. This inequality is derived as a simplified version of the inequality that is obtained from concavity of the function G_1 of the previous section.

13 INEQUALITIES AND EXPANSIONS FOR GURLAND'S RATIO

The first result about the ratio of Gamma functions

$$T(x,y) = \frac{\Gamma(x)\Gamma(y)}{\Gamma^2\left(\frac{x+y}{2}\right)}, \quad x,y > 0,$$

appeared in 1956, in John Gurland's paper [10], where the following inequality was presented:

$$(13.1) \qquad \frac{\Gamma(x)\Gamma(x+2\beta)}{\Gamma^2(x+\beta)} \geq 1 + \frac{\beta^2}{x}, \qquad x > 0, x + 2\beta > 0.$$

There is the following relationship between T and Gautschi's ratio Q:

$$(13.2) \qquad T(x, x+2\beta) = \frac{Q(x+\beta, \beta)}{Q(x, \beta)},$$

and, naturally, this relationship can be used to produce inequalities of Gurland type from inequalities of Gautshi type. However, techniques explained in previous sections can be used here as well. The following properties of Gurland's ratio are proved in [22]:

Theorem 13.1.

(i) For any $\beta \in I = (0, +\infty)$, the functions

$$x \mapsto T(x, x+2\beta) \quad \text{and} \quad x \mapsto \log T(x, x+2\beta)$$

are completely monotonic on I.

(ii) For any $\beta \in I$ the function $x \mapsto T(x, x+2\beta)$ is decreasing in $x \in I$ from $+\infty$ to 1.

(iii) For any $x \in I$, the function $\beta \mapsto T(x, x+2\beta)$ is increasing in $\beta \in I$ from 1 to $+\infty$.

(iv) *The function $(x, y) \mapsto F(x, y)$ is Schur-convex on $I \times I$, that is, for any $x, y \in I$ such that $x < y$ and $0 < \varepsilon < (y - x)/2$,*

$$T(x + \varepsilon, y - \varepsilon) < T(x, y).$$

(v) *For any $\beta \in I$, the functions*

$$x \mapsto T(x, x + 2\beta), \quad x \mapsto \log T(x, x + 2\beta), \quad x \mapsto \log \log T(x, x + 2\beta)$$

are convex on I.

The initial interest for Gurland's ratio was related to the Cramér-Rao inequality in Statistics. There were many attempts to improve inequality (13.1) by using different versions of the Cramér-Rao inequality. A survey of this early work can be found in [28].

However, G.N. Watson [40] for the case $\beta = 1/2$ and A.V.Boyd [4] for the general case, noticed that (13.1) is a simple consequence of Gauss' formula for the hypergeometric function (see [41, 14.11]):

$$(13.3) \qquad \frac{\Gamma(x)\Gamma(x + 2\beta)}{\Gamma^2(x + \beta)} = F(-\beta, -\beta, x, 1) = 1 + \sum_{k=1}^{\infty} \frac{\left((-\beta)_k\right)^2}{k!(x)_k},$$

where $(z)_k = z(z + 1) \cdots (z + k - 1)$ and F is the hypergeometric function. The series is convergent whenever $x + 2\beta > 0$. If, in addition, $x > 0$, then all terms are nonnegative and, by retaining a finite number of terms in the series, we get (13.1) and its improvements.

We will give here some examples of inequalities of Gurland type.

From the convexity of the function F_2 in Section 11, and Jensen's inequality

$$F_2\left(\frac{x + y}{2}\right) \leq \frac{F_2(x) + F_2(y)}{2},$$

we get the inequality [16]:

$$(13.4) \qquad T(x, y) \geq \frac{x^x y^y}{\left(\frac{x+y}{2}\right)^{x+y}},$$

which can be turned into an expansion using a π_n-transform:

$$T(x, y) \underset{\sim}{\geq} \frac{(x + n)^{x+n} (y + n)^{y+n}}{\left(\frac{x+y}{2} + n\right)^{x+y+2n}} \rho(x, y, n).$$

A general method of producing double inequalities of Gurland type is the following. Suppose that the function

$$(13.5) \qquad F(x) = \log Q(x, \beta) + \log D(x, \beta),$$

is convex with respect to $x \in I$, for a fixed $\beta \in (0, 1)$. Then from Jensen's inequality

$$(13.6) \qquad F(x) \leq \beta F(x - 1 + \beta) + (1 - \beta)F(x + \beta), \quad x > 1 - \beta$$

we find, writing for simplicity $Q(x, \beta) = Q(x)$ and $D(x, \beta) = D(x)$:

$$(13.7) \qquad Q(x)D(x) \leq Q^{\beta}(x - 1 + \beta)Q^{1-\beta}(x + \beta)D^{\beta}(x - 1 + \beta)D^{1-\beta}(x + \beta).$$

Now note that

$$Q(x-1+\beta) = \frac{\Gamma(x-1+2\beta)}{\Gamma(x-1+\beta)} = \frac{x-1+\beta}{x-1+2\beta} \cdot \frac{\Gamma(x+2\beta)}{\Gamma(x+\beta)} = \frac{x-1+\beta}{x-1+2\beta} \cdot Q(x+\beta),$$

which finally yields, via (13.7) and the relation (13.2).

$$(13.8) \qquad T(x, x+2\beta) \geq \left(\frac{x-1+2\beta}{x-1+\beta}\right)^{\beta} \cdot \frac{D(x,\beta)}{D^{\beta}(x-1+\beta,\beta)D^{1-\beta}(x+\beta,\beta)},$$

where $x > 1-\beta$. An upper bound may be found with the same function (13.5), but starting with Jensen's inequality

$$(13.9) \qquad\qquad F(x+\beta) \leq (1-\beta)F(x) + \beta F(x+1), \quad x > 0$$

instead of (13.6). In that way, we find

$$(13.10) \qquad T(x, x+2\beta) \leq \left(\frac{x+\beta}{x}\right)^{\beta} \cdot \frac{D^{\beta}(x+1,\beta)D^{1-\beta}(x,\beta)}{D(x+\beta,\beta)}, \quad x \in I.$$

The same procedure can be applied if F is concave, with $\leq$ and $\geq$ being interchanged.

It is easy to see that the function $x \mapsto Q(x,\beta)$ is log-concave; therefore, in light of previous sections, the function D should be log-convex.

The simplest double inequality of this type is obtained with $F(x) = \log Q(x,\beta)$:

$$\left(1+\frac{\beta}{x}\right)^{\beta} \leq T(x, x+2\beta) \leq \left(1+\frac{\beta}{x-1+\beta}\right)^{\beta},$$

and the corresponding expansions via π_n-transform:

$$\rho(x, x+2\beta, n) \cdot \left(1+\frac{\beta}{x+n}\right)^{\beta} \underset{\sim}{\leq} T(x, x+2\beta)$$

$$\underset{\sim}{\leq} \rho(x, x+2\beta, n) \cdot \left(1+\frac{\beta}{x+n-1+\beta}\right)^{\beta},$$

where $x > 1-\beta$ and $0 \leq \beta \leq 1$.

Inequalities for the Trigamma function can yield convex or concave functions related to the Gamma function; this method works well for both types of inequalities. For example, it is proved in [22] that, for $x > 0$:

$$(13.11) \qquad \frac{1}{x+1} + \frac{1}{x^2} + \frac{1}{2(x+1)^2} < \Psi'(x) < \frac{1}{x+1} + \frac{1}{x^2} + \frac{1}{(x+1)^2}.$$

These inequalities imply that, for $x > 0$, the function $x \mapsto \log\Gamma(x+1) - x\log(x+1)$ is concave, and the function $x \mapsto \log\Gamma(x+1) - (x+1/2)\log(x+1)$ is convex.

For a more complete survey of Gurland type inequalities and their applictions, see [22].

REFERENCES

[1] M. Abramowitz and I.A. Stegun, *A Handbook of Mathematical Functions*, New York, 1965.

[2] E. Artin, *The Gamma Function*, Holt, Rinehart and Winston, New York 1964, translation from the German original of 1931.

[3] H. Bohr and J. Mollerup, *Laerbog i matematisk Analyse, III*, Kopenhagen 1922.

[4] A.V. Boyd, Gurland's inequality for the Gamma function, *Skand. Aktuarietidiskr.*, **43** (1961), 134–135.

[5] A.V. Boyd, A note on a paper by Uppuluri, *Pacific J. Math.*, **22** (1967), 9–10.

[6] J.T. Chu. A modified Wallis product and some applications, *Amer. Math.Monthly*, **69**(5) (1962), 402–404.

[7] P.J. Davis, Leonhard Euler's integral: A historical profile of the Gamma function, *Amer. Math. Monthly*, **66** (1959), 849–869.

[8] A.M. Fink, Kolmogorov-Landau inequalities for monotone functions, *J. Math. Anal. Appl.*, **90** (1982), 251–258.

[9] W. Gautschi, Some elementary inequalities relating to the gamma and incomplete GAMMA function, *J. Math. and Phys.*, **38** (1959), 77–81.

[10] J. Gurland, An inequality satisfied by the Gamma function, *Skand. Aktuarietidiskr.*, **39** (1956), 171–172.

[11] G.H. Hardy, J.E. Littlewood and G. Pólya, *Inequalities*, Cambridge University Press, 1st edition 1934, 2nd edition 1952.

[12] H. Haruki, A new characterization of Euler's gamma function by a functional equation, *Aequationes Math.*, **31**(2-3) (1986), 173–183.

[13] O. Hölder, Über die Eigenschaft der Gamma Funktion keiner algebraische Differential-gleichung zu genügen, *Math. Ann.*, **28** (1887), 1–13.

[14] M.E.H. Ismail, L. Lorch and M.E. Muldoon, Completely monotonic functions associated with the Gamma function and its q-analogues, *J. Math. Anal. Appl.*, **116** (1986), 1–9.

[15] H.H. Kairies, Über die logarithmische Ableitung der Gammafunktion, *Math. Ann.*, **184** (1970), 157–162.

[16] J.D. Kečkić and P.M. Vasić, Some inequalities for the Gamma function, *Publ. Inst. Math. Beograd. N. Ser.*, **11(25)** (1971), 107–114.

[17] D. Kershaw, Some extensions of W. Gautschi's inequalities for the gamma function, *Math. Comp.*, **41** (1983), 607–611.

[18] W. Krull, Bemerkungen zur Differenzengleichung $g(x + 1) - g(x) = \varphi(x)$, *Math. Nachrichten*, **1** (1948), 365–376.

[19] M. Kuczma, *Functional Equations in a Single Variable*, Polish Scientific Publishers, Warszawa 1968.

[20] I. Lazarević and A Lupaş, Functional equations for Wallis and Gamma functions, *Univ. Beograd, Publ. Elektrotehn.Fak.Ser.Mat.Fiz.* $N^0$461-497 (1979), 245-251.

[21] A. Marshall and I. Olkin, *Inequalities: Theory of Majorization and Its Applications*, Academic Press, New York, 1979.

[22] M. Merkle, Gurland's ratio for the Gamma function, *Computers and Math. with Applications*, **49** (2005), 389-406.

[23] M. Merkle, Representation of the error term in Jensen's and some related inequalities with applications, *J. Math. Analysis Appl.*, **231** (1999), 76–90.

[24] M. Merkle, Conditions for convexity of a derivative and some applications to the Gamma function, *Aequ. Math.*, **55** (1998), 273–280.

[25] M. Merkle, Logarithmic convexity and inequalities for the Gamma function, *J. Math. Analysis Appl.*, **203** (1996), 369–380.

[26] M. Merkle, Logarithmic concavity of distribution functions, *Proc. Internat. Memorial Conference "D.S. Mitrinović"*, Niš, 1996. Collection: G.V. Milovanović (ed.), *Recent Progress in Inequalities*, Kluwer Academic Publishers, Dordrecht, 1998, 481–484.

[27] M. Merkle, Convexity, Schur-convexity and bounds for the Gamma function involving the Digamma function, *Rocky Mountain J. Math.*, **28**(3) (1998), 1053–1066.

[28] D.S. Mitrinović, *Analytic Inequalities*, Berlin-Heidelberg-New York, 1970.

[29] T. Popoviciu, *Les fonctions convexes*, Actualités Sci. Indust. 992, Paris 1944.

[30] B.R. Rao, On a generalization of Gautschi's inequality, *Skand. Aktuarietidiskr.* 1970, 10–14.

[31] A.W. Roberts and D.E. Varberg, *Convex Functions*, Academic Press, New York, 1973.

[32] R.T. Rockafellar, *Convex Analysis*, Princeton Math. Ser., No 28, Princeton University Press, Princeton, New Jersey, 1970.

[33] A.L. Rubel, A survey of transcendentally transcendental functions, *Amer. Math. Monthly*, **96**(9) (1989), 777–788.

[34] I. Schur, Über eine Klasse von Mittelbildungen mit Anwendungen die Determinanten, *Theorie Sitzungsber. Berlin. Math. Gesellschaft*, **22** (1923), 9–20; also in: *Issai Schur Collected Works*, A. Brauer and H. Rohrbach eds., Vol. II, pp 416-427, Springer Verlag, Berlin (1973).

[35] D.N. Shanbhag, On some inequalites satisfied by the gamma function, *Skand. Aktuarietidiskr.* (1964).

[36] J. Stoer and C. Witzgall, *Convexity and Optimization in Finite Dimensions*, Vol.1, Springer Verlag, 1970.

[37] M. Tomić, Théorème de Gauss relatif au centre de gravité et son application, *Bull. Soc. Math. Phys. Serbie*, **1** (1949), 31–40.

[38] J.G. Wendel, Note on the gamma function, *Amer. Math. Monthly*, **55** (1948), 653-564.

[39] H. Weyl, Inequalities between two kinds of eigenvalues of a linear transformation, *Proc. Nat. Acad. Sci. USA*, **35** (1949), 408–411.

[40] G.N. Watson, A note on Gamma function, *Proc. Edin. Math, Soc.*, **11** (1959), Notes, 7-9.

[41] E.T. Whittaker and G.N. Watson, *A Course of Modern Analysis*, part II, Chapter 12, 235-264, Cambridge University Press, Fourth Edition, Cambridge 1962.

[42] D.V. Widder, *The Laplace Transform*, Princeton University Press, Princeton 1941.

In: Advances in Inequalities for Special Functions   ISBN 978-1-60021-919-1
Editors: P. Cerone and S. S. Dragomir, pp. 101–105 © 2008 Nova Science Publishers, Inc.

Some Inequalities for Hyperharmonic Series

István Mező

Vincellér str. 2.
Debrecen, Hungary
E-mail address: mistvan4@hotmail.com

ABSTRACT. The notion of hyperharmonic numbers is rather new. The series involving harmonic numbers have been investigated by a number of authors. Since hyperharmonic numbers are recently defined, there are no such results. We fill a part of this gap. Moreover, an upper bound for Ramsey numbers is also presented.

1991 Mathematics Subject Classification: 11B83

Key words and phrases: harmonic numbers, hyperharmonic numbers, Ramsey numbers

1 INTRODUCTION

The nth harmonic number H_n is defined by

$$H_n := \sum_{k=1}^{n} \frac{1}{k} \quad (n \in \mathbb{N}).$$

For these numbers the following estimates are well-known (see [2]):

(1.1) $$\frac{1}{2(n+1)} + \ln(n) + \gamma < H_n < \frac{1}{2n} + \ln(n) + \gamma \quad (n \in \mathbb{N}),$$

where $\gamma = 0.5772\ldots$ is the Euler-Mascheroni constant.

Hyperharmonic numbers were given by Conway and Guy in [1]. The nth hyperharmonic number of order $r > 1$ is

$$H_n^{(r)} = \sum_{k=1}^{n} H_k^{(r-1)},$$

with the agreement that $H_n^{(1)} = H_n$. There is a useful connection between harmonic and higher order harmonic numbers ([1]):

(1.2) $$H_n^{(r)} = \binom{n+r-1}{r-1}(H_{n+r-1} - H_{r-1}).$$

Our aim is to study the convergence of some series involving higher order harmonic numbers. These investigations help us to see the growth of these numbers.

2   HYPERHARMONIC SERIES

Theorem 2.1. *Let us fix an order $r \geq 2$. We have*

$$
\text{(2.1)} \qquad\qquad \sum_{n=1}^{\infty} \frac{H_n^{(r)}}{n^r} = \infty,
$$

$$
\text{(2.2)} \qquad \frac{\zeta(s+1)}{(r-1)!} < \sum_{n=1}^{\infty} \frac{H_n^{(r)}}{n^{r+s}} < \frac{3}{2}\frac{(2r)^r}{(r-1)!}\zeta(s) \quad (s > 1),
$$

$$
\text{(2.3)} \qquad\qquad \sum_{n=1}^{\infty} \frac{n^{r-1}}{H_n^{(r)}} = \infty,
$$

$$
\text{(2.4)} \qquad \frac{2}{3}\frac{(r-1)!}{(2r)^r}\zeta(s) < \sum_{n=1}^{\infty} \frac{n^{r-s}}{H_n^{(r)}} < (r-1)!\zeta(s-1) \quad (s > 2),
$$

where ζ is the Riemann zeta function.

To prove these relations, we need upper and lower estimations for hyperharmonic numbers, which are not the sharpest ones but more usable in analytical calculations.

Lemma 2.2. *We have*

$$
\frac{1}{(r-1)!}n^{r-1} < H_n^{(r)} < \frac{3}{2}\frac{(2r)^r}{(r-1)!}n^r,
$$

for all $n \in \mathbb{N}$ and $r \geq 2$.

Proof (Proof of Lemma 2.2). As we have seen,

$$
H_n^{(r)} = \binom{n+r-1}{r-1}(H_{n+r-1} - H_{r-1}).
$$

First, we prove the upper estimation.

$$
\binom{n+r-1}{r-1} = \frac{(n+1)(n+2)\cdots(n+r-1)}{(r-1)!} < \frac{(n+r)^{r-1}}{(r-1)!},
$$

and

$$
H_{n+r-1} - H_{r-1} < \frac{1}{2(n+r-1)} + \ln(n+r-1) + \gamma - \left(\frac{1}{2r} + \ln(r-1) + \gamma\right)
$$
$$
< \frac{1}{2} + \ln\left(\frac{n+r}{r-1}\right).
$$

From these inequalities we get

$$
H_n^{(r)} < \frac{(n+r)^{r-1}}{(r-1)!}\left(\frac{1}{2} + \ln\left(\frac{n+r}{r-1}\right)\right)
$$
$$
< \frac{(n+r)^{r-1}}{(r-1)!}\left(\frac{1}{2} + \frac{n+r}{r-1}\right)
$$
$$
= \frac{(n+r)^{r-1}}{2(r-1)!} + \frac{(n+r)^r}{(r-1)(r-1)!}
$$
$$
< \frac{(n+r)^r}{(r-1)!}\left(\frac{1}{2} + \frac{1}{r-1}\right) \leq \frac{3}{2}\frac{(n+r)^r}{(r-1)!}.
$$

Furthermore,

$$(n+r)^r = \sum_{k=0}^{r} \binom{r}{k} n^k r^{r-k} < \sum_{k=0}^{r} \binom{r}{k} n^k r^r = r^r (n+1)^r < (2rn)^r.$$

The lower estimation can be obtained easily:

$$\binom{n+r-1}{r-1} > \frac{n^{r-1}}{(r-1)!}.$$

Since $H_{n+r-1} - H_{r-1} > 1$, we have obtained the desired relations. □

Proof (Proof of Theorem 2.1). Since

$$H_n^{(r)} > \frac{1}{(r-1)!} n^{r-1},$$

we get immediately that

$$\frac{H_n^{(r)}}{n^r} > \frac{1}{(r-1)!} \frac{1}{n}.$$

This relation and the comparison test prove our first statement.
In the same way as above,

$$\frac{H_n^{(r)}}{n^{r+s}} > \frac{1}{(r-1)!} \frac{1}{n^{s+1}}.$$

$$\sum_{n=1}^{\infty} \frac{H_n^{(r)}}{n^{r+s}} > \frac{1}{(r-1)!} \sum_{n=1}^{\infty} \frac{1}{n^{s+1}} = \frac{1}{(r-1)!} \zeta(s+1) \quad (s > 0).$$

By the lemma,

$$\sum_{n=1}^{\infty} \frac{H_n^{(r)}}{n^{r+s}} < \frac{3}{2} \frac{(2r)^r}{(r-1)!} \sum_{n=1}^{\infty} \frac{1}{n^s} = \frac{3}{2} \frac{(2r)^r}{(r-1)!} \zeta(s) \quad (s > 1).$$

The divergence of (2.3) can be deduced by using Lemma 2.2. and the comparison test:

$$\frac{1}{H_n^{(r)}} > \frac{2}{3} \frac{(r-1)!}{n^r (2r)^r},$$

therefore

$$\sum_{n=1}^{\infty} \frac{n^{r-1}}{H_n^{(r)}} > \frac{2}{3} \frac{(r-1)!}{(2r)^r} \sum_{n=1}^{\infty} \frac{1}{n} = \infty.$$

If we change n^{r-1} to n^{r-s} $(s > 1)$ in the numerator, we get the left-hand side inequality of (2.4).

The last relation of the theorem can be proved also easily. Since

$$\frac{1}{H_n^{(r)}} < \frac{(r-1)!}{n^{r-1}},$$

$$\sum_{n=1}^{\infty} \frac{n^{r-s}}{H_n^{(r)}} < (r-1)! \sum_{n=1}^{\infty} \frac{1}{n^{s-1}} = (r-1)! \zeta(s-1) \quad (s > 2).$$

□

3 An Upper Estimation of Ramsey Numbers Involving Hyperharmonic Numbers

For two positive integers r and n, the Ramsey number $R(r, n)$ is the smallest integer R so that every graph on R vertices contains either a clique of size r or an independent set of size n. Or, equivalently, the $R(r, n)$ Ramsey number gives the solution to the question 'What is the minimum number of guests $R(r, n)$ that must be invited so that at least r will know each other or at least n will not know each other?'. Such a number exists for all r and n.

The following statement is known as the Theorem of Erdős and Szekeres: for all $r, n \in \mathbb{N}$

$$R(r, n) \leq \binom{n + r - 2}{r - 1}.$$

Since

$$\binom{n + r - 2}{r - 1} = \frac{n(n + 1) \cdots (n + r - 2)}{(r - 1)!},$$

and

$$\binom{n + r - 1}{r - 1} = \frac{(n + 1) \cdots (n + r - 1)}{(r - 1)!},$$

we can express the upper bound of the Ramsey numbers with hyperharmonic numbers. Indeed,

$$\binom{n + r - 2}{r - 1} = \frac{n}{n + r - 1} \binom{n + r - 1}{r - 1}.$$

Moreover, we know (see (1.2)) that

$$H_n^{(r)} = \binom{n + r - 1}{r - 1}(H_{n+r-1} - H_{r-1}) = \frac{n + r - 1}{n}\binom{n + r - 2}{r - 1}(H_{n+r-1} - H_{r-1}),$$

whence

$$R(r, n) \leq \binom{n + r - 2}{r - 1} = \frac{n}{n + r - 1}\frac{H_n^{(r)}}{(H_{n+r-1} - H_{r-1})}.$$

If we consider the article of A. Benjamin, D. Gaebler and R. Gaebler ([3]), we can give an equivalent form of the above estimation.

The $\begin{bmatrix} n \\ k \end{bmatrix}_r$ r-Stirling number is the number of the permutations of the set $\{1, \ldots, n\}$ having k disjoint, non-empty cycles, in which the elements 1 through r are restricted to appear in different cycles.

In [3] one can find the interesting equality

$$H_n^{(r)} = \frac{\begin{bmatrix} n+r \\ r+1 \end{bmatrix}_r}{n!}.$$

Thus, we have proved the following

Proposition 3.1. *For all $r, n \in \mathbb{N}$*

$$R(r, n) \leq \frac{n}{n + r - 1}\frac{H_n^{(r)}}{(H_{n+r-1} - H_{r-1})} = \frac{n}{n + r - 1}\frac{\begin{bmatrix} n+r \\ r+1 \end{bmatrix}_r}{n!(H_{n+r-1} - H_{r-1})}.$$

REFERENCES

[1] J.H. Conway and R.K. Guy, *The Book of Numbers*, Springer-Verlag, New York, p. 258-259 (1996).

[2] Eric W. Weisstein et al., *Harmonic Number*, From MathWorld – A Wolfram Web Resource. http://mathworld.wolfram.com/HarmonicNumber.html

[3] A.T. Benjamin, D. Gaebler and R. Gaebler, A combinatorial approach to hyperharmonic numbers, *INTEGERS: The Electornic Journal of Combinatorial Number Theory*, **3** (2003), pp. 1–9, #A15.

In: Advances in Inequalities for Special Functions   ISBN 978-1-60021-919-1
Editors: P. Cerone and S. S. Dragomir, pp. 107–117 © 2008 Nova Science Publishers, Inc.

The Hermite-Hadamard Inequalities for Double Dirichlet Averages and Their Applications to Special Functions

Edward Neuman

Department of Mathematics
Mailcode 4408, 1245 Lincoln Drive
Southern Illinois University
Carbondale, IL 62901, USA
E-mail address: edneuman@math.siu.edu

ABSTRACT. The Hermite-Hadamard type inequalities for double Dirichlet averages of a univariate function are established. Applications to special functions with emphasis on Lauricella's hypergeometric function F_B and Jacobi polynomials are included.

1991 Mathematics Subject Classification: 26D07, 26B25, 33C45, 33C65

Key words and phrases: Double Dirichlet averages, Hermite-Hadamard inequalities, convex functions, logarithmically-convex functions, Lauricella's hypergeometric function F_B, Jacobi polynomials.

1   INTRODUCTION AND DEFINITIONS

Many of the most important special functions admit representations in terms of so-called Dirichlet averages. For the reader's convenience we recall first the definition of the single Dirichlet average, also called the Dirichlet average, of a univariate function. Let f be a real-valued holomorphic function on the closed interval I. By

$$E_{m-1} = \{u = (u_1, \ldots, u_m) : u_i \geq 0, \ 1 \leq i \leq m, \ u_1 + \cdots + u_m = 1\}$$

$(m = 2, 3, \ldots)$ we will denote the Euclidean simplex in $\mathbb{R}^{m-1}$. In what follows we will always choose $u_m = 1 - (u_1 + \cdots + u_{m-1})$. For $b \in \mathbb{R}^m_>$, where $\mathbb{R}_> = \{t : t > 0\}$, let $B(b)$ denote the multivariate beta function and

$$\mu_b(u) = \frac{1}{B(b)} \prod_{i=1}^{m} u_i^{b_i - 1}$$

is the Dirichlet measure on E_{m-1}.

Definition 1. *Let $x \in I^m$. The Dirichlet average of the function f with parameters b and variables x, denoted by $F(b; x)$, is defined by [5, (5.2-1)]*

$$(1.1) \qquad F(b; x) = \int_{E_{m-1}} f(u \cdot x) \mu_b(u) \, du,$$

where $u \cdot x = u_1 x_1 + \cdots + u_m x_m$ is the dot product of vectors u and x and $du = du_1 \ldots du_{m-1}$.

Special functions reached in this way include the celebrated Gauss hypergeometric function $_2F_1$, Kummer's confluent hypergeometric function $_1F_1$, Bessel functions of the first kind, to mention the most important ones. This method, however, has its limitations. For instance, unrestricted Lauricella hypergeometric functions F_A, F_B, and F_C have no known representations in terms of single Dirichlet averages of elementary transcendental functions. In [3] B.C. Carlson has introduced the notion of the double Dirichlet average $\mathcal{F}$ of f.

Let $X = [x_{kl}]$ ($1 \le k \le m$, $1 \le l \le n$) be a real matrix and let $J = [\min(x_{kl}), \max(x_{kl})]$. Further, let $d \in \mathbb{R}^n_>$ and let $\mu_d(v)$ denote the Dirichlet measure on the Euclidean simplex E_{n-1}. Assume that f is a real-valued holomorphic function on the domain $\mathcal{D}$ and let $J \subset \mathcal{D}$.

Definition 2. *The double Dirichlet average $\mathcal{F}$ of f is defined by*

$$(1.2) \qquad \mathcal{F}(b; X; d) = \int_{E_{n-1}} \int_{E_{m-1}} f(u \cdot X \cdot v) \mu_b(u) \mu_d(v) \, du \, dv,$$

where $v = (v_1, \ldots, v_n) \in E_{n-1}$ with $v_n = 1 - (v_1 + \cdots + v_{n-1})$, $dv = dv_1 \ldots dv_{n-1}$, and

$$u \cdot X \cdot v = \sum_{k=1}^{m} \sum_{l=1}^{n} u_k x_{kl} v_l \, .$$

If m or n is unity, the corresponding integration is omitted and if $m = n = 1$, we define $\mathcal{F} = f$.

For the reader's convenience we list some elementary properties of the double Dirichlet average. They can be found in [3].

(a) Row symmetry (symmetry in indices $1, \ldots, m$, which label the b-parameters and the rows of X);

(b) Column symmetry (symmetry in indices $1, \ldots, n$, which label the d-parameters and the columns of X);

(c) Transposition property: $\mathcal{F}(b; X; d) = \mathcal{F}(d; X^T; b)$;

(d) Two or more identical rows (columns) can be replaced by a single row (column) if the corresponding b-parameters (d-parameters) are replaced by their sum;

(e) A vanishing b-parameter (d-parameter) can be omitted along with the corresponding row (column) of X;

(f) Let $|b| := b_1 + \cdots + b_m$ and $|d| = d_1 + \cdots + d_n$. The average $\mathcal{F}$ can be continued analytically in the parameters and variables as long as $|b|$, $|d| \ne 0, -1, \ldots$ and all x_{kl} remain in $\mathcal{D}$, provided $\mathcal{D}$ is an open interval in $\mathbb{R}$;

(g) The double Dirichlet average $\mathcal{F}$ is holomorphic in the elements of b, d and X on its domain of definition.

Properties of the Dirichlet average F can be deduced easily from the above list.

Special functions which can be represented by the double Dirichlet averages include Lauricella hypergeometric functions F_A, F_B, and F_C, Jacobi polynomials, the unrestricted hypergeometric function $_3F_2$, to mention the most important ones (see [3], [4]).

Some integral formulas for the double Dirichlet averages are obtained in [11]. Therein, these averages have been employed to obtain new results for the Gegenbauer functions. In [13] the authors have used the double Dirichlet averages to study the moments of the multivariate Dirichlet splines.

Dirichlet averages are closely related to one of the most important inequalities for convex functions. Let $f : I \to \mathbb{R}$ be a convex function and let $\alpha, \beta \in I$ ($\alpha \neq \beta$). The classical result which is due to Hermite and Hadamard states

$$f\left(\frac{\alpha + \beta}{2}\right) \leq \frac{1}{\beta - \alpha} \int_\alpha^\beta f(t)\, dt \leq \frac{f(\alpha) + f(\beta)}{2}$$

(see, e.g., [6], [14]). A generalization of this result can be found in [5, Ex. 5.2–1]

$$(1.3) \qquad f\left(\sum_{i=1}^m w_i x_i\right) \leq \int_{E_{m-1}} f(u \cdot x)\mu_b(u)\, du \leq \sum_{i=1}^m w_i f(x_i),$$

where $w_i = b_i/|b|$, $1 \leq i \leq m$, $x = (x_1, \ldots, x_m) \in I^m$. Comparison with (1.1) shows that the middle term in (1.3) is the Dirichlet average F, thus

$$(1.4) \qquad f\left(\sum_{i=1}^m w_i x_i\right) \leq F(b; x) \leq \sum_{i=1}^m w_i f(x_i).$$

Generalizations of (1.3) to the case when f is a multivariate convex function can be found in [12], [10], and [1]. Some of the results in [1] apply to the logarithmically-convex functions.

The goal of this paper is to establish the Hermite-Hadamard inequalities for the double Dirichlet averages. These results are contained in Section 2. Applications to Lauricella's F_B and Jacobi polynomials are presented in Section 3.

2   THE HERMITE-HADAMARD INEQUALITIES FOR DOUBLE DIRICHLET AVERAGES

In this section we deal with the inequalities for double Dirichlet averages of convex functions. Some of these results can be regarded as generalizations of inequalities (1.4).

To this end we will always assume that $b \in \mathbb{R}_>^m$, $d \in \mathbb{R}_>^n$ ($m, n \geq 1$). For later use we define the weights r_k ($1 \leq k \leq m$) and s_l ($1 \leq l \leq n$), where

$$(2.1) \qquad r_k = b_k/|b|$$

and

$$(2.2) \qquad s_l = d_l/|d|.$$

Let $X = [x_{kl}]$ be an m by n real matrix. We will assume that not all entries of X are equal. In what follows, the symbols $_kX$ and X_l will stand for the kth row and the lth column of X, respectively. Also, we will use the symbol J which has been introduced in Section 1. In order to present the first result of this section we introduce the vector $Y = (y_1, \ldots, y_n)$, where

$$(2.3) \qquad y_l = \sum_{k=1}^m r_k x_{kl}$$

($1 \leq l \leq n$) and the vector $Z = (z_1, \ldots, z_m)$, with

$$(2.4) \qquad z_k = \sum_{l=1}^n s_l x_{kl}$$

($l \leq k \leq m$).

We are in a position to state and prove the following.

Theorem 2.1. *Let $f : \mathrm{Int}(J) \to \mathbb{R}$. If f is a convex function, then*

$$(2.5) \qquad F(d; Y) \leq \mathcal{F}(b; X; d) \leq \sum_{k=1}^{m} r_k F(d; {}_kX)$$

and

$$(2.6) \qquad F(b; Z) \leq \mathcal{F}(b; X; d) \leq \sum_{l=1}^{n} s_l F(b; X_l).$$

Inequalities (2.5) and (2.6) are reversed if f is a concave function and they become equalities if f is an algebraic polynomial of degree at most one.

Proof. We shall prove inequalities (2.5) and (2.6) when f is a convex function. We need the following formula [3, (2.8)]

$$
\begin{aligned}
(2.7) \qquad \mathcal{F}(b; X; d) &= \int_{E_{n-1}} F(b; {}_1X \cdot v, \dots, {}_mX \cdot v)\mu_d(v)\,dv \\
&= \int_{E_{m-1}} F(d; u \cdot X_1, \dots, u \cdot X_n)\mu_b(u)\,du.
\end{aligned}
$$

For the proof of (2.5) we introduce a vector $W = (w_1, \dots, w_m)$ where $w_k = {}_kX \cdot v$ $(1 \leq k \leq m)$, $v \in E_{n-1}$. Then

$$\sum_{k=1}^{m} r_k w_k = \sum_{k=1}^{m} r_k({}_kX \cdot v) = \sum_{k=1}^{m} r_k \left(\sum_{l=1}^{n} x_{kl} v_l \right) = \sum_{l=1}^{n} \left(\sum_{k=1}^{m} r_k x_{kl} \right) v_l = \sum_{l=1}^{n} y_l v_l = Y \cdot v.$$

Thus

$$(2.8) \qquad \sum_{k=1}^{m} r_k w_k = Y \cdot v.$$

It follows from (1.4) that

$$f\left(\sum_{k=1}^{m} r_k w_k \right) \leq F(b; W) \leq \sum_{k=1}^{m} r_k f(w_k).$$

Application of (2.8) to the last inequality gives

$$f(Y \cdot v) \leq F(b; {}_1X \cdot v, \dots, {}_mX \cdot v) \leq \sum_{k=1}^{m} r_k f({}_kX \cdot v).$$

Multiplying all members of the last inequality by $\mu_d(v)$ and next integrating over E_{n-1} we obtain

$$
\begin{aligned}
\int_{E_{n-1}} f(Y \cdot v)\mu_d(v)\,dv &\leq \int_{E_{n-1}} F(b; {}_1X \cdot v, \dots, {}_mX \cdot v)\mu_d(v)\,dv \\
&\leq \sum_{k=1}^{m} r_k \int_{E_{n-1}} f({}_kX \cdot v)\mu_d(v)\,dv.
\end{aligned}
$$

Application of (1.1) to the first and third members of the last inequality and use of (2.7) completes the proof of (2.5). Inequalities (2.6) can be established in a similar fashion. We define $W = (w_1, \ldots, w_n)$ with $w_l = u \cdot X_l$ $(1 \leq l \leq n)$. Easy computation shows that

$$(2.9) \qquad \sum_{l=1}^{n} s_l w_l = Z \cdot u,$$

where $u \in E_{m-1}$ and the components of the vector Z are defined in (2.4). We employ (1.4) again to obtain

$$f\left(\sum_{l=1}^{n} s_l w_l\right) \leq F(d; W) \leq \sum_{l=1}^{n} s_l f(w_l).$$

Making use of (2.9) and utilizing the definition of the vector W we obtain

$$f(Z \cdot u) \leq F(d; u \cdot X_1, \ldots, u \cdot X_n) \leq \sum_{l=1}^{n} s_l f(u \cdot X_l).$$

To complete the proof of (2.6) we multiply all members of the last inequality by $\mu_b(u)$ and next integrate over E_{m-1}. Application of (1.1) and (2.7) to the resulting inequality gives the desired result. $\qquad\square$

Before we state and prove a corollary of Theorem 2.1 let us introduce more notation. Following [3] the double Dirichlet average of $f(t) = t^{-a}$ $(t > 0)$ will be denoted by $\mathcal{R}(b; X; d)$ provided the vectors b and d are such that $|b| = |d| = a$. Also, we will write R_{-a} for the single Dirichlet average of the power function $t \to t^{-a}$.

Corollary 2.2. *Let the numbers y_l $(1 \leq l \leq n)$ and z_k $(1 \leq k \leq m)$ be the same as in (2.3) and (2.4), respectively. Assume that all the entries x_{kl} of the matrix are positive numbers. Then the following inequalities*

$$(2.10) \qquad \prod_{l=1}^{n} y_l^{-d_l} \leq \mathcal{R}(b; X; d) \leq \sum_{k=1}^{m} r_k \prod_{l=1}^{n} x_{kl}^{-d_l}$$

and

$$(2.11) \qquad \prod_{k=1}^{m} z_k^{-b_k} \leq \mathcal{R}(b; X; d) \leq \sum_{l=1}^{n} s_l \prod_{k=1}^{n} x_{kl}^{-b_k}$$

are valid.

Proof. Let $x = (x_1, \ldots, x_m) \in \mathbb{R}_{>}^{m}$. It is known ([5, (6.6–5)]) that

$$R_{-a}(b; x) = \prod_{k=1}^{m} x_k^{-b_k}$$

provided $|b| = a$. Applying this result to the first and third members of (2.5) and (2.6), with $f(t) = t^{-a}$, we obtain the desired inequalities (2.10)–(2.11). $\qquad\square$

For later use, let $Y = [y_{kl}]$ be an m by n real matrix all of whose entries are not equal. Let $K = [\min(y_{kl}), \max(y_{kl})]$. For $0 < t < 1$ we define a matrix Z, where $Z = tX + (1-t)Y$ and X has the same meaning as in Theorem 2.1. Also, for $\tau_1, \tau_2 \in \mathbb{R}$ let $\tau = t\tau_1 + (1-t)\tau_2$. Our next result reads as follows.

Theorem 2.3. *Let* $f : \text{Int}(J \cup K) \to \mathbb{R}_>$ *be a logarithmically-convex function. Then*

$$(2.12) \qquad\qquad \mathcal{F}(b; Z; d) \le [\mathcal{F}(b; X; d)]^t [\mathcal{F}(b; Y; d)]^{1-t}.$$

If $x_{kl} > 0$ *for* $1 \le k \le m$, $1 \le l \le n$ *and if* $\tau_1 \ne \tau_2$, *then*

$$(2.13) \qquad\qquad \mathcal{R}_\tau(b; X; d) < [\mathcal{R}_{\tau_1}(b; X; d)]^t [\mathcal{R}_{\tau_2}(b; X; d)]^{1-t}.$$

Proof. We shall establish (2.12) first. Logarithmic convexity of f implies the following inequality

$$f(u \cdot Z \cdot v) \le [f(u \cdot X \cdot v)]^t [f(u \cdot Y \cdot v)]^{1-t}.$$

We multiply both sides by $\mu_b(u)\mu_d(v)$, next integrate over E_{m-1} and E_{n-1} and apply Hölder's inequality to obtain

$$\mathcal{F}(b; Z; d)$$
$$\le \int_{E_{n-1}} \int_{E_{m-1}} [f(u \cdot X \cdot v)\mu_b(u)\mu_d(v)]^t [f(u \cdot Y \cdot v)\mu_b(u)\mu_d(v)]^{1-t} \, du \, dv$$
$$\le \left[\int_{E_{n-1}} \int_{E_{m-1}} f(u \cdot X \cdot v)\mu_b(u)\mu_d(v) \, du \, dv \right]^t \left[\int_{E_{n-1}} \int_{E_{m-1}} f(u \cdot Y \cdot v)\mu_b(u)\mu_d(v) \, du \, dv \right]^{1-t}$$
$$= [\mathcal{F}(b; X; d)]^t [\mathcal{F}(b; Y; d)]^{1-t}.$$

The proof of (2.12) is complete. In order to establish inequality (2.13) we use the following result [2, Theorem 4]

$$R_\tau(d; x) < [R_{\tau_1}(d; x)]^t [R_{\tau_2}(d; x)]^{1-t},$$

where $x \in \mathbb{R}_>^n$. Letting $x = u \cdot X = (u \cdot X_1, \ldots, u \cdot X_n)$ ($u \in E_{m-1}$) and next integrating against the Dirichlet measure $\mu_b(u)$ over the simplex E_{m-1} we obtain

$$\int_{E_{m-1}} R_\tau(d; u \cdot X)\mu_b(u) \, du < \int_{E_{m-1}} \left[R_{\tau_1}(d; u \cdot X)\mu_b(u) \right]^t \left[R_{\tau_2}(d; u \cdot X)\mu_b(u) \right]^{1-t} du$$
$$< \left[\int_{E_{m-1}} R_{\tau_1}(d; u \cdot X)\mu_b(u) \, du \right]^t \left[\int_{E_{m-1}} R_{\tau_2}(d; u \cdot X)\mu_b(u) \, du \right]^{1-t}$$

where in the last step we have used Hölder's inequality. Taking into account that $u \cdot X = (u \cdot X_1, \ldots, u \cdot X_n)$ and utilizing (2.7) one obtains the desired result (2.13). $\qquad\square$

3 Applications to Special Functions

This section deals with applications of inequalities, established in the previous section, to special functions. Emphasis is on Lauricella's hypergeometric function F_B and Jacobi polynomials.

3.1 Bounds for Lauricella's Function $\mathbf{F_B}$

In what follows we will use Appell's symbol (a, n) ($a \ne 0$, $n \in \mathbb{N}_0$ – set of all nonnegative integers), where $(a, 0) = 1$ and $(a, n) = a(a+1) \cdots (a+n-1)$ $(n > 0)$. For $i = (i_1, \ldots, i_n) \in \mathbb{N}_0^n$ and $\alpha, \beta \in \mathbb{C}^n$ we define

$$(\alpha, i) = (\alpha_1, i_1) \cdots (\alpha_n, i_n), \qquad (\beta, i) = (\beta_1, i_1) \cdots (\beta_n, i_n).$$

Also, we will employ the multi-index notation:

$$|i| = i_1 + \cdots + i_n, \quad i! = i_1! \cdots \cdots i_n!, \quad x^i = x_1^{i_1} \cdots \cdots x_n^{i_n},$$

where $x \in \mathbb{C}^n$.

For $a, \beta \in \mathbb{C}^n$, $\gamma \in \mathbb{C}$ ($\gamma \neq 0, -1, \ldots$) and $x \in \mathbb{C}^n$, with $|x_i| < 1$ ($1 \leq i \leq n$), the Lauricella hypergeometric function F_B is defined by (see e.g., [9], [7])

$$F_B(\alpha, \beta; \gamma; x) = \sum \frac{(\alpha, i)(\beta, i)}{(\gamma, |i|)i!} x^i,$$

where the summation extends over all multi-indices $i \in \mathbb{N}_0^n$. When $n = 1$, F_B becomes the celebrated Gauss hypergeometric function $_2F_1$:

$$(3.1) \qquad _2F_1(\alpha, \beta; \gamma; x) = \sum_{i=0}^{i} \frac{(\alpha, i)(\beta, i)}{(\gamma, i)i!} x^i.$$

Also, we will use Lauricella's hypergeometric function F_D. For $\alpha, \gamma \in \mathbb{C}$ ($\gamma \neq 0, -1, \ldots$) and $\beta, x \in \mathbb{C}^n$ ($|x_i| < 1, 1 \leq i \leq n$) the function in question is defined by

$$(3.2) \qquad F_D(\alpha, \beta; \gamma; x) = \sum \frac{(\alpha, |i|)(\beta, i)}{(\gamma, |i|)i!} x^i,$$

where the summation extends over all multi-indices $i \in \mathbb{N}_0^n$ (see [9], [7]).

Both functions F_B and F_D admit representations in terms of Dirichlet averages. In what follows the symbol $\mathcal{R}_{-a}$ will stand for the double Dirichlet average of the power function $t \to t^{-a}$ ($t > 0$). It is known [3, (5.4)] that

$$(3.3) \qquad F_B(\alpha, \beta; \gamma; x) = \mathcal{R}_{-|\alpha|}(\alpha; X; \beta, \gamma - |\beta|),$$

where

$$(3.4) \qquad X = \begin{bmatrix} 1 - x_1 & 1 & \cdots & 1 & 1 \\ 1 & 1 - x_2 & \cdots & 1 & 1 \\ \vdots & & \ddots & \vdots & \vdots \\ 1 & 1 & \cdots & 1 - x_n & 1 \end{bmatrix}.$$

Function F_D is represented by a single Dirichlet average:

$$(3.5) \qquad F_D(\alpha, \beta; \gamma; x) = R_{-\alpha}(\beta, \gamma - |\beta|; 1 - x, 1)$$

(see, e.g., [5, Ex. 6.3–5]). Here $1 - x = (1 - x_1, \ldots, 1 - x_n)$.

Our first result reads as follows.

Proposition 3.1. *Let* $\alpha, \beta \in \mathbb{R}_>^n$, $\gamma > 0$ *and let* $x \in \mathbb{R}^n$. *If* $\gamma > |\beta|$ *and* $x_i < 1$ ($1 \leq i \leq n$), *then*

$$(3.6) \qquad F_D(|\alpha|, \beta; \gamma; rx) \leq F_B(\alpha, \beta; \gamma; x) \leq \sum_{k=1}^{n} r_k \big[_2F_1(|\alpha|, \beta_k; \gamma; x_k) \big],$$

where

$$(3.7) \qquad r_k = \alpha_k / |\alpha|$$

(1 ≤ k ≤ n) and $r.x := (r_1 x_1, \ldots, r_n x_n)$.

Proof. We shall use inequality (2.5) with $m = n$, $n := n + 1$, $f(t) = t^{-|\alpha|}$ $(t > 0)$, $b = \alpha$, and $d = (\beta, \gamma - |\beta|)$. Making use of (2.3) one obtains easily

$$y_l = \begin{cases} 1 - r_l x_l, & 1 \le l \le n \\ 1, & l = n + 1. \end{cases}$$

Thus $Y = (1 - r_1 x_1, \ldots, 1 - r_n x_n, 1)$. Using (3.5) we obtain $F(d; Y) = R_{-|\alpha|}(\beta, \gamma - |\beta|; 1 - rx, 1) = F_D(|\alpha|, \beta; \gamma; rx)$. This is the first term in the inequality (3.6). The middle one is equal to $F_B(\alpha, \beta; \gamma; x)$ because

$$\mathcal{F}(b; X; d) = \mathcal{R}_{-|\alpha|}(\alpha; X; \beta, \gamma - |\beta|) = F_B(\alpha, \beta; \gamma; x),$$

where the last equality follows from (3.3). Here the matrix X is defined in (3.4). The third member of (2.5) is computed as follows

$$\sum_{k=1}^{n} r_k F(d; {}_k X) = \sum_{k=1}^{n} r_k R_{-|\alpha|}(\beta, \gamma - |\beta|; 1, \ldots, 1 - x_k, \ldots, 1, 1)$$

$$= \sum_{k=1}^{n} r_k R_{-|\alpha|}(\beta_k, \gamma - \beta_k; 1 - x_k, 1)$$

$$= \sum_{k=1}^{n} r_k \left[{}_2F_1(|\alpha|, \beta_k; \gamma; x_k) \right].$$

Here we have used Property (d) and the formula (3.5) with $n = 1$. The proof is complete.
$\square$

Computable bounds for Lauricella's function F_B are given in the next proposition. To facilitate presentation, let us introduce more notation. We define

$$(3.8) \qquad\qquad s_k = \beta_k/\gamma \quad (1 \le k \le n),$$

$$(3.9) \qquad\qquad K_1 = \prod_{l=1}^{n} (1 - r_l x_l)^{-\beta_l},$$

$$(3.10) \qquad\qquad K_2 = \prod_{k=1}^{n} (1 - s_k x_k)^{-\alpha_k},$$

$$(3.11) \qquad\qquad L_1 = 1 + \sum_{l=1}^{n} r_l \left[(1 - x_l)^{-\beta_l} - 1 \right],$$

$$(3.12) \qquad\qquad L_2 = 1 + \sum_{k=1}^{n} s_k \left[(1 - x_k)^{-\alpha_k} - 1 \right],$$

where the weights $r_1, \ldots, r_n$ are defined in (3.7).

Proposition 3.2. *Let $\alpha, \beta \in \mathbb{R}^n_>$, let $\gamma > 0$, and let $x \in \mathbb{R}^n$. If $\gamma > \max(|\alpha|, |\beta|)$ and $x_i < 1$ for $1 \le i \le n$, then the following inequalities*

$$(3.13) \qquad\qquad \max\{K_1, K_2\} \le F_B(\alpha, \beta; \gamma; x) \le \min\{L_1, L_2\}$$

are valid.

Proof. We shall employ another representation of F_B as the double Dirichlet average of the power function $t \to t^{-\gamma}$ $(t > 0)$. Following [3, (5.11)]

(3.14) $$F_B(\alpha, \beta; \gamma; x) = \mathcal{R}(\alpha, \gamma - |\alpha|; Z; \beta, \gamma - |\beta|),$$

where

$$Z = \begin{bmatrix} 1 - x_1 & 1 & \cdots & 1 & 1 \\ 1 & 1 - x_2 & \cdots & 1 & 1 \\ \vdots & \vdots & \ddots & & \\ 1 & 1 & \cdots & 1 - x_n & 1 \\ 1 & 1 & \cdots & 1 & 1 \end{bmatrix}.$$

The weights associated with the rows of Z are equal to r_l $(1 \leq l \leq n + 1)$ (see (3.7)) where $r_{n+1} = 1 - (r_1 + \cdots + r_n)$ and the weights associated with the columns of Z are equal to s_k $(1 \leq k \leq n + 1)$ (see (3.8)) where $s_{n+1} = 1 - (s_1 + \cdots + s_n)$. Making use of (2.3) and (2.4) with $m = n := n + 1$ we obtain

$$y_l = \begin{cases} 1 - r_l x_l, & 1 \leq l \leq n \\ 1, & l = n + 1 \end{cases}$$

and

$$z_k = \begin{cases} 1 - s_k x_k, & 1 \leq k \leq n \\ 1, & k = n + 1. \end{cases}$$

In order to obtain the lower bounds K_1 and K_2 we apply the first members of (2.10) and (2.11) to (3.14). The upper bounds L_1 and L_2 are derived in a similar fashion. □

Proposition 3.3. *Let $\alpha, \beta \in \mathbb{R}^n_>$ and let $\gamma > 0$. Assume that $\gamma > |\beta|$. Further, let $X = [x_{kl}]$ and $Y = [y_{kl}]$ be real m by n matrices such that $x_{kl} < 1$ and $y_{kl} < 1$ for all k and l. If $0 < t < 1$, then*

$$F_B(\alpha, \beta; \gamma; tX + (1 - t)Y) \leq \left[F_B(\alpha, \beta; \gamma; X)\right]^t \left[F_B(\alpha, \beta; \gamma; Y)\right]^{1-t}.$$

Proof. We apply (2.12) to (3.3) to obtain the assertion. □

3.2 An Inequality for Jacobi Polynomials

The Jacobi polynomial $P_n^{(\alpha,\beta)}(x)$ of order (α, β) and degree n in variable x is defined by [7, Ex. 7.1–3]

$$P_n^{(\alpha,\beta)}(x) = \sum_{k=0}^{n} \binom{\alpha + n}{k} \binom{\beta + n}{n - k} \left(\frac{x + 1}{2}\right)^k \left(\frac{x - 1}{2}\right)^{n-k}.$$

G. Gasper [8] has shown that if $\beta \geq \alpha > -\frac{1}{2}$ and $|x| \leq 1$, then the polynomials in question satisfy the Turán type inequality

(3.15) $$S_{n-1}^{(\alpha,\beta)}(x) S_{n+1}^{(\alpha,\beta)}(x) \leq \left[S_n^{(\alpha,\beta)}(x)\right]^2,$$

where $S_n^{(\alpha,\beta)}(x) = P_n^{(\alpha,\beta)}(x)/P_n^{(\alpha,\beta)}(1)$. Equality holds in (3.15) if and only if $|x| = 1$.
For later use we define

(3.16) $$V_n^{(\alpha,\beta)}(z) = \frac{P_n^{(\alpha,\beta)}(z)}{P_n^{(\alpha,\beta)}(1) P_n^{(\alpha,\beta)}(-1)}.$$

We are in a position to prove the following.

Proposition 3.4. *Let $\alpha, \beta > -\frac{1}{2}$, $n \geq 1$, and let $|z| \geq 1$. Then*

$$(3.17) \qquad \left[V_n^{(\alpha,\beta)}(z)\right]^2 < \gamma_n V_{n-1}^{(\alpha,\beta)}(z) V_{n+1}^{(\alpha,\beta)}(z),$$

where

$$(3.18) \qquad \gamma_n = \frac{n(2n+1)}{(n+1)(2n-1)}.$$

Proof. For the proof of (3.17) we define $b = \left(\alpha + \frac{1}{2}, \alpha + \frac{1}{2}\right)$, $d = \left(\beta + \frac{1}{2}, \beta + \frac{1}{2}\right)$, and

$$X = \begin{bmatrix} r+s & r-s \\ -r+s & -r-s \end{bmatrix},$$

where $r^2 = (1+x)(1+y)/4$, $s^2 = (1-x)(1-y)/4$, with $|x|, |y| \leq 1$. We shall prove first that

$$(3.19) \qquad \mathcal{R}_{2n}(b; X; d) = (-1)^n \frac{\left(\frac{1}{2}, n\right)}{n!} \left(\frac{x+y}{2}\right)^n V_n^{(\alpha,\beta)}\left(\frac{1+xy}{x+y}\right),$$

where $\mathcal{R}_{2n}$ stands for the double Dirichlet average of the power function $t \to t^{2n}$. Also, we will write R_n for the single Dirichlet average of $t \to t^n$. The later average is also called the R-hypergeometric polynomial (see [5]). In ([5, Ex. 7.1–3])

$$P_n^{(\alpha,\beta)}(z) = \frac{(\lambda + n, n)}{2^n n!} R_n(-\alpha - n, -\beta - n; z+1, z-1)$$

($\lambda = \alpha + \beta + 1$) we let $z = \frac{1+xy}{x+y}$. Taking into account that R_n is a homogeneous function of degree n in its variables we obtain

$$\left(\frac{x+y}{2}\right)^n P_n^{(\alpha,\beta)}\left(\frac{1+xy}{x+y}\right) = \frac{(\lambda + n, n)}{n!} R_n(-\alpha - n, -\beta - n; r^2, s^2).$$

Combining this with ([4, (5.9)])

$$(\alpha + 1, n)(\beta + 1, n)\mathcal{R}_{2n}(b; X; d) = \left(\frac{1}{2}, n\right)(\lambda + n, n) R_n(-\alpha - n, -\beta - n; r^2, s^2)$$

and taking into account that

$$P_n^{(\alpha,\beta)}(1) = \frac{(\alpha + 1, n)}{n!}, \quad P_n^{(\alpha,\beta)}(-1) = (-1)^n \frac{(\beta + 1, n)}{n!}$$

we obtain (3.19). To complete the proof of the inequality (3.17) use (3.19) together with the inequality (2.13). Letting $t = 1/2$, $\tau_1 = 2n - 2$, and $\tau_2 = 2n + 2$ in (2.13) we obtain the desired result. Let us note that if $|x| \leq 1$ and $|y| \leq 1$, then $|z| = \left|\frac{1+xy}{x+y}\right| \geq 1$. $\square$

We close this section with the remark that the members of the sequence (3.18) satisfy the inequality $1 < \gamma_n \leq 1.5$ and they decrease monotonically as n increases.

REFERENCES

[1] M. Klaričić Bakula, E. Neuman, J.E. Pečarić, and V. Šimić, Hermite-Hadamard's inequalities for multivariate g-convex functions, *Math. Inequal. Appl.*, **8** (2005), 305–316.

[2] B.C. Carlson, A hypergeometric mean value, *Proc. Amer. Math. Soc.*, **16** (1965), 759–766.

[3] B.C. Carlson, Appell functions and multiple averages, *SIAM J. Math. Anal.*, **2** (1971), 420–430.

[4] B.C. Carlson, Inequalities for Jacobi polynomials and Dirichlet averages, *SIAM J. Math. Anal.*, **5** (1974), 586–596.

[5] B.C. Carlson, *Special Functions of Applied Mathematics*, Academic Press, New York, 1977.

[6] S.S. Dragomir and C.E.M. Pearce, *Selected Topics in Hermite-Hadamard Inequalities and Applications*, Rgmia Monographs, Victoria University 2000. (Online: http://rgmia.vu.edu.au/monographs/hermite_hadamard.html)

[7] A. Erdélyi, W. Magnus, F. Oberhettinger and F.G. Tricomi, *Higher Transcendental Functions*, McGraw-Hill, New York, 1953.

[8] G. Gasper, An inequality of Turán type for Jacobi polynomials, *Proc. Amer. Math. Soc.*, **32** (1972), 435–439.

[9] G. Lauricella, Sulle funzioni ipergeometriche a piu variabli, *Rend. Circ. Mat. Palermo*, **7** (1893), 111–158.

[10] E. Neuman, Inequalities involving multivariate convex functions II, *Proc. Amer. Math. Soc.*, **109** (1990), 965–974.

[11] E. Neuman, Dirichlet averages and their applications to Gegenbauer functions, *Int. J. Math. Stat. Sci.*, **5** (1996), 85–101.

[12] E. Neuman and J.E. Pečarić, Inequalities involving multivariate convex functions, *J. Math. Anal. Appl.*, **137** (1989), 541–549.

[13] E. Neuman and P. Van Fleet, Moments of Dirichlet splines and their applications to hypergeometric functions, *J. Comput. Appl. Math.*, **53** (1994), 225–241.

[14] J.E. Pečarić, F. Proschan and Y.L. Tong, *Convex Functions, Partial Orderings and Statistical Applications*, Academic Press, Boston, 1992.

In: Advances in Inequalities for Special Functions   ISBN 978-1-60021-919-1
Editors: P. Cerone and S. S. Dragomir, pp. 119–124 © 2008 Nova Science Publishers, Inc.

On New Inequalities Involving Convex Functions

B. G. Pachpatte

57 Shri Niketan Colony, Near Abhinay Talkies
Aurangabad (Maharashtra) India
E-mail address: bgpachpatte@gmail.com

ABSTRACT. In the present paper we establish some new integral inequalities involving convex functions by using fairly elementary analysis.

1991 Mathematics Subject Classification: 26D15, 26D20.

Key words and phrases: Integral inequalities, convex functions, Hadamard inequality, log-convex functions.

1   INTRODUCTION

One of the classical and important inequalities used in analysis is the Hadamard inequality:

$$\text{(1.1)} \qquad f\left(\frac{a+b}{2}\right) \le \frac{1}{b-a} \int_a^b f(x)\, dx \le \frac{f(a)+f(b)}{2},$$

where $f : I \to \mathbb{R}$ is a convex function on the interval I of real numbers $\mathbb{R}$, $a, b \in I$ with $a < b$, see [2, 11]. Recently, in [8] the present author has established some new integral inequalities, analogues to that of Hadamard, involving the product of two convex functions. One of the main results proved in [8] can be stated as follows:

Let f and g be real-valued, nonnegative convex functions on $[a, b]$. Then

$$\text{(1.2)} \qquad \frac{1}{b-a} \int_a^b f(x)\, g(x)\, dx \le \frac{1}{3} M(a,b) + \frac{1}{6} N(a,b),$$

$$\text{(1.3)} \qquad 2f\left(\frac{a+b}{2}\right) g\left(\frac{a+b}{2}\right) \le \frac{1}{b-a} \int_a^b f(x)\, g(x)\, dx + \frac{1}{6} M(a,b) + \frac{1}{3} N(a,b),$$

where

$$M(a,b) = f(a)\, g(a) + f(b)\, g(b), \qquad N(a,b) = f(a)\, g(b) + f(b)\, g(a).$$

For numerous inequalities for convex functions, see the books [2, 3, 5, 6, 11] and for the inequalities involving the product of two and more convex functions, see the recent papers [1], [4], [7] – [10]. The main purpose of this paper is to establish some new integral inequalities involving convex functions. The analysis used in the proof is elementary and our results provide new estimates on these types of inequalities.

This paper is dedicated to the memory of my wife Barbara.

2   STATEMENT OF RESULTS

Let I be a suitable interval of real numbers $\mathbb{R}$. A function $f : I \to \mathbb{R}$ is called convex if

$$f\left(\lambda x + (1 - \lambda) y\right) \le \lambda f(x) + (1 - \lambda) f(y),$$

for all $x, y \in I$ and $\lambda \in (0, 1)$. A function $f : I \to (0, \infty)$ is said to be a log-convex function, if for all $x, y \in I$ and $t \in [0, 1]$ one has the inequality (see [12, p. 7]):

$$f\left(tx + (1 - t) y\right) \le \left[f(x)\right]^t \left[f(y)\right]^{1-t}.$$

Let $f, g : [a, b] \to \mathbb{R}$ $(a < b)$ be convex functions. We shall define the mappings $F(x, y)(t), G(x, y)(t) : [0, 1] \to \mathbb{R}$ as follows:

$$F(x, y)(t) = \frac{1}{2}\left[f\left(tx + (1 - t) y\right) + f\left((1 - t) x + ty\right)\right],$$

$$G(x, y)(t) = \frac{1}{2}\left[g\left(tx + (1 - t) y\right) + g\left((1 - t) x + ty\right)\right],$$

for $x, y \in I$.

Our main results are given in the following theorems.

Theorem 2.1. *Let f and g be real-valued, nonnegative convex functions on $[a, b]$ and the mappings $F(x, y)(t)$ and $G(x, y)(t)$ be as defined above. Then for all $t \in [0, 1]$ we have*

$$(2.1) \quad \frac{1}{b - a} \int_a^b F\left(x, \frac{a + b}{2}\right)(t) G\left(x, \frac{a + b}{2}\right)(t)\, dx$$

$$\le \frac{1}{4(b - a)} \int_a^b f(x) g(x)\, dx + \frac{3}{16}\left[M(a, b) + N(a, b)\right]$$

and

$$(2.2) \quad \frac{2}{(b - a)^2} \int_a^b \int_a^b F(x, y)(t) G(x, y)(t)\, dx\, dy$$

$$\le \frac{1}{b - a} \int_a^b f(x) g(x)\, dx + \frac{1}{4}\left[M(a, b) + N(a, b)\right],$$

where

$$M(a, b) = f(a) g(a) + f(b) g(b), \qquad N(a, b) = f(a) g(b) + f(b) g(a).$$

Theorem 2.2. *Let $f, g, h : I \to (0, \infty)$ be log-convex functions on I and $a, b \in I$ with $a < b$. Then we have*

$$(2.3) \quad \frac{2}{b - a} \int_a^b \left[f(x) g(x) + g(x) h(x) + h(x) f(x)\right] dx$$

$$\le \left[f(a) + f(b)\right] L\left(f(a), f(b)\right) + \left[g(a) + g(b)\right] L\left(g(a), g(b)\right)$$
$$+ \left[h(a) + h(b)\right] L\left(h(a), h(b)\right),$$

$$(2.4) \quad \frac{4}{b - a} \int_a^b f(x) g(x) h(x)\left[f(x) + g(x) + h(x)\right] dx$$

$$\le \left[f(a) + f(b)\right]\left[f^2(a) + f^2(b)\right] L\left(f(a), f(b)\right)$$
$$+ \left[g(a) + g(b)\right]\left[g^2(a) + g^2(b)\right] L\left(g(a), g(b)\right)$$
$$+ \left[h(a) + h(b)\right]\left[h^2(a) + h^2(b)\right] L\left(h(a), h(b)\right),$$

where $L\left(p, q\right) = \frac{p-q}{\log p - \log q}$ $(p \neq q)$ is the logarithmic mean of the positive real numbers p, q (for $p = q$, we put $L(p, p) = p$).

3 PROOF OF THEOREM 2.1

Since f and g are convex on $[a, b]$, then for $t \in [0, 1]$, it is easy to observe that

(3.1)
$$F\left(x, \frac{a+b}{2}\right)(t) \leq \frac{1}{2}\left[f\left(x\right) + f\left(\frac{a+b}{2}\right)\right]$$

and

(3.2)
$$G\left(x, \frac{a+b}{2}\right)(t) \leq \frac{1}{2}\left[g\left(x\right) + g\left(\frac{a+b}{2}\right)\right].$$

From (3.1) and (3.2) we observe that

(3.3)
$$F\left(x, \frac{a+b}{2}\right)(t) G\left(x, \frac{a+b}{2}\right)(t) \leq \frac{1}{4}\left[f\left(x\right) + f\left(\frac{a+b}{2}\right)\right]\left[g\left(x\right) + g\left(\frac{a+b}{2}\right)\right]$$
$$= \frac{1}{4}\left[f\left(x\right) g\left(x\right) + f\left(x\right) g\left(\frac{a+b}{2}\right)\right.$$
$$\left. + f\left(\frac{a+b}{2}\right) g\left(x\right) + f\left(\frac{a+b}{2}\right) g\left(\frac{a+b}{2}\right)\right].$$

Integrating (3.3) on $[a, b]$ and making use of the inequality (1.1) we observe that

(3.4)
$$\int_a^b F\left(x, \frac{a+b}{2}\right)(t) G\left(x, \frac{a+b}{2}\right)(t)\, dx$$
$$\leq \frac{1}{4}\left[\int_a^b f\left(x\right) g\left(x\right)\, dx + g\left(\frac{a+b}{2}\right)\int_a^b f\left(x\right)\, dx\right.$$
$$\left. + f\left(\frac{a+b}{2}\right)\int_a^b g\left(x\right)\, dx + (b-a) f\left(\frac{a+b}{2}\right) g\left(\frac{a+b}{2}\right)\right]$$
$$\leq \frac{1}{4}\left[\int_a^b f\left(x\right) g\left(x\right)\, dx + \left\{\frac{1}{b-a}\int_a^b g\left(x\right)\, dx\right\}\left\{\frac{1}{b-a}\int_a^b f\left(x\right)\, dx\right\}(b-a)\right.$$
$$+ \left\{\frac{1}{b-a}\int_a^b f\left(x\right)\, dx\right\}\left\{\frac{1}{b-a}\int_a^b g\left(x\right)\, dx\right\}(b-a)$$
$$\left. + (b-a)\left\{\frac{1}{b-a}\int_a^b f\left(x\right)\, dx\right\}\left\{\frac{1}{b-a}\int_a^b g\left(x\right)\, dx\right\}\right]$$
$$= \frac{1}{4}\int_a^b f\left(x\right) g\left(x\right)\, dx + \frac{3}{4}(b-a)\left\{\frac{1}{b-a}\int_a^b f\left(x\right)\, dx\right\}\left\{\frac{1}{b-a}\int_a^b g\left(x\right)\, dx\right\}$$
$$\leq \frac{1}{4}\int_a^b f\left(x\right) g\left(x\right)\, dx + \frac{3}{4}(b-a)\left\{\frac{f\left(a\right) + f\left(b\right)}{2}\right\}\left\{\frac{g\left(a\right) + g\left(b\right)}{2}\right\}$$

$$= \frac{1}{4} \int_a^b f(x) g(x) \, dx + \frac{3}{16} (b-a) [M(a,b) + N(a,b)].$$

Rewriting (3.4) we get the required inequality in (2.1).

Since f and g are convex on $[a, b]$, it is easy to observe that

$$(3.5) \qquad F(x,y)(t) \le \frac{1}{2} [f(x) + f(y)]$$

and

$$(3.6) \qquad G(x,y)(t) \le \frac{1}{2} [g(x) + g(y)],$$

for $t \in [0, 1]$. From (3.5) and (3.6) we observe that

$$(3.7) \qquad F(x,y)(t) G(x,y)(t) \le \frac{1}{4} [f(x) + f(y)] [g(x) + g(y)]$$

$$= \frac{1}{4} [f(x) g(x) + f(x) g(y) + f(y) g(x) + f(y) g(y)].$$

Integrating (3.7) on $[a,b] \times [a,b]$ and using the right half of the inequality in (1.1) we get

$$(3.8) \qquad \int_a^b \int_a^b F(x,y)(t) G(x,y)(t) \, dx \, dy$$

$$\le \frac{1}{4} \left[(b-a) \int_a^b f(x) g(x) \, dx + \left(\int_a^b f(x) \, dx \right) \left(\int_a^b g(y) \, dy \right) \right.$$

$$\left. + \left(\int_a^b f(y) \, dy \right) \left(\int_a^b g(x) \, dx \right) + (b-a) \int_a^b f(y) g(y) \, dy \right]$$

$$= \frac{1}{2} (b-a) \int_a^b f(x) g(x) \, dx$$

$$+ \frac{1}{2} (b-a)^2 \left(\frac{1}{b-a} \int_a^b f(x) \, dx \right) \left(\frac{1}{b-a} \int_a^b g(x) \, dx \right)$$

$$\le \frac{1}{2} (b-a) \int_a^b f(x) g(x) \, dx + \frac{1}{2} (b-a)^2 \left(\frac{f(a) + f(b)}{2} \right) \left(\frac{g(a) + g(b)}{2} \right)$$

$$= \frac{1}{2} (b-a) \int_a^b f(x) g(x) \, dx + \frac{1}{8} (b-a)^2 [M(a,b) + N(a,b)].$$

Rewriting (3.8) we get the desired inequality in (2.2).

4   PROOF OF THEOREM 2.2

Since f, g, h are log-convex functions, we have

$$(4.1) \qquad f(ta + (1-t)b) \le [f(a)]^t [f(b)]^{1-t},$$

$$(4.2) \qquad g(ta + (1-t)b) \le [g(a)]^t [g(b)]^{1-t}$$

and

$$(4.3) \qquad h(ta + (1-t)b) \le [h(a)]^t [h(b)]^{1-t}$$

for $t \in [0, 1]$. It is easy to observe that

$$(4.4) \quad \int_a^b \left[f(x) g(x) + g(x) h(x) + h(x) f(x) \right] dx$$

$$= (b - a) \int_0^1 \left[f(ta + (1 - t) b) g(ta + (1 - t) b) + g(ta + (1 - t) b) h(ta + (1 - t) b) \right.$$

$$\left. + h(ta + (1 - t) b) f(ta + (1 - t) b) \right] dt.$$

Using the elementary inequality (see [5]) $c_1 c_2 + c_2 c_3 + c_3 c_1 \leq c_1^2 + c_2^2 + c_3^2$ (for c_1, c_2, c_3 reals) and (4.1), (4.2), (4.3) on the right hand side of (4.4) and making the change of variables, we have

(4.5)

$$\int_a^b \left[f(x) g(x) + g(x) h(x) + h(x) f(x) \right] dx$$

$$\leq (b - a) \int_0^1 \left[\{ f(ta + (1 - t) b) \}^2 + \{ g(ta + (1 - t) b) \}^2 + \{ h(ta + (1 - t) b) \}^2 \right] dt$$

$$\leq (b - a) \int_0^1 \left[\left\{ [f(a)]^t [f(b)]^{1-t} \right\}^2 + \left\{ [g(a)]^t [g(b)]^{1-t} \right\}^2 + \left\{ [h(a)]^t [h(b)]^{1-t} \right\}^2 \right] dt$$

$$= (b - a) \left\{ f^2(b) \int_0^1 \left[\frac{f(a)}{f(b)} \right]^{2t} dt + g^2(b) \int_0^1 \left[\frac{g(a)}{g(b)} \right]^{2t} dt + h^2(b) \int_0^1 \left[\frac{h(a)}{h(b)} \right]^{2t} dt \right\}$$

$$= (b - a) \left\{ \frac{1}{2} f^2(b) \int_0^2 \left[\frac{f(a)}{f(b)} \right]^{\sigma} d\sigma + \frac{1}{2} g^2(b) \int_0^2 \left[\frac{g(a)}{g(b)} \right]^{\sigma} d\sigma + \frac{1}{2} h^2(b) \int_0^2 \left[\frac{h(a)}{h(b)} \right]^{\sigma} d\sigma \right\}$$

$$= \frac{1}{2} (b - a) \left\{ f^2(b) \left[\frac{\left[\frac{f(a)}{f(b)} \right]^{\sigma}}{\log \frac{f(a)}{f(b)}} \right]_0^2 + f^2(b) \left[\frac{\left[\frac{g(a)}{g(b)} \right]^{\sigma}}{\log \frac{g(a)}{g(b)}} \right]_0^2 + h^2(b) \left[\frac{\left[\frac{h(a)}{h(b)} \right]^{\sigma}}{\log \frac{h(a)}{h(b)}} \right]_0^2 \right\}$$

$$= \frac{1}{2} (b - a) \left\{ [f(a) + f(b)] \frac{f(a) - f(b)}{\log f(a) - \log f(b)} + [g(a) + g(b)] \frac{g(a) - g(b)}{\log g(a) - \log g(b)} \right.$$

$$\left. + [h(a) + h(b)] \frac{h(a) - h(b)}{\log h(a) - \log h(b)} \right\}$$

$$= \frac{1}{2} (b - a) \left\{ [f(a) + f(b)] L(f(a), f(b)) + [g(a) + g(b)] L(g(a), g(b)) \right.$$

$$\left. + [h(a) + h(b)] L(h(a), h(b)) \right\}.$$

The desired inequality in (2.3) follows by rewriting (4.5).

It is easy to observe that

$$(4.6) \quad \int_a^b f(x) g(x) h(x) \left[f(x) + g(x) + h(x) \right] dx$$

$$= (b - a) \int_0^1 f(ta + (1 - t) b) g(ta + (1 - t) b) h(ta + (1 - t) b)$$

$$\times \left[f(ta + (1 - t) b) + g(ta + (1 - t) b) + h(ta + (1 - t) b) \right] dt.$$

Using the elementary inequalities (see [5])

$$c_1 c_2 c_3 \left[c_1 + c_2 + c_3 \right] \leq \frac{1}{3} \left(c_1 c_2 + c_2 c_3 + c_3 c_1 \right)^2,$$

$$c_1 c_2 + c_2 c_3 + c_3 c_1 \leq c_1^2 + c_2^2 + c_3^2 \qquad \text{and} \qquad (c_1 + c_2 + c_3)^2 \leq 3\left(c_1^2 + c_2^2 + c_3^2\right)$$

(for c_1, c_2, c_3 reals), we observe that

$$\int_a^b f(x) g(x) h(x) \left[f(x) + g(x) + h(x)\right] dx$$

$$\leq (b-a) \int_0^1 \left[\left\{ [f(a)]^t [f(b)]^{1-t} \right\}^4 + \left\{ [g(a)]^t [g(b)]^{1-t} \right\}^4 \right.$$

$$\left. + \left\{ [h(a)]^t [h(b)]^{1-t} \right\}^4 \right] dt.$$

The rest of the proof can be completed by following the proof of inequality (2.3) with suitable modifications. Here we omit the further details.

References

[1] G. Cristescu, Improved integral inequalities for product of convex functions, *J. Inequal. Pure and Appl. Math.*, **6**(2) (2005), Art. 35.

[2] S.S. Dragomir and C.E.M. Pearce, *Selected topics on Hermite-Hadamard inequalities and Applications*, RGMIA Monographs, Victoria University, 2000.

[3] G.H. Hardy, J.E. Littlewood and G. Pólya, *Inequalities*, Cambridge Univ.Press, 1934.

[4] M. Klaričić Bakula and J.E. Pečarić, Note on some Hadamard-type inequalities, *J. Inequal. Pure and Appl. Math.*, **5**(3) (2004), Art.74.

[5] D.S. Mitrinović, *Analytic Inequalities*, Springer-Verlag, Berlin, New York, 1970 .

[6] D.S. Mitrinović, J.E. Pečarić and A.M. Fink, *Classical and New Inequalities in Analysis*, Kluwer Academic Publishers, Dordrecht, 1993.

[7] B.G. Pachpatte, On some integral inequalities involving convex functions, *RGMIA Res.Rep.Coll.*, **3**(3) (2000), 487–492.

[8] B.G. Pachpatte, On some inequalities for convex functions, *RGMIA Res. Rep. Coll.*, **6**(E) (2003), Art. 1.

[9] B.G. Pachpatte, A note on integral inequalities involving two log-convex functions, *Math. Inequal.Appl.*, **7** (2004), 511–515.

[10] B.G. Pachpatte, A note on Hadamard type integral inequalities involving several log-convex functions, *Tamkang J. Math.*, **36** (2004), 43–47.

[11] B.G. Pachpatte, *Mathematical Inequalities*, North-Holland Mathematical Library, Elsevier, 2005.

[12] J.E. Pečarić, F. Proschan and Y.L. Tong, *Convex Functions, Partial Orderings and Statistical Applications*, Academic Press, New York, 1991.

In: Advances in Inequalities for Special Functions   ISBN 978-1-60021-919-1
Editors: P. Cerone and S. S. Dragomir, pp. 125–132 © 2008 Nova Science Publishers, Inc.

On Growth Rates of Weierstraß $\wp'(z)$ and $\wp(z)$

Tibor K. Pogány

Faculty of Maritime Studies
University of Rijeka
51000 Rijeka, Studentska 2, Croatia
E-mail address: poganj@brod.pfri.hr

ABSTRACT.   Non–negative functions L, R are given such that $L(z) \leq |\wp'(z)| \leq R(z)$, where
$L(z) = \mathcal{O}(H(2|z|)\delta_z^{-4})$, $R(z) = \mathcal{O}(\delta_z^{-3})$ and $\delta_z := \inf_{\mathbb{Z}^2} |z - \mathbb{Z}^2|$, $z \in \mathbb{C}$. Here

$$H(r) := \frac{\min\{r^2 - [r^2], [r^2] + 1 - r^2\}}{2r + 1/\sqrt{2}} \qquad (r \geq 0),$$

with $[a]$ being the integer part of a. Using this result growth rates are deduced for $|\wp(z)|$.

1991 Mathematics Subject Classification: 33E20, 33E30, 34A30

Key words and phrases: Bounding inequality; Jacobi θ; Weierstraß invariants $\mathfrak{g}_2, \mathfrak{g}_3$; Weierstraß $\wp(z), \wp'(z)$; Weierstraß $\sigma(z)$

1   INTRODUCTION

According to [10, Chapter XX] we introduce the Weierstraßian elliptic function

$$(1.1) \qquad \wp(z) = z^{-2} + \sideset{}{'}\sum_{(m,n)\in\mathbb{Z}^2} \left((z - \Omega_{m,n})^{-2} - \Omega_{m,n}^{-2} \right),$$

where, for brevity, we write $\Omega_{m,n} := m + ni$ and Σ' means that the summation excludes simultaneously zero values of m and n. The series converges absolutely and uniformly (with respect to z) except near its double poles $\Omega_{m,n}$. Therefore $\wp(z)$ is analytic throughout the set $\mathbb{C} \setminus \mathbb{Z}^2$ and its legitimate term by term differentiation results in

$$(1.2) \qquad \wp'(z) = -2 \sideset{}{'}\sum_{(m,n)\in\mathbb{Z}^2} (z - \Omega_{m,n})^{-3}.$$

The function $\wp'(z)$ is analytic except at its poles. Both functions are elliptic [10, p.435]. The main result which connects $\wp$ and $\wp'$ is the differential equation

$$(1.3) \qquad {\wp'}^2(z) = 4\wp^3(z) - \mathfrak{g}_2\wp(z) - \mathfrak{g}_3 \qquad (z \in \mathbb{C} \setminus \mathbb{Z}^2)$$

where

$$(1.4) \qquad \mathfrak{g}_2 = 60 \sideset{}{'}\sum_{(m,n)\in\mathbb{Z}^2} \Omega_{m,n}^{-4}, \qquad \mathfrak{g}_3 = 140 \sideset{}{'}\sum_{(m,n)\in\mathbb{Z}^2} \Omega_{m,n}^{-6}$$

are the so–called Weierstraß invariants, defined by appropriate Eisenstein series (1.4). Recently Dienstfrey and Huang reported [1, p.2] that the square lattice sums mentioned above possess the integral representations

$$E_k(\mathrm{i}) = \sideset{}{'}\sum_{(m,n)\in\mathbb{Z}^2} (m+n\mathrm{i})^{-k} = \frac{8}{(k-1)!} \int_0^\infty \frac{\lambda^{k-1}\cos^2(\lambda/2)}{e^\lambda - 2\cos(\lambda) + e^{-\lambda}}\, d\lambda$$

for $k \equiv 0 \pmod 4$, $E_k(\mathrm{i}) = 0$ otherwise. Therefore we conclude

$$(1.5) \qquad\qquad \mathfrak{g}_2 = 60E_4(\mathrm{i}), \qquad \mathfrak{g}_3 = 0\,.$$

Actually, the second relation in (1.5) is a consequence of the fact that the so–called *period cell* of $\wp(z)$ is congruent to the unit square $[0,1]^2$, i.e. $\Omega_{m,n} = m\cdot 1 + n\cdot\mathrm{i}$, [3, p.31]. So

$$(1.6) \qquad\qquad \wp'^2(z) = 4\wp^3(z) - \mathfrak{g}_2\wp(z) \qquad (z \in \mathbb{C}\setminus\mathbb{Z}^2)\,.$$

We shall next introduce the Weierstraß Sigma–function defined as

$$\sigma(z) = z \sideset{}{'}\prod_{(m,n)\in\mathbb{Z}^2} \left(1 - \frac{z}{m+n\mathrm{i}}\right) \exp\left\{\frac{z}{m+n\mathrm{i}} + \frac{z^2}{2(m+n\mathrm{i})^2}\right\},$$

where the dashed product means that the factor with $m = n = 0$ is omitted. The classical connections between $\wp$ and σ are presented e.g. in [3, §52], [10, p.447]. In this short essay we will exploit certain growth estimates of $\sigma(z)$. However, the local growth estimation of Weierstraß Sigma does not have a rather recent history. The first result of this kind known by the author is given in [6], where $\ln M_\sigma(r) \sim \pi r^2/2$; $r \to \infty$ is proved ($M_\sigma(r)$ stands for the maximum modulus of σ on the circle $|z| = r$), see also [9, Chapter 4/§1, Problem 49], where this result is quoted from the book [6]. After that Hayman proved that there exist absolute constants $\mathbf{K}_1, \mathbf{K}_2$ with $\mathbf{K}_1 < \mathbf{K}_2$, for which

$$(1.7) \qquad \mathbf{K}_1\,\delta_z\,e^{\pi|z|^2/2} \le |\sigma(z)| \le \mathbf{K}_2\,\delta_z\,e^{\pi|z|^2/2} \qquad (z \in \mathbb{C}),$$

where $\delta_z = \inf_{\mathbb{Z}^2}|z - \mathbb{Z}^2|$. Finally, we pointed out that the uniform numerical values of Hayman constants were obtained [7, 8], which reads as follows

$$(1.8) \qquad \mathbf{K}_1 = K_1(1/\sqrt{2}) = \left(1 - \frac{\pi^4}{360}\right)\left(1 - \frac{\pi^2}{24}\left(\boldsymbol{G} - \frac{\pi^2}{15}\right)\right)^2 e^{-\frac{\pi}{4}}, \qquad \mathbf{K}_2 = K_2(0)\,.$$

Here $\boldsymbol{G} = \sum_{n\in\mathbb{N}}(-1)^{n-1}(2n-1)^{-2}$ is the famous Catalan's constant and $K_j(\cdot), j = 1, 2$ are explicitly given by (2.7) and (2.8) respectively.

The second important result we will need in the sequel connects $\wp(z)$ and $\sigma(z)$. Namely, the identity

$$(1.9) \qquad\qquad \wp(z) - \wp(y) = -\frac{\sigma(z+y)\,\sigma(z-y)}{\sigma^2(z)\,\sigma^2(y)}$$

hold and it is given in [10, *Example 1.*, p.451], for example.

Our main task will be here to establish two non–negative guard–bound functions L, R depending only on δ_z and on the modulus $|z|$. These guard functions appear in the bounding inequality

$$L(z) \le |\wp'(z)| \le R(z).$$

Further questions arise immediately, such as the

(1) existence of absolute constants $\mathbf{L}, \mathbf{R} > 0$ that $L(z) = \mathbf{L}\,\delta_z^{-\alpha}$, $R(z) = \mathbf{R}\delta_z^{-\beta}$;

(2) belonging bounding inequality for $|\wp(z)|$.

We will give some answers to these questions after establishing the main results of the article.

2   Main Results

The function $H(\cdot)$ was introduced previously (see the Abstract). So

$$H(r) = \frac{\min\{r^2 - [r^2], [r^2] + 1 - r^2\}}{2r + 1/\sqrt{2}} \qquad (r \geq 0),$$

where $[a]$ denotes the integer part of $a \in \mathbb{R}$. The function $H(\cdot)$ will play one of the most crucial roles in the formulation of our main result.

Theorem 2.1. *There are non–negative real guard–functions*

$$(2.1) \qquad L(z) = \frac{\mathbf{K}_1 H(2|z|)}{\delta_z^4} \exp\left\{\frac{\pi}{4}\left(1 - \frac{8}{3}\pi^2 \mathbf{G}\,\delta_z^4\right)\right\},$$

$$(2.2) \qquad R(z) = \frac{2\exp\{8\pi^2\,\mathbf{G}\delta_z^4/3 + 2\pi\delta_z(2\delta_z - H(2|z|))\}}{\delta_z^3\left(1 - \frac{\pi^4}{90}\delta_z^4\right)^4\left(1 - \left(\frac{\pi^2\mathbf{G}}{6} - \frac{\pi^4}{90}\right)\delta_z^4\right)^8}$$

such that

$$(2.3) \qquad L(z) \leq |\wp'(z)| \leq R(z)$$

except at the poles of $\wp(z)$; $\mathbf{K}_1$ is described in (1.8).

Proof. Firstly we will connect $\wp'(z)$ and $\sigma(z)$ by

$$(2.4) \qquad \wp'(z) = -\frac{\sigma(2z)}{\sigma^4(z)} \qquad (z \in \mathbb{C} \setminus \mathbb{Z}^2).$$

Indeed, putting $z + \Delta z \mapsto z$, $z \mapsto y$ in (1.9) we get

$$\frac{\wp(z + \Delta z) - \wp(z)}{\Delta z} = -\frac{\sigma(2z + \Delta z)\,\sigma(\Delta z)}{\sigma^2(z + \Delta z)\,\sigma^2(z)\,\Delta z}.$$

Letting $\Delta z \to 0$ we arrive at (2.4), because near to zero $\sigma(\Delta z) \sim \Delta z$.

As the next step, we give the bilateral bounding estimate

$$(2.5) \qquad H(2|z|) \leq \delta_{2z} \leq 2\delta_z \qquad (z \in \mathbb{C}).$$

The left–hand inequality is proved earlier in [7, Lemma 1]. The right–hand estimate is straightforward. Indeed, we have

$$\delta_{2z} = \inf_{(m,n)\in\mathbb{Z}^2} |2z - m - ni| \leq \inf_{(m,n)\in\mathbb{Z}^2} |z - m - ni| + \inf_{(k,\ell)\in\mathbb{Z}^2} |z - k - \ell i| = 2\delta_z.$$

The suitable estimates for the Sigma–function are [7, Theorem 1]:

$$(2.6) \qquad \delta_z K_1(\delta_z) \leq |\sigma(z)| \exp\left\{-\frac{\pi}{2}|z|^2\right\} \leq \delta_z K_2(\delta_z),$$

where

$$(2.7) \qquad K_1(\delta_z) = \left(1 - \frac{\pi^4 \delta_z^4}{90}\right)\left(1 - \left(\frac{\pi^2 G}{6} - \frac{\pi^4}{90}\right)\delta_z^4\right)^2 \exp\left\{-\frac{\pi}{2}\delta_z^2\right\};$$

$$(2.8) \qquad K_2(\delta_z) = \exp\left\{\frac{\pi^2 G}{6}\delta_z^4 - \frac{\pi}{2}\delta_z^2\right\}.$$

Now, combining (2.5), (2.6), (2.7) and (2.8) we arrive at

$$(2.9)$$

$$|\wp'(z)| \leq \frac{\delta_{2z} K_2(\delta_{2z}) \exp\{\pi|2z|^2/2\}}{\delta_z^4 K_1^4(\delta_z)\exp\{2\pi|z|^2\}}$$

$$= \frac{\delta_{2z}\exp\left\{\frac{\pi^2 G}{6}\delta_{2z}^4 - \frac{\pi}{2}\delta_{2z}^2 + 2\pi\delta_z^2\right\}}{\delta_z^4\left(1 - \frac{\pi^4\delta_z^4}{90}\right)^4\left(1 - \left(\frac{\pi^2 G}{6} - \frac{\pi^4}{90}\right)\delta_z^4\right)^8}$$

$$\leq \frac{2\exp\left\{\frac{8\pi^2 G}{3}\delta_z^4 + \frac{\pi}{2}\left(4\delta_z^2 - \delta_{2z}^2\right)\right\}}{\delta_z^3\left(1 - \frac{\pi^4\delta_z^4}{90}\right)^4\left(1 - \left(\frac{\pi^2 G}{6} - \frac{\pi^4}{90}\right)\delta_z^4\right)^8}.$$

Having in mind (2.5), we get

$$4\delta_z^2 - \delta_{2z}^2 = (2\delta_z + \delta_{2z})(2\delta_z - \delta_{2z}) \leq 4\delta_z(2\delta_z - H(2|z|)).$$

Applying this estimate to the numerator of (2.9) we easily deduce the functional upper bound (2.2), which is denoted by $R(z)$.

On the other hand we derive $L(z)$ by a similar procedure. Indeed, we have

$$|\wp'(z)| \geq \frac{\delta_{2z}K_1(\delta_{2z})\exp\{\pi|2z|^2/2\}}{\delta_z^4 K_2^4(\delta_z)\exp\{2\pi|z|^2\}}$$

$$= \frac{\delta_{2z}\left(1 - \frac{\pi^4\delta_z^4}{90}\right)\left(1 - \left(\frac{\pi^2 G}{6} - \frac{\pi^4}{90}\right)\delta_z^4\right)^2\exp\left\{-\frac{\pi}{2}\delta_{2z}^2\right\}}{\delta_z^4 \exp\{2\pi^2 G\delta_z^4/3 - 2\pi\delta_z^2\}}$$

$$\geq \frac{H(2|z|)\displaystyle\min_{\delta_{2z}\in[0,1/\sqrt{2}]}\left(1 - \frac{\pi^4\delta_z^4}{90}\right)\left(1 - \left(\frac{\pi^2 G}{6} - \frac{\pi^4}{90}\right)\delta_z^4\right)^2}{\delta_z^4 \exp\{2\pi^2 G\delta_z^4/3\}}$$

$$\geq \frac{H(2|z|)\left(1 - \frac{\pi^4}{360}\right)\left(1 - \frac{\pi^2}{24}\left(\mathbf{G} - \frac{\pi^2}{15}\right)^2\right)^2}{\delta_z^4 \exp\{2\,\pi^2\,\mathbf{G}\delta_z^4/3\}}$$

(2.10)
$$= \frac{\mathbf{K}_1\,H(2|z|)\,e^{\pi/4}}{\delta_z^4}\,e^{-\frac{2}{3}\pi^2\mathbf{G}\delta_z^4}.$$

The proof is complete. $\qquad\qquad\square$

Theorem 2.2. *The bounds*

(2.11) $$\mathbf{L}\,H(2|z|)\,\delta_z^{-4} \leq |\wp'(z)| \leq \mathbf{R}\,\delta_z^{-3}$$

hold true, where

(2.12) $$\mathbf{L} := \mathbf{K}_1\,\exp\left\{\frac{\pi}{4}\left(1 - \frac{2\pi\mathbf{G}}{3}\right)\right\}$$

(2.13) $$\mathbf{R} := 2\mathbf{K}_1^{-4}\,\exp\left\{\frac{2}{3}\pi^2\mathbf{G}\right\}.$$

Proof. Maximizing $\rho(z) := R(z)\delta_z^3$ and minimizing $\lambda(z) := L(z)\big(H(2|z|)\big)^{-1}\delta_z^4$ on the whole range of $\delta_z \in [0, 1/\sqrt{2}]$ we clearly conclude that $\mathbf{R} = \rho(1/\sqrt{2})$, $\mathbf{L} := \lambda(1/\sqrt{2})$ are the desired uniform constants. $\qquad\square$

Lastly, let us consider the belonging evaluation of modulus of Weierstraß Pe–function $|\wp(z)|$ in the light of the bounds derived here for $|\wp'(z)|$. But at first, we prove that $\mathfrak{g}_2 > 0$. At this point let us introduce the *Jacobi Theta function*

(2.14) $$\theta(x) = \sum_{n\in\mathbb{Z}} e^{-n^2 x} \qquad (x \in \mathbb{R}).$$

consult for example [2, p.62].

Theorem 2.3. *There holds true*

(2.15) $$\mathfrak{g}_2 = \frac{2\pi^2(2\pi^2 + \mathbf{G})}{3} - 80\int_0^\infty \left(\frac{\partial}{\partial x}\theta(x)\right)^2 x^3\,dx \geq \frac{8\pi^2}{3}\left(2\pi^2 - 15\mathbf{G}\right).$$

Proof. By direct calculation we have

(2.16) $$\mathfrak{g}_2 = 60\sum_{(m,n)\in\mathbb{Z}^2}{}' \frac{1}{(m+ni)^4} = 240\left(\zeta(4) + \sum_{(m,n)\in\mathbb{N}^2} \frac{m^4 + n^4 - 6m^2n^2}{(m^2+n^2)^4}\right)$$

$$= 240\left(\zeta(4) + \sum_{(m,n)\in\mathbb{N}^2} \frac{1}{(m^2+n^2)^2} - 8\sum_{(m,n)\in\mathbb{N}^2} \frac{m^2n^2}{(m^2+n^2)^4}\right),$$

where $\zeta(s) = \sum_{n\in\mathbb{N}} n^{-s}$ denotes the Riemann Zeta function. By a Borwein & Borwein result [8, Theorem 1] we have

$$\sum_{(m,n)\in\mathbb{N}^2} \frac{1}{(m^2+n^2)^2} = \frac{\pi^2}{6}\left(\mathbf{G} - \frac{\pi^2}{15}\right),$$

therefore $\mathfrak{g}_2$ becomes

$$(2.17) \qquad \mathfrak{g}_2 = 40\pi^2 \boldsymbol{G} - 1920 \sum_{(m,n)\in\mathbb{N}^2} \frac{m^2 n^2}{(m^2+n^2)^4}.$$

Taking the familiar formula

$$\frac{1}{\alpha^s} = \frac{1}{\Gamma(s)} \int_0^\infty e^{-\alpha x} x^{s-1}\, dx,$$

in which we set $\alpha = m^2 + n^2$, $s = 4$, it is straightforward that

$$\sum_{(m,n)\in\mathbb{N}^2} \frac{m^2 n^2}{(m^2+n^2)^4} = \frac{1}{6} \int_0^\infty \left(\sum_{n\in\mathbb{N}} n^2 e^{-n^2 x}\right)^2 x^3\, dx = \frac{1}{24} \int_0^\infty \left(\frac{\partial}{\partial x}\theta(x)\right)^2 x^3\, dx.$$

Now, by all these transformations (2.17) becomes the asserted formula (2.15).

It remains to prove the lower bound in (2.15). However, by the Arithmetic mean–Geometric mean inequality we have

$$\sum_{(m,n)\in\mathbb{N}^2} \frac{4m^2 n^2}{(m^2+n^2)^4} \leq \sum_{(m,n)\in\mathbb{N}^2} \frac{1}{(m^2+n^2)^2} = \frac{\pi^2}{6}\left(\boldsymbol{G} - \frac{\pi^2}{15}\right).$$

Inserting this estimate into (2.17), we arrive at the lower bound in (2.15). $\qquad\square$

Theorem 2.4. *Let $z \in \mathbb{C}\setminus\mathbb{Z}^2$ fixed. Then*

$$(2.18) \quad |\wp(z)|$$

$$\leq \begin{cases} \dfrac{\mathbf{R}^{2/3}}{2\delta_z^2}\left(1 + \sqrt[3]{1 + \sqrt{1 - \dfrac{\mathfrak{g}_2^3 \delta_z^{12}}{27\mathbf{R}^4}}}\right) =: Q^+(z) & |\wp'(z)| > (\mathfrak{g}_2/3)^{3/4} \\[3mm] 2\sqrt{\dfrac{\mathfrak{g}_2}{3}}\cos\left(\dfrac{1}{3}\arctan\sqrt{\dfrac{\mathfrak{g}_2^3 \delta_z^{16}}{27\mathbf{L}^4 \mathbf{H}^4 (2|z|)} - 1}\right) =: Q^-(z) & |\wp'(z)| \leq (\mathfrak{g}_2/3)^{3/4} \end{cases}.$$

Proof. Let us see that there holds

$$(2.19) \quad |\wp(z)| \leq T$$

$$:= \begin{cases} \dfrac{1}{2}\left(\sqrt[3]{|\wp'(z)|^2 + \sqrt{|\wp'(z)|^4 - (\mathfrak{g}_2/3)^2}}\right. \\ \qquad \left. + \left(\sqrt[3]{|\wp'(z)|^2 - \sqrt{|\wp'(z)|^4 - (\mathfrak{g}_2/3)^2}}\right)\right) & |\wp'(z)| > (\mathfrak{g}_2/3)^{3/4} \\[3mm] 2\sqrt{\mathfrak{g}_2/3}\cos\left(\dfrac{1}{3}\arctan\sqrt{\dfrac{\mathfrak{g}_2^3}{27|\wp'(z)|^4} - 1}\right) & |\wp'(z)| \leq (\mathfrak{g}_2/3)^{3/4} \end{cases}.$$

Indeed, consider (1.6). By the previous theorem $\mathfrak{g}_2 > 0$. For $z \in \mathbb{C}\setminus\mathbb{Z}^2$ and $t = |\wp(z)|$, from $|(\wp'(z))^2 + \mathfrak{g}_2 t| = 4t^3$ we deduce $4t^3 - \mathfrak{g}_2 t - |\wp'(z)|^2 \leq 0$. The cubic function $\phi(t) = 4t^3 - \mathfrak{g}_2 t - |\wp'(z)|^2$ attains its minimal value $\phi(t_1 = \sqrt{\mathfrak{g}_2/3}/2) = -(\mathfrak{g}_2/3)^{3/2} - |\wp'(z)|^2 < 0$ and $\phi(t)$ decreases for $t \in [0, t_1)$ and increases for $t > t_1$. Moreover, since $\phi(0) = -|\wp'(z)|^2 < 0$, it is not hard to see that there exists the unique, positive zero T of this function. Therefore $\phi(t) \leq 0$ for all $t \in [0, T]$. Now, it remains to get T by the Cardano formula from $4t^3 - \mathfrak{g}_2 t - |\wp'(z)|^2 = 0$. This results in (2.19).

Assume that $|\wp'(z)| > (\mathfrak{g}_2/3)^{3/4}$. Now, having in mind the bounding inequalities (2.3) and (2.11) we easily deduce

$$
\begin{aligned}
(2.20) \quad T &= \frac{1}{2}\left(\sqrt[3]{|\wp'(z)|^2 + \sqrt{|\wp'(z)|^4 - (\mathfrak{g}_2/3)^2}} \right. \\
&\quad \left. + \left(\sqrt[3]{|\wp'(z)|^2 - \sqrt{|\wp'(z)|^4 - (\mathfrak{g}_2/3)^2}} \right) \right) \\
&\leq \frac{1}{2}\left(\sqrt[3]{R^2(z) + \sqrt{R^4(z) - (\mathfrak{g}_2/3)^2}} + R^{2/3}(z) \right) \\
&= \frac{R^{2/3}(z)}{2}\left(1 + \sqrt[3]{1 + \sqrt{1 - \frac{\mathfrak{g}_2^3}{27R^4(z)}}} \right) \\
&\leq \frac{\mathbf{R}^{2/3}}{2\delta_z^2}\left(1 + \sqrt[3]{1 + \sqrt{1 - \frac{\mathfrak{g}_2^3\,\delta^{12}}{27\mathbf{R}^4}}} \right) =: Q^+(z).
\end{aligned}
$$

For the opposite case, i.e. when $|\wp'(z)| \leq (\mathfrak{g}_2/3)^{3/4}$, by similar argument (2.20) becomes

$$
T \leq 2\sqrt{\mathfrak{g}_2/3}\, \cos\left(\frac{1}{3}\arctan\sqrt{\frac{\mathfrak{g}_2^3}{27L^4(z)} - 1} \right).
$$

Now, by minimizing $L(z)$ we conclude

$$
Q^-(z) := 2\sqrt{\frac{\mathfrak{g}_2}{3}}\, \cos\left(\frac{1}{3}\arctan\sqrt{\frac{\mathfrak{g}_2^3\,\delta_z^{16}}{27\mathbf{L}^4 H^4(2|z|)} - 1} \right).
$$

This finishes the proof of the Theorem. $\qquad\square$

3 FINAL REMARKS

A. The bounding inequality (2.3) has a sharper form including δ_{2z} instead of $H(2|z|)$. However, an estimate like $\delta_{2z} \geq C_z \cdot \delta_z$, $C_z > 0$ does not exist in the general case. Indeed, $z = 1 + i/2$ is a working counterexample; it is not hard to see that $C_{1+i/2} \equiv 0$. Therefore, we are forced to evaluate δ_{2z} in different manner than in terms of δ_z. This results in (2.5) for example.

B. The sharpness of bounding inequality (2.3) is an open question. However, we are not without any result in this direction. Namely, (2.6) is sharp in the sense that the inequality $e^t \geq 1 + t$, $(t \in \mathbb{R})$ is used in getting it. Therefore, (2.3) is sharp in the same manner that $e^t \geq 1 + t$ is. The same remark could be made for (2.11).

C. In evaluating $|\wp(z)|$ we could use the formula

$$
48\wp^4(z) - 24\mathfrak{g}_2\wp^2(z) - 48\mathfrak{g}_3\wp(z) = \mathfrak{g}_2^2 + \frac{16\sigma(3z)}{\sigma^9(z)};
$$

from [5], bearing in mind (1.5), then this formula becomes

$$
(3.1) \qquad 48\wp^4(z) - 24\mathfrak{g}_2\wp^2(z) = \mathfrak{g}_2^2 + \frac{16\sigma(3z)}{\sigma^9(z)}.
$$

Solving this biquadric equation with respect to $\wp(z)$, we get a suitable expression in terms of $\sigma(3z), \sigma(z)$ and $\mathfrak{g}_2$. Then certain convenient transformations lead to bounds for $|\wp(z)|$.

D. Finally, it is not hard to see that

$$Q^+(z) \leq \frac{\mathbf{R}^{2/3}(1 + \sqrt[3]{2})}{2\delta_z^2} =: \mathbf{Q}\delta_z^{-2}, \qquad Q^-(z) \leq 2\sqrt{\frac{\mathfrak{g}_2}{3}}.$$

However, the constants under consideration in the article have the following numerical values:

Constant	Numerical Value
$\mathbf{K}_1$	0.26574548
$\mathbf{K}_2$	1
$\mathbf{L}$	0.129197476
$\mathbf{R}$	166107.8756
$\mathbf{Q}$	3414.470914
$\mathfrak{g}_2$	189.073

It remains to remark that the lower bound obtained for the Weierstraß invariant $\mathfrak{g}_2$ is approximately equal to 157.9.

References

[1] A. Dienstfrey and Jingfang Huang, Integral representations for elliptic functions. *J. Math. Anal. Appl.* (to appear).

[2] H. Davenport, *Multiplicative Number Theory.* 2nd ed. Springer-Verlag, New York-Berlin, 1980.

[3] P. Du Val, *Elliptic Functions and Elliptic Curves.* London Mathematical Society Lecture Notes Series **9**. Cambridge University Press, Cambridge, 1973.

[4] W.K. Hayman, On the local growth of power series: a survey of the Wiman–Valiron method. *Canad. Math. Bull.* **17(3)** (1974), pp.317-358.

[5] http://functions.wolfram.com/EllipticFunctions/WeierstrassP/27/07/01

[6] A. Hurwitz and R. Courant, *Allgemeine Funktionentheorie und elliptische Funktionen. Geometrische Funktionentheorie.* J. Springer, Berlin, 1922.

[7] T.K. Pogány, Local growth of Weierstraß σ–function and Whittaker type derivative sampling. *Georgian Math. J.* **10/1**(2003), pp.157–164.

[8] T.K. Pogány, Whittaker–Type Derivative Sampling Reconstruction of Stochastic $L^\alpha(\Omega)$–Processes. (submitted)

[9] G. Pólya and G. Szegő, *Aufgaben und Lehrsätze aus der Analysis. Band II: Funktionentheorie. Nullstellen. Polynome. Determinanten. Zahlentheorie.* Dritte berichtigte Auflage. Die Grundlehren der Mathematischen Wisseschaften, Band 20. Springer–Verlag, Berlin–New York, 1964. (Russian translation: Nauka, Moscow, 1978).

[10] E.T. Whittaker and G.N. Watson, *A Course of Modern Analysis.* Fourth Edition(Reprinted). University Press, Cambridge, 1952.

On Certain Special Functions of Number Theory and Mathematical Analysis

József Sándor

Department of Mathematics and Computer Sciences
Babeș-Bolyai University
Str. Kogălniceanu Nr.1
400084 Cluj-Napoca, Romania
E-mail address: jjsandor@hotmail.com

ABSTRACT. We offer a survey of results on certain special number theoretical functions as well as their real variable analogues initiated by the author.

1991 Mathematics Subject Classification: 11A25, 11N37, 26D15, 33B15, 33D05, 33E99, 40A05.

Key words and phrases: Arithmetic functions, asymptotic results, Smarandache functions, Sándor type functions, gamma functions, infinite series, inequalities.

1 INTRODUCTION

A. In 1887, J. Neuberg (see [7]) determined the least positive integer m such that $m! = 1 \cdot 2 \cdots m$ is divisible by a given power of a prime number, but overlooked exceptional cases. These were corrected in 1918 by A.J. Kempner [8] (see also [7]), who introduced the function $S(n) = m$ such that $m!$ is the smallest factorial divisible by n (his notation was $\mu(n)$ for $S(n)$). Kempner established some basic properties of $S(n)$, e.g. $\mu(p^k) = ps$ for a prime p, and $k \geq 1$ integer, where $s \leq p$; or $S(n) = \max\{S(p_1^{\alpha_1}), \ldots, S(p_r^{\alpha_r})\}$, if $n = p_1^{\alpha_1} \cdots p_r^{\alpha_r}$ is the prime factorization of n.

In 1980 F. Smarandache [42] rediscovered this arithmetical function. This rediscovery, and the many new problems related to this function, have opened the way for much interesting research in Number theory and related areas ([43], [44], [25], [16]).

In 1999 the author [17] (see also [18]) introduced a very large generalization of the Smarandache (or Neuberg-Kempner-Smarandache) function. Let $\mathbb{N}^* = \{1, 2, \ldots\}$, $\phi \neq A \subset \mathbb{N}^*$, $f : \mathbb{N}^* \to \mathbb{N}^*$, and defined

$$(1.1) \qquad F_f^A(n) = \min\{k \in A : \ n | f(k)\},$$

if there exists at least a $k \in A$ such that $n | f(k)$. Similarly, the "dual" function of (1.1) will be defined by

$$(1.2) \qquad G_g^A(n) = \max\{k \in A : \ g(k) | n\},$$

Dedicated to the 70th Anniversary of Professor József Kolumbán.

(where $g : \mathbb{N}^* \to \mathbb{N}^*$ is a given function, and $A \subset \mathbb{N}^*$ is a given nonvoid subset of positive integers), if this is possible.

Some particular cases of the F_f^A and G_g^A functions are important to note. For $f(k) = k!$ one obtains the "Smarandache function of a set" (see [20])

$$(1.3) \qquad S_A(n) = \min\{k \in A : n|k!\}$$

and its dual

$$(1.4) \qquad S_{A_*}(n) = \max\{k \in A : k!|n\}.$$

For $A = \mathbb{N}^*$, (1.3) provides the Smarandache function $S(n)$, while (1.4) the "Smarandache dual function" $S_*(n)$:

$$(1.5) \qquad S(n) = \min\{k \in \mathbb{N}^* : n|k!\}, \quad S_*(n) = \max\{k \in \mathbb{N}^* : k!|n\}.$$

The function S_* was first introduced and studied in [17].

Let $A = P$ - set of prime numbers. Then (1.3) gives an arithmetical function denoted by us by $P(n)$:

$$(1.6) \qquad P(n) = \min\{p \text{ prime} : n|p!\}.$$

Let φ denote the Euler totient function (see e.g. [32], [38]). Then for $A = \mathbb{N}^*$, $f(k) = \varphi(k)$ in (1.1) one obtains the "Euler minimum function"

$$(1.7) \qquad E(n) = \min\{k \geq 1 : n|\varphi(k)\},$$

introduced for the first time by P. Moree and H. Roskam [13], and rediscovered independently by the author in [17]. For $A = \mathbb{N}^*$, $g(k) = \varphi(k)$ in (1.2) one obtains the "Euler maximum function"

$$(1.8) \qquad E_*(n) = \max\{k \geq 1 : \varphi(k)|n\},$$

introduced and studied for the first time by the author in [17], [40]. For the exponential-totient function φ_e of the author [15], the corresponding $E_e(n)$ can be found in [36] ($E_{e_*}(n)$ does not exist).

Let A = set of perfect squares, and A_1 = set of squarefree numbers. For $f(k) = k!$ we get the arithmetical functions

$$(1.9) \qquad Q(n) = \min\{m^2 \geq 1 : n|(m^2)!\}, \quad Q_1(n) = \min\{m \geq 1 \text{ squarefree} : n|m!\}.$$

For properties of Q and Q_1, see [20].

Let $d(n)$ and $\sigma(n)$ denote the number, resp. sum-of divisors of n. It is immediate that $D_*(n) = \max\{k \geq 1 : d(k)|n\}$ is not well-defined, as e.g. for any prime p we have $d(p^{n-1}) = n$ and p^{n-1} is unbounded as $p \to \infty$. For a finite set $A \subset \mathbb{N}$, however $D_*^A(n) = \max\{k \in A : d(k)|n\}$ does exist. Let

$$(1.10) \qquad D(n) = \min\{k \geq 1 : n|d(k)\},$$

$$(1.11) \qquad \Sigma(n) = \min\{k \geq 1 : n|\sigma(k)\}, \quad \Sigma_*(n) = \max\{k \geq 1 : \sigma(k)|n\}.$$

For $D(n)$, see [27], while for the function $\Sigma(n)$, and $\Sigma_*(n)$, see [35].

The "Smarandache minimum and maximum functions" have been introduced by the author recently in [39] as

(1.12) $$S_{min}(n) = \min\{k \geq 1 : n|S(k)\}, \quad S_{max}(n) = \max\{k \geq 1 : S(k)|n\}$$

Let $\varphi^*(n)$ be the unitary analogue of the totient function. This function was introduced in the 1960's by E. Cohen (see e.g. [6]). The "unitary totient minimum and maximum functions" have been denoted by us as $E^*(n)$ and $E^*_*(n)$:

(1.13) $$E^*(n) = \min\{k \geq 1 : n|\varphi^*(k)\}, \quad E^*_*(n) = \max\{k \geq 1 : \varphi^*(k)|n\}.$$

For properties of those functions, see [37].

Let $T(n) = \prod_{i|n} i$ denote the product of all divisors of n. Properties of $T(n)$ in connection with "multiplicatively perfect numbers" have been studied in [23]. For related results on exponential divisors and e-perfect numbers, see [31]. For other asymptotic properties of $T(n)$, see [14]. For divisibility properties of $T(\sigma(n))$ with $T(n)$, see [11], while for asymptotic properties of sums of type $\sum_{n \leq x} 1/T(n)$, see [45]. See also the monograph [32].

Let

(1.14) $$\mathcal{T}(n) = \min\{k \geq 1 : n|T(k)\}, \quad \mathcal{T}_*(n) = \max\{k \geq 1 : T(k)|n\},$$

be the "product-of-divisors minimum, resp. maximum functions". For their properties, see [33].

In 1996 K. Kashihara (see [25]) introduced the case $A = \mathbb{N}^*$, $f(k) = \frac{k(k+1)}{2}$ of (1.1), obtaining the so-called "pseudo-Smarandache function" $Z(n)$ (see also [21]):

(1.15) $$Z(n) = \min\left\{k \geq 1 : n\left|\frac{k(k+1)}{2}\right.\right\}.$$

The dual function has been introduced and studied for the first time in [26]:

(1.16) $$Z_*(n) = \max\left\{k \geq 1 : \left.\frac{k(k+1)}{2}\right|n\right\}.$$

For many results of a new type for $Z(n)$, $Z_*(n)$, see our book [25]. See also [41].

Let $k!! = 1 \cdot 3 \cdot 5 \cdots k$, if k is odd; $= 2 \cdot 4 \cdot 6 \cdots k$, if k is even. The Smarandache "double-factorial function" (see [44]) is obtained for $A = \mathbb{N}^*$, $f(k) = k!!$ in (1.1):

(1.17) $$SDF(n) = \min\{k : n|k!!\}.$$

Its dual function has been introduced in [22]:

(1.18) $$SDF_*(n) = \max\{k : k!!|n\}.$$

For $A = \mathbb{N}^*$, $f(k) = k! + (k-1)! = (k-1)!(k+1)$ (here $0! = 1$ by definition) in (1.1), we get the "modification of the Smarandache function" introduced in [30] by us as

(1.19) $$F(n) = \min\{k \geq 1 : n|(k-1)!(k+1)\}$$

Another Smarandache-type function, not of type (1.2) has been introduced by us in [19] (see also [25, p. 169-170]) as

(1.20) $$C(n) = \max\left\{k : 1 \leq k < n-1, \ n\left|\binom{n}{k}\right.\right\},$$

where $\binom{n}{k} = C_n^k$ denotes a binomial coefficient.

The "Smarandache simple function" (see [43]) is defined by

$$(1.21) \qquad\qquad S_p(n) = \min\{k \geq 1 : p^n|k!\},$$

where p is a fixed prime number. The dual $S_{a^*}(n)$ of this function

$$(1.22) \qquad\qquad S_{a^*}(n) = \max\{k \geq 1 : k!|a^n\},$$

where a is a given positive integer, as well as some extensions, has been introduced and studied in [29].

B. The additive analogue of $T_f^A(n)$ given by (1.1) can be defined as

$$(1.23) \qquad\qquad S_f^A(x) = \min\{k \in A : x \leq f(k)\}, \quad x \in B \subset \mathbb{R},$$

where $A \subset \mathbb{N}^*$, $f : \mathbb{N}^* \to \mathbb{N}^*$ are given. Its dual is

$$(1.24) \qquad\qquad T_g^A(x) = \max\{k \in A : g(k) \leq x\}, \quad x \in C \subset \mathbb{R}.$$

For example, when $f(k) = k!$, $A = \mathbb{N}$, $B = (1, \infty)$, one obtains

$$(1.25) \qquad\qquad S(x) = \min\{k \geq 1 : x \leq k!\}, \quad x \in (1, +\infty),$$

while for $g(k) = k!$, $x \in [1, +\infty)$ one obtains from (1.24) the dual of S, namely

$$(1.26) \qquad\qquad S_*(x) = \max\{k \geq 1 : k! \leq x\}, \quad x \in [1, \infty).$$

Functions (1.25) and (1.26) were introduced in 2001 ([24]) and are called "Sándor's functions". Generally speaking, such functions have been called by various authors as Sándor type functions. C. Adiga and T. Kim [1] have provided a generalization of Sándor's function by using the Euler gamma function in place of the factorial. By using the q-gamma function of F.H. Jackson, in 2003 C. Adiga, T. Kim, D.D. Somashekara and N. Fathima [2] introduced and studied a q-analogue of (1.25) and (1.26).

The author has also introduced additive analogues of the Pseudo-Smarandache functions (1.15) and (1.16), as well as the Smarandache simple functions (1.21) and (1.22) as follows ([28]):

$$Z(x) = \min\left\{k \geq 1 : x \leq \frac{k(k+1)}{2}\right\}, \quad x \in (0, \infty),$$

(1.27)

$$Z_*(x) = \max\left\{k \geq 1 : \frac{k(k+1)}{2} \leq x\right\}, \quad x \in [1, \infty),$$

$$P(x) = \min\{k \geq 1 : p^x \leq k!\}, \quad p > 1, \ x \in (0, \infty),$$

(1.28)

$$P_*(x) = \max\{k \geq 1 : k! \leq p^x\}, \quad p > 1, \ x \in [1, \infty).$$

The q-analogues of (1.27) and (1.28) have been studied by C. Adiga, T. Kim and J.H. Han [3].

Let $A = \mathbb{N}^*$, $f(k) = e^k$, $B = [1, \infty)$ in (1.23), $g(k) = e^k$, $C = [e, +\infty)$ in (1.24). These particular cases have been considered by N. Anitha [4], who denoted these functions by

$$G(x) = \min\{k \geq 1 : x \leq e^k\}, \quad x \in [1, \infty),$$

(1.29)

$$G_*(x) = \max\{k \geq 1 : e^k \leq x\}, \quad x \in [e, +\infty)$$

For an interesting connection of these functions with the prime numbers, see the next section of this paper.

The additive analogues of the Euler minimum and maximum functions are introduced in our paper [34]:

(1.30)
$$\mathcal{E}(x) = \min\{k \geq 1 : x \leq \varphi(k)\}, \quad x \in \mathbb{R}$$

$$\mathcal{E}_*(x) = \max\{k \geq 1 : \varphi(k) \leq x\}, \quad x \in [1, \infty).$$

For $f(k) = k!$, k even, $A =$ set of even integers; while for k odd $A =$ set of odd integers, (1.23) gives a function denoted as Sdf_1 by Z. Minhui [12]:

(1.31)
$$Sdf_1(2x) = \min\{k \geq 1 : 2x \leq (2k)!!\}, \quad x \in (1, \infty)$$

$$Sdf_1(2x + 1) = \min\{k \geq 1 : 2x + 1 \leq (2k + 1)!!\}, \quad x \in (1, \infty)$$

For their asymptotic properties, see the next section.

2   Main Results

As we have seen in the Introduction, many new Smarandache and Sándor-type functions are known in the literature. In what follows, we shall select for review some basic properties of the considered functions.

2.1   Inequalities

First we state some inequalities for the functions $S(n)$ and $S_*(n)$ given by (1.5).

If p is a prime and $x \leq y$ are positive integers, then

(2.1)
$$S(p^x) \leq S(p^y) \text{ for } 0 \leq x \leq y,$$

(2.2)
$$\frac{S(p^x)}{p^x} \geq \frac{S(p^{x+1})}{p^{x+1}} \text{ for } x \geq 0,$$

(2.3)
$$S(p^x) \leq S(q^x) \text{ for } p \leq q \text{ primes, } x \text{ arbitrary,}$$

(2.4)
$$(p - 1)x + 1 \leq S(p^x) \leq px.$$

For composite n, one has

(2.5)
$$\frac{S(n)}{n} \leq \frac{2}{3}.$$

Clearly

(2.6)
$$S(n) \leq n,$$

with equality only for $n = 1, 4, p$ (prime). Properties (2.1) – (2.6) are well-known standard results, see Smarandache Notions Journal collection.

For all positive integers m, n one has (see [25], [16])

$$(2.7) \qquad \max\{S(m), S(n)\} \leq S(mn) \leq S(m) + S(n).$$

Since for $m \geq 2$, $S(m) \geq 2$, it is immediate that for all $m, n \geq 1$ one has $S(m) + S(n) \leq S(mn)$, thus (2.7) refines the inequality

$$(2.8) \qquad S(mn) \leq S(m)S(n)$$

which shows that S is a "sub-multiplicative" function.

If n is an even number, $n > 4$, then

$$(2.9) \qquad S(n^2) \leq n,$$

and if $n \neq p, 2p, 8$ or 9, then

$$(2.10) \qquad S(n^2) \leq n - 1.$$

For many related properties, see our book [25], or paper [16].

Let $S_*(n)$ be the dual of the Smarandache function, introduced by the author in [17]. Then

$$(2.11) \qquad S_*(k!m) \geq k \text{ for all } k, m \geq 1,$$

$$(2.12) \qquad \max\{S_*(a), S_*(b)\} \leq S_*(a, b) \text{ for all } a, b \geq 1,$$

$$(2.13) \qquad S_*[x(x-1)\ldots(x-a+1)] \geq a \text{ for all } x \geq a \text{ positive integers}$$

$$(2.14) \qquad S_*((2k)!(2k+2)!) = 2k + 2, \text{ if } 2k + 3 \text{ is a prime}.$$

The author conjectured that

$$(2.15) \qquad S_*((2k-1)!(2k+1)!) = q_k - 1,$$

where q_k is the first prime following $2k + 1$. This conjecture has been proved by F. Luca [10], K.T. Atanassov [5], and M. Le [9].

Let $P(n)$ be the function defined by (1.6). In [17], [18] we have proved that

$$(2.16) \qquad 2p + 1 \leq P(p^2) \leq 3p - 1,$$

for all primes p, and that

$$(2.17) \qquad mp + 1 \leq P(p^m) \leq (m+1)p - 1$$

for all $m \geq 1$, and all primes $p \geq p_0$. One has also

$$S(n) \leq P(n) \leq 2S(n) - 1,$$

$$(2.18)$$

$$P(mn) \leq 2[P(n) + P(m)] - 1,$$

for all $m, n \geq 1$.

Let $E(n)$ and $E_*(n)$ be the Euler minimum, respectively maximum functions defined by (1.7) and (1.8). If p_i $(i = \overline{1, r})$ are distinct primes, and $\alpha_i \geq 1$ are integers, then (see [40])

$$(2.19) \qquad \max\{E(p_i^{\alpha_i}) : \ i = \overline{1, r}\} \leq E(n) \leq [E(p_1^{\alpha_1}), \ldots, E(p_r^{\alpha_r})],$$

where $n = p_1^{\alpha_1} \cdots p_r^{\alpha_r}$ and $[\,,]$ denotes the l.c.m. of numbers.

More generally, for $A = \mathbb{N}^*$, write F_f for F_f^A given by (1.1).

Suppose that f has the following property:

$$(2.20) \qquad a | b \ \Rightarrow \ f(a) | f(b) \quad (a, b \geq 1).$$

Then

$$(2.21) \qquad F_f(p_1^{\alpha_1} \cdots p_r^{\alpha_r}) \leq [F(p_1^{\alpha_1}), \ldots, F(p_r^{\alpha_r})]$$

if f satisfies the following stronger property than (2.20):

$$(2.22) \qquad a \leq b \ \Rightarrow \ f(a) | f(b),$$

then

$$(2.23) \qquad F_f(p_1^{\alpha_1} \cdots p_r^{\alpha_r}) = \max\{F_f(p_i^{\alpha_i}) : \ i = \overline{1, r}\}.$$

For example, when $f(n) = n!$, $F_f(n) = S(n)$, one reobtains the Kempner-Smarandache property stated at the beginning:

$$(2.24) \qquad S(n) = \max\{S(p_1^{\alpha_1}), \ldots, S(p_r^{\alpha_r})\}$$

The function $E_*(n)$ takes infinitely many times the same value, as (see [40])

$$(2.25) \qquad E_*(2 \cdot 7^k) = 6 \ \text{ for all } \ k \geq 1,$$

but as

$$(2.26) \qquad E_*(m!) \geq \frac{(m!)^2}{\varphi(m!)},$$

it follows that

$$(2.27) \qquad \lim_{m \to \infty} \frac{E_*(m!)}{m!} = +\infty.$$

We now quote some inequalities for $\Sigma(n)$ and $\Sigma_*(n)$ given by (1.11). Our results are contained in [35].

For all primes p one has

$$(2.28) \qquad \Sigma(p + 1) \leq p \leq \Sigma_*(p + 1)$$

For all primes p one has also

$$(2.29) \qquad \Sigma_*(p + 1) = p.$$

and if $(p + 1)/n$, then

$$(2.30) \qquad \Sigma_*(n) \geq p$$

Let p be a prime such that $p \notin \sigma(\mathbb{N}^*)$. Then

$$(2.31) \qquad \Sigma_*(p) = 1$$

More generally, if for all $d > 1$, $d|n$ one has $d \notin \sigma(\mathbb{N}^*)$, then

$$(2.32) \qquad \Sigma_*(n) = 1.$$

Let n be odd and suppose that $\Sigma_*(n) \neq 1, 2$. Then

$$(2.33) \qquad \Sigma_*(n) \leq \left(\frac{-1 + \sqrt{4n - 3}}{2} \right)^2.$$

If $n \geq 4$, then

$$(2.34) \qquad \Sigma(n) > n^{2/3}.$$

For all $m \geq 2$,

$$(2.35) \qquad (2^{m+1} - 1)^{2/3} < \Sigma(2^{m+1} - 1) \leq 2^m.$$

Let $f : [1, \infty) \to [1, \infty)$, $f(x) = x + x \log x$. Then

$$(2.36) \qquad \Sigma(n) \geq f^{-1}(n),$$

where f^{-1} is the inverse function of f.

For all Mersenne primes p one has

$$(2.37) \qquad \Sigma(p) \leq \frac{p + 1}{2}.$$

For the Smarandache minimum and maximum functions given by (1.12) the following inequalities are true (see [39]):

$$(2.38) \qquad S_{min}(n) \geq n \text{ for all } n \geq 1,$$

with equality only for $n = 1, 4, p$ (prime)

$$(2.39) \qquad S_{min}(n) \leq n! \leq S_{max}(n) \text{ for all } n \geq 1.$$

For all primes p one has

$$(2.40) \qquad S_{max}(p) = p!,$$

and

$$(2.41) \qquad S_{min}(2p) \leq p^2 \leq S_{max}(2p).$$

More generally, for all $m \leq p$,

$$(2.42) \qquad S_{min}(mp) \leq p^m \leq S_{max}(mp).$$

For all primes p and q, $p < q$ one has

$$(2.43) \qquad S_{min}(pq) \leq q^p \leq p^q \leq S_{max}(pq).$$

(2.43) is true also when $p = 2$ and $q \geq 5$.

Let now $E^*(n)$ and $E_*^*(n)$ be the unitary totient minimum and maximum functions. The following results are selected from [37]:

$$(2.44) \qquad \varphi^*(E_*^*(n))|n|\varphi^*(E^*(n)) \text{ for all } n \geq 1.$$

In particular,

$$(2.45) \qquad \varphi^*(E_*^*(n)) \leq n$$

and

$$(2.46) \qquad \varphi^*(E^*(n)) \geq n$$

One has

$$(2.47) \qquad E^*(n) \geq (n^{1/r} + 1)^r \geq n+1 \text{ for all } n \geq 2,$$

where r = number of distinct prime divisors of $E^*(n)$.

For all odd primes p one has

$$(2.48) \qquad E^*(p-1) = p,$$

but for all primes p,

$$(2.49) \qquad E_*^*(p-1) \geq p.$$

One has

$$(2.50) \qquad P_1(E_*^*(p-1)) \leq p \text{ for } p \geq 3,$$

where $P_1(m)$ here denotes the greatest prime factor of m.

The following result relies on certain diophantine equations:

$$(2.51) \qquad E_*^*(p^k) = \begin{cases} 2m, & \text{if } p=2, \text{ where } m \text{ is a positive integer;} \\ 2, & \text{if } p \geq 5 \text{ is not a Mersenne prime;} \\ 2^k, & \text{if } p = 2^k - 1 \text{ is a Mersenne prime.} \end{cases}$$

For the arithmetical functions $T(n)$ and $T_*(n)$ given by (1.14) the following results are true (see [33]):

Let $f : [1, \infty) \to [0, \infty)$, $f(x) = \sqrt{x} \log x$. Then

$$(2.52) \qquad f^{-1}(\log n) < T(n) \leq n$$

for all $n \geq 1$, where f^{-1} denotes the inverse function of f.

If n is squarefree, then

$$(2.53) \qquad T_*(n) = P(n),$$

where $P(n)$ is the greatest prime factor of n, but

$$(2.54) \qquad T_*(p^k) = p^\alpha$$

for a prime p and integer $k \geq 1$, where α is the greatest integer such that

$$\frac{\alpha(\alpha+1)}{2} \leq k.$$

If p, q are distinct primes, then

$$(2.55) \qquad T_*(p^s q) = \begin{cases} \max\{p, q\}, & \text{if} \quad s \text{ is not a triangular number,} \\ \max\{p^m, q\}, & \text{if} \quad s = \frac{m(m+1)}{2} = \text{triangular number.} \end{cases}$$

There are many inequalities related to the pseudo-Smarandache functions $Z(n)$ and $Z_*(n)$ given by (1.16). The following results are extracted from [21] and [26]. See also the book [25]

$$(2.56) \qquad Z(n) \leq \begin{cases} n, & \text{for} \quad n \quad \text{odd,} \\ 2n - 1, & \text{for} \quad n \quad \text{even,} \end{cases}$$

$$(2.57) \qquad Z(n) \geq -\frac{1}{2} + \sqrt{2n + \frac{1}{4}}, \quad \text{for all} \quad n \geq 1$$

which is best possible. As applications, one can deduce that

$$(2.58) \qquad \liminf_{n \to \infty} \frac{Z(n)}{n} = 0, \quad \limsup_{n \to \infty} \frac{Z(n)}{n} = 2,$$

$$(2.59) \qquad \liminf_{n \to \infty} |Z(2n) - Z(n)| = 0, \quad \limsup_{n \to \infty} |Z(2n) - Z(n)| = +\infty,$$

$$(2.60) \qquad \liminf_{n \to \infty} |S(Z(n)) - Z(S(n))| \leq 1, \quad \limsup_{n \to \infty} |S(Z(n)) - Z(S(n))| = +\infty,$$

$$(2.61) \qquad Z_*(n) \leq \frac{\sqrt{8n + 1} - 1}{2} \text{ for all } n \geq 1.$$

As a consequence,

$$(2.62) \qquad \liminf_{n \to \infty} \frac{Z_*(n)}{\sqrt{n}} = 0, \quad \limsup_{n \to \infty} \frac{Z_*(n)}{\sqrt{n}} = \sqrt{2}.$$

One has, for all $n, a, b \geq 1$ the chain of inequalities

$$(2.63) \qquad 1 \leq Z_*(n) \leq Z(n),$$

$$(2.64) \qquad \max\{Z_*(a), Z_*(b)\} \leq Z_*(ab),$$

$$(2.65) \qquad \max\{Z_*(a), Z_*(b)\} \leq \max\{Z(a), Z(b)\} \leq Z(ab).$$

The above inequalities may be used to study arithmetic properties of $Z(n)$ and $Z_*(n)$. For example, the series

$$(2.66) \qquad \sum_{n \geq 1} Z_*(n)/n! \text{ and } \sum_{n \geq 1} (-1)^{n-1} Z_*(n)/n!$$

are irrational.

We now state some inequalities for the additive analogues of Euler minimum and maximum functions, given by (1.30) (see [34]).

One has

$$E(n) \geq \mathcal{E}(n) \text{ and } E_*(n) \leq \mathcal{E}_*(n);$$

(2.67)
$$\max\{\varphi(1), \varphi(2), \ldots, \varphi(\mathcal{E}(n) - 1)\} < n \leq \varphi(\mathcal{E}(n));$$

$$\varphi(\mathcal{E}_*(n)) \leq n < \min\{\varphi(\mathcal{E}_*(n) + l) : l \geq 1\}.$$

For all $n \geq 2$,

(2.68)
$$\mathcal{E}(n) \geq n + 1, \quad \mathcal{E}_*(n) \geq n + 1,$$

but

$$\mathcal{E}_*(n) < n^{3/2} \text{ for } n \geq 12, \quad \mathcal{E}(n) < n^{3/2} + 1 \text{ for } n \geq 30.$$

For the number-of-divisors minimum function $D(n)$ of (1.10), in paper [27] we have proved that

(2.69)
$$D(n) \leq 2^{n-1} \text{ for all } n,$$

with equality for $n = $ prime.

For the function $S_{a*}(n)$ given by (1.22) we note the following: If $a = p_1^{\alpha_1} \cdots p_r^{\alpha_r}$ is the prime factorization of $a > 1$; $p_1 < \cdots < p_r$; and if $p \neq p_i$ ($i = \overline{1, r}$), then

(2.70)
$$S_{a*}(n) \leq p - 1.$$

In particular, $S_{p*}(n) = 1$ if $p \geq 3$, $= 2$ if $p = 2$, for any prime p.

For the function $F(n)$ of (1.19) we have:

$$F(p) = p - 1 \text{ for all primes } p,$$

$$F(n) \leq n - 1 \text{ for } n \geq 2, \quad F(k!) = k + 1 \ (k \geq 3), \quad F(1) = F(2) = 1.$$

As a corollary, $F(n) < S(n)$ and $F(m) > S(m)$ are true for infinitely many numbers n and m.

2.2 Asymptotic Properties

In 2001 the author [24] studied the real functions $S(x)$ and $S_*(x)$. It is immediate that

(2.71)
$$S_*(x) \leq S(x) \leq S_*(x) + 1,$$

thus from some point of view, it is sufficient to study properties of $S_*(x)$. The function S_* (defined on $[1, +\infty)$) is a surjective and increasing function; is continuous for all $x \in [1, \infty) \setminus A$, where $A = \{k! : k \geq 2\}$, and S_* is continuous from the right in $x = k!$ ($k \geq 2$), but it is not continuous from the left. The function S_* is differentiable on $(1, \infty) \setminus A$, and has a right derivative in $A \cup \{1\}$. The function S_* is Riemann integrable on $[a, b] \subset \mathbb{R}$ for all $a < b$.

The following results are also true:

(2.72)
$$S_*(x) \sim \frac{\log x}{\log \log x} \text{ as } x \to \infty.$$

The series

(2.73) $$\sum_{n=1}^{\infty} \frac{1}{n(S_*(m))^{\alpha}} \quad \text{is} \quad \begin{cases} \text{convergent} & \text{for } \alpha > 1 \\ \text{divergent} & \text{for } \alpha \le 1. \end{cases}$$

Let Γ be the Euler gamma function. In the paper [1], C. Adiga and T. Kim defined the following generalization of $S(x)$ and $S_*(x)$:

(2.74)
$$T_a(x) = \min\{k \ge 1 : x \le \Gamma(a + k)\} \text{ for } x \in (\Gamma(a + 1), \infty)$$
$$T_{a_*}(x) = \max\{k \ge 1 : \Gamma(a + k) \le x\} \text{ for } x \in [\Gamma(a + 1), \infty)$$

where a is a fixed positive real number. They proved similar results to (2.68) and (2.69):

(2.75) $$T_{a_*}(x) \sim \frac{\log x}{\log \log x} \text{ as } x \to \infty.$$

The series

(2.76) $$\sum_{n=1}^{\infty} \frac{1}{n(T_{a_*}(n))^{\alpha}} \quad \text{is} \quad \begin{cases} \text{convergent} & \text{for } \alpha > 1 \\ \text{divergent} & \text{for } \alpha \le 1. \end{cases}$$

Let $q > 0$ be a fixed real number. By defining the q-factorial of n by $(n!)_q = 1 \cdot (1 + q)(1 + q + q^2) \cdots (1 + q + q^2 + \cdots + q^{n-1})$, F.H. Jackson (see [2]) defined the q-analogue of the Gamma function by

(2.77) $$\Gamma_q(x) = \frac{(q; q)_\infty}{(q^x; q)_\infty}(1 - q)^{1-x}, \quad 0 < q < 1,$$

and

$$\Gamma_q(x) = \frac{(q^{-1}; q^{-1})_\infty}{(q^{-x}; q^{-1})_\infty}(q - 1)^{1-x}q^{\binom{x}{2}}, \quad q > 1,$$

where $(a; q)_\infty = \prod_{n=0}^{\infty}(1 - aq^n)$.

Now defining S_q and S_{q_*} as in (2.74), replacing $a = 1$ and Γ with Γ_q, in [2] the following results are proved:

(2.78) $$S_{q_*}(x) \sim \frac{\log x}{\log\left(\frac{1}{1-q}\right)} \text{ for } 0 < q < 1.$$

The series

(2.79) $$\sum_{n=1}^{\infty} \frac{1}{n(S_{q_*}(n))^{\alpha}} \quad \text{is} \quad \begin{cases} \text{convergent} & \text{for } \alpha > 1 \\ \text{divergent} & \text{for } \alpha \le 1 \quad (0 < q < 1). \end{cases}$$

Clearly $S_q(x) \to S(x)$, $S_{q_*}(x) \to S_*(x)$ as $q \to 1-$.

In the paper [28] we studied the asymptotic properties of the functions $Z(x)$ and $P(x)$, etc. given by (1.27) and (1.28). These are the following:

(2.80) $$Z_*(x) \sim \frac{1}{2}\sqrt{8x + 1} \quad (x \to \infty),$$

(2.81) $$\log p_*(x) \sim \log x \quad (x \to \infty).$$

The series

$$(2.82) \qquad \sum_{n=1}^{\infty} \frac{1}{(Z_*(n))^\alpha} \quad \text{is} \quad \begin{cases} \text{convergent} & \text{for } \alpha > 2 \\ \text{divergent} & \text{for } \alpha \leq 2. \end{cases}$$

The series

$$(2.83) \qquad \sum_{n=1}^{\infty} \frac{1}{n} \left(\frac{\log \log n}{\log P_*(n)} \right)^\alpha \quad \text{is} \quad \begin{cases} \text{convergent} & \text{for } \alpha > 1 \\ \text{divergent} & \text{for } \alpha \leq 1. \end{cases},$$

Recently, C. Adiga, T. Kim and J.H. Han [3], by using the theory of q-gamma functions, have defined

$$(2.84) \qquad Z_q(x) = \min \left\{ \frac{1 - q^k}{1 - q} : x \leq \frac{\Gamma_q(k+2)}{2\Gamma_q(k)} \right\}, \quad k \geq 1, \ x \in (0, \infty),$$

where $0 < q < 1$. Z_{q_*} will be its dual. Similarly, let

$$(2.85) \qquad P_q(x) = \min\{k \geq 1 : p^x \leq \Gamma_q(k+1)\}, \quad p > 1, \ x \in (0, \infty),$$

$$(2.86) \qquad P_{q_*}(x) = \max\{k \geq 1 : \Gamma_q(k+1) \leq p^x\}, \quad p > 1, \ x \in [1, \infty).$$

They proved the following results:

$$(2.87) \qquad \frac{\sqrt{1 + 8xq} - (1 + 2q)}{2q^2} < Z_{q_*}(x) \leq \frac{\sqrt{1 + 8xq} - 1}{2q}, \quad x \geq \frac{\Gamma_q(3)}{2\Gamma_q(1)}$$

and that

$$(2.88) \qquad P_*(x) \sim \frac{x \log p}{\log \left(\frac{1}{1-q} \right)} \quad (x \to \infty)$$

Sándor's result (2.80) is reobtained from (2.87), by letting $q \to 1-$.

In [4] N. Anitha studied the asymptotic properties of functions G and G_*, given by (1.29). She proved the following estimates:

$$(2.89) \qquad \pi(x) \sim \frac{x}{G_*(x)} \quad \text{as } x \to \infty,$$

where $\pi(x)$ denotes the number of all primes $\leq x$; and

$$(2.90) \qquad G_*(x) \sim \log x.$$

The series

$$(2.91) \qquad \sum_{n=1}^{\infty} \frac{1}{n[G_*(n)]^\alpha} \quad \text{is} \quad \begin{cases} \text{convergent} & \text{for } \alpha > 1 \\ \text{divergent} & \text{for } \alpha \leq 1. \end{cases},$$

Y. Yi and W. Zhang [46] have recently considered the mean value of the Sándor function:

$$(2.92) \qquad \sum_{n \leq x} S(n) = \frac{x \log x}{\log \log x} + O(x)$$

(Here $S(n)$ is the value of the Sándor function at the positive integer n, and should not be confused with the Smarandache function value).

Z. Minhui [12] has proved the following mean value theorem for the Sándor type function Sdf_1 given by (1.31):

$$(2.93) \qquad \sum_{n \le x} Sdf_1(n) = \frac{2x \log x}{\log \log x} + O\left(\frac{x(\log x)(\log \log \log x)}{(\log \log x)^2}\right).$$

Finally we state the asymptotic estimates for the author's functions $\mathcal{E}(x)$ and $\mathcal{E}_*(x)$ of (1.30):

$$(2.94) \qquad \begin{aligned} \log \mathcal{E}_*(x) &\sim \log x, \quad \text{and} \\ \log \mathcal{E}(x) &\sim \log x, \text{ as } x \to \infty \end{aligned}$$

For other estimates, and graphical representations of these functions, see [34]. For asymptotic results on $S_p(n)$ of (1.21), see [47], [48]. For asymptotic results on the Smarandache function, see the Smarandache Notions Journal Collection.

We conclude this review by mentioning that only a part of the results have been presented here. In particular, no results on $SDF(n)$ of (1.17), or $C(n)$ of (1.20) are included. We propose the interested reader to consult the references (e.g. our book [25], where many further references are pointed out), as well as internet search engines.

References

[1] C. Adiga and T. Kim, On a generalization of Sándor's function, *Proc. Jangjeon Math. Soc.*, **5**(2) (2002), 121–124.

[2] C. Adiga, T. Kim, D.D. Somashekara and N. Fathima, On a q-analogue of Sándor's function, *J. Inequal. in Pure & Appl. Math.*, **4**(4) (2003), 1–5.

[3] C. Adiga, T. Kim and J.H. Han, A note on q-analogue of Sándor's functions, *Math. Ineq. Appl.* (to appear).

[4] N. Anitha, A note on Sándor's type functions, *J. Inequal. in Pure & Appl. Math.*, **6**(4) (2005), Art. 127.

[5] K.T. Atanassov, Remark on József Sándor and Florian Luca's theorem, *C.R. Acad. Bulg. Sci.*, **55**(10) (2002), 9–14.

[6] E. Cohen, Arithmetical functions associated with the unitary divisors of an integer, *Math. Z.*, **74** (1960), 66–80.

[7] L.E. Dickson, *History of the Theory of Numbers*, vol. I, AMS Chelsea Publ., 1919, reprinted in 1999, see p.263.

[8] A.J. Kempner, Concerning the smallest integer $m!$ divisible by a given integer n, *Amer. Math. Monthly*, **25** (1918), 204–210.

[9] M. Le, A conjecture concerning the Smarandache dual function, *Smarandache Notion J.*, **14** (2004), 153–155.

[10] F. Luca, On a divisibility property involving factorials, *C.R. Acad. Bulg. Sci.*, **53**(6) (2000), 35–38.

[11] F. Luca, On the product of divisors of n and $\sigma(n)$, *J. Inequal. in Pure & Appl. Math.*, **4**(2) (2003), 7pp (electronic).

[12] Z. Minhui, Mean value of the additive analogue of Smarandache function, *Scientia Magna*, **1**(1) (2005), 179–182.

[13] P. Moree and H. Roskam, On an arithmetical function related to Euler's totient and the discriminator, *Fib. Quart.*, **33** (1995), 332–340.

[14] T. Šalát and J. Tomanová, On the product of divisors of a positive integer, *Math. Slovaca*, **52**(3) (2002), 271–287.

[15] J. Sándor, On an exponential totient function, *Studia Univ. Babeş-Bolyai, Math.*, **XLI**(3) (1996), 91–94.

[16] J. Sándor, On certain inequalities involving the Smarandache function, *Abstracts of Papers Presented to the Amer. Math. Soc.*, **17** (1996), 583.

[17] J. Sándor, On certain generalizations of the Smarandache function, *Notes Numb. Theory Discr. Math.*, **5**(2) (1999), 41–51.

[18] J. Sándor, On certain generalizations of the Smarandache function, *Smarandache Notions J.*, **11**(1-2-3) (2000), 202–212.

[19] J. Sándor, On a new Smarandache type function, *Smarandache Notions J.*, **12** (2001), 247–249.

[20] J. Sándor, The Smarandache function of a set, *Octogon Math. Mag.*, **9**(1) (2001), 369–372.

[21] J. Sándor, On the pseudo-Smarandache function, *Smarandache Notions J.*, **12**(1-2-3) (2001), 59–61.

[22] J. Sándor, On certain arithmetic functions, *Smarandache Notions J.*, **12** (2001), 260–262.

[23] J. Sándor, On multiplicatively perfect numbers, *J. Inequal. in Pure & Appl. Math.*, **2**(1) (2001), Art. 3, 6pp (electronic).

[24] J. Sándor, On an additive analogue of the function S, *Notes Numb. Th. Discr. Math.*, **7**(2) (2001), 91–95.

[25] J. Sándor, *Geometric theorems, diophantine equations, and arithmetic functions*, American Research Press, New Mexico, 2002.

[26] J. Sándor, On a dual of the pseudo-Smarandache function, *Smarandache Notions J.*, **13**(1-2-3) (2002), 18-23.

[27] J. Sándor, A note on the divisor minimum function, *Octogon Math. Mag.*, **12**(1) (2004), 273–275.

[28] J. Sándor, On additive analogues of certain arithmetic functions, *Smarandache Notions J.*, **14** (2004), 128–133.

[29] J. Sándor, On duals of the Smarandache simple function, *Octogon Math. Mag.*, **12**(1) (2004), 161–164.

[30] J. Sándor, On a modification of the Smarandache function, *Octogon Math. Mag.*, **12**(2A) (2004), 521–523.

[31] J. Sándor, On multiplicatively e-perfect numbers, *J. Inequal. in Pure & Appl. Math.*, **5**(4) (2004), article 114.

[32] J. Sándor (in coop. with B. Crstici), *Handbook of Number Theory*, II, Springer Verlag, 2004.

[33] J. Sándor, The product-of-divisors minimum and maximum functions, *RGMIA Research Report Collection*, **7**(2) (2004), art. 18, 11pp.

[34] J. Sándor, An additive analogue of the Euler minimum function, *Adv. Stud. Contemp. Math.*, **10**(1) (2005), no.1, 53-62.

[35] J. Sándor, The sum-of-divisors minimum and maximum functions, *RGMIA Research Report Collection*, **8**(1) (2005), art.20.

[36] J. Sándor, A note on exponential divisors and related arithmetical functions, *Scientia Magna*, **1**(1) (2005), 97–101.

[37] J. Sándor, The unitary totient minimum and maximum functions, *Studia Univ. Babeş-Bolyai Math.*, **50**(2) (2005), 91–100.

[38] J. Sándor and D.S. Mitrinović (in coop. with B. Crstici), *Handbook of Number Theory I*, Springer Verlag, 2005.

[39] J. Sándor, The Smarandache minimum and maximum functions, *Scientia Magna*, **1**(2) (2005), 162–166.

[40] J. Sándor, On the Euler minimum and maximum functions, *RGMIA Research Report Collection*, **8**(1) (2005), article 1.

[41] J. Sándor, On the pseudo-Smarandache minimum and maximum functions, to appear.

[42] F. Smarandache, A function in the number theory, *An. Univ. Timişoara, Ser. Mat.*, **38** (1980), 79–88.

[43] F. Smarandache, *Only Problems, Not Solutions!*, Chicago, Xiquan Publ. House, 1993.

[44] F. Smarandache, *Definitions, solved and unsolved problems, conjectures, and theorems in number theory and geometry*, edited by M.L. Perez, Xiquan Publ. House (USA), 2000.

[45] Z. Weiyi, On the divisor product sequence, *Smarandache Notions J.*, **14** (2004), 144–146.

[46] Y. Yi and W. Zhang, Mean value of the additive analogue of Smarandache function, *Scientia Magna*, **1**(1) (2005), 145–147.

[47] Y. Yi, On the primitive numbers of power p and its asymptotic property, *Scientia Magna*, **1**(1) (2005), 175–179.

[48] W. Zhang and D. Liu, Primitive numbers of power p and its asymptotic property, *Smarandache Notions J.*, **13** (2002), 173–175.

In: Advances in Inequalities for Special Functions   ISBN 978-1-60021-919-1
Editors: P. Cerone and S. S. Dragomir, pp. 149–160 © 2008 Nova Science Publishers, Inc.

On the Operator $\oplus_B^k$ Related to the Bessel-wave Equation and Laplacian-Bessel

Mehmet Zeki Sarikaya and Hüseyin Yildirim

Department of Mathematics
Faculty of Science and Arts
Afyon Kocatepe University, Afyon-TURKEY
E-mail addresses: {sarikaya,hyildir}@aku.edu.tr

ABSTRACT. In this article, we study the Green function of the operator $\oplus_B^k$, iterated $k-$times and is defined by

$$\oplus_B^k = \left[\left(B_{x_1} + B_{x_2} + \cdots + B_{x_p} \right)^4 - \left(B_{x_{p+1}} + \cdots + B_{x_{p+q}} \right)^4 \right]^k$$

where $p+q = n$, $B_{x_i} = \frac{\partial^2}{\partial x_i^2} + \frac{2v_i}{x_i} \frac{\partial}{\partial x_i}$, where $2v_i = 2\alpha_i + 1$, $\alpha_i > -\frac{1}{2}$ [6], $i = 1, 2, \ldots, n$, k is a nonnegative integer and n is the dimension of the space $\mathbb{C}^n$. At first we study the elementary solution or the Green function of the operator $\oplus_B^k$ and then such a solution is related to the solution of the Bessel wave equation and the Laplacian Bessel. We found that the relationships of such solutions which depend on the conditions of p, q and k.

1991 Mathematics Subject Classification: 46F10, 35L82, 35A55.

Key words and phrases: Diamond Operator, Tempered Distribution, Convolution Algebra.

1 INTRODUCTION

Gelfand and Shilov were the first to introduce the elementary solution of the $n-$dimensional classical diamond operator [2]. Later Yıldırım, Sarikaya and Ozturk showed that the solution of the convolution form $u(x) = (-1)^k S_{2k}(x) * R_{2k}(x)$ is a unique elementary solution of $\Diamond_B^k u(x) = \delta$ [9]. Kananthai, Suantai and Longani have studied the elementary solution of the $n-$dimensional classical operator $\oplus^k$ and the classical operator $\oplus^k$ related to the wave equation and Laplacian [3]. In this paper, firstly we introduce the operator $\oplus_B^k$ as (1.4). Later we can find the elementary solution $K(x)$ of the operator $\oplus_B^k$, that is $\oplus_B^k K(x) = \delta$ where δ is the Dirac-delta distribution. Moreover, we can find the relationship between $K(x)$ and the elementary solution of the Bessel wave operator defined by (1.8) depending on the conditions of p, q and k of (1.4) with $p = 1$, $q = n - 1$, $k = 1$ and $x_1 = t(\text{time})$.

Also, we found that $K(x)$ relates to the elementary solutions of the Laplacian Bessel defined by (1.9) and (1.10) depending on the conditions of q and k of (1.4) with $q = 0$ and $k = 1$.

In this article, we will define the Bessel ultra-hyperbolic type operator iterated $k-$times with $x \in \mathbb{R}_n^+ = \{x : x = (x_1, \ldots, x_n), x_1 > 0, \ldots, x_n > 0\}$

$$(1.1) \qquad \Box_B^k = (B_{x_1} + B_{x_2} + \cdots + B_{x_p} - B_{x_{p+1}} - \cdots - B_{x_{p+q}})^k, \quad p+q = n.$$

We showed in [9] that the generalized function $R_{2k}^H(u)$ as defined by (1.12) is the unique elementary solution of the operator $\Box_B^k$, that is $\Box_B^k R_{2k}^H(u) = \delta$ where $x \in \mathbb{R}_n^+$ and δ is the

Dirac-delta distribution. S is the Schwarz space of any testing functions and S' is a space of tempered distribution.

Furthermore, we showed in [9] that the function $R^{\epsilon}_{2k}(v)$ as defined by (1.15) is an elementary solution of the Laplace-Bessel operator iterated $k-$times

$$(1.2) \qquad \Delta^k_B = (B_{x_1} + B_{x_2} + \cdots + B_{x_n})^k$$

that is, $\Delta^k_B R^{\epsilon}_{2k}(v) = \delta$, where $x \in \mathbb{R}^+_n$.

The operator $\Diamond^k_B$ was first introduced by Yıldırım, Sarikaya and Ozturk [9] and named as the Bessel Diamond operator iterated $k-$times, defined by

$$(1.3) \qquad \Diamond^k_B = \left[\left(B_{x_1} + B_{x_2} + \cdots + B_{x_p} \right)^2 - \left(B_{x_{p+1}} + \cdots + B_{x_{p+q}} \right)^2 \right]^k.$$

The operator $\Diamond^k_B$ can be expressed as the product of the operators $\Box_B$ and Δ_B, that is

$$\Diamond^k_B = \left[\left(\sum_{i=1}^{p} B_{x_i} \right)^2 - \left(\sum_{i=p+1}^{p+q} B_{x_i} \right)^2 \right]^k$$

$$= \left[\sum_{i=1}^{p} B_{x_i} - \sum_{i=p+1}^{p+q} B_{x_i} \right]^k \left[\sum_{i=1}^{p} B_{x_i} + \sum_{i=p+1}^{p+q} B_{x_i} \right]^k$$

$$= \Box^k_B \Delta^k_B.$$

In this paper we define that the operator $\oplus^k_B$ can be expressed in the form

$$(1.4) \qquad \oplus^k_B = \left[\left(\sum_{i=1}^{p} B_{x_i} \right)^2 - \left(\sum_{j=p+1}^{p+q} B_{x_j} \right)^2 \right]^k$$

$$\times \left[\sum_{i=1}^{p} B_{x_i} + i \sum_{j=p+1}^{p+q} B_{x_j} \right]^k \left[\sum_{i=1}^{p} B_{x_i} - i \sum_{j=p+1}^{p+q} B_{x_j} \right]^k,$$

where $p + q = n$ is the dimension of $\mathbb{C}^n$, $i = \sqrt{-1}$ and k is a nonnegative integer.

Let us denote the operators

$$(1.5) \qquad \Lambda_1 = \sum_{i=1}^{p} B_{x_i} + i \sum_{j=p+1}^{p+q} B_{x_j}$$

and

$$(1.6) \qquad \Lambda_2 = \sum_{i=1}^{p} B_{x_i} - i \sum_{j=p+1}^{p+q} B_{x_j}.$$

Thus (1.4) can be written as

$$(1.7) \qquad \oplus^k_B = \Diamond^k_B \Lambda^k_1 \Lambda^k_2.$$

By putting $k = 1$, $p = 1$ and $x_1 = t$(time) in (1.1) then we obtain the Bessel wave operator

$$(1.8) \qquad \Box_B = B_t - \sum_{i=1}^{n-1} B_{x_i}$$

and from (1.4) with $k = 1$ and $q = 0$, we obtain

(1.9) $$\oplus_B = \triangle_{B,p}^4,$$

where

(1.10) $$\triangle_{B,p} = \sum_{i=1}^{p} B_{x_i}.$$

Denote by T^y the generalized shift operator acting according to the law [6]

$$T_x^y \varphi(x) = C_v^* \int_0^\pi \cdots \int_0^\pi \varphi\left(\sqrt{x_1^2 + y_1^2 - 2x_1 y_1 \cos\theta_1}, \ldots, \sqrt{x_n^2 + y_n^2 - 2x_n y_n \cos\theta_n}\right)$$
$$\times \left(\prod_{i=1}^{n} \sin^{2v_i - 1}\theta_i\right) d\theta_1 \ldots d\theta_n,$$

where $x, y \in \mathbb{R}_n^+$, $C_v^* = \prod_{i=1}^{n} \frac{\Gamma(v_i+1)}{\Gamma(\frac{1}{2})\Gamma(v_i)}$. We remark that this shift operator is closely connected with the Bessel differential operator [6]

$$\frac{d^2 U}{dx^2} + \frac{2v}{x}\frac{dU}{dx} = \frac{d^2 U}{dy^2} + \frac{2v}{y}\frac{dU}{dy}$$
$$U(x,0) = f(x)$$
$$U_y(x,0) = 0.$$

The convolution operator determined by the T^y is as follows

(1.11) $$(f * \varphi)(y) = \int_{\mathbb{R}_n^+} f(y) T_x^y \varphi(x) \left(\prod_{i=1}^{n} y_i^{2v_i}\right) dy.$$

Convolution (1.11) is known as a B-convolution. We note the following properties of the B-convolution and the generalized shift operator.

a. $T_x^y 1 = 1$

b. $T_x^0 f(x) = f(x)$

c. If $f(x), g(x) \in C(\mathbb{R}_n^+)$, $g(x)$ is a bounded function for all $x > 0$ and

$$\int_0^\infty |f(x)| \left(\prod_{i=1}^{n} x_i^{2v_i}\right) dx < \infty$$

then

$$\int_{\mathbb{R}_n^+} T_x^y f(x) g(y) \left(\prod_{i=1}^{n} y_i^{2v_i}\right) dy = \int_{\mathbb{R}_n^+} f(y) T_x^y g(x) \left(\prod_{i=1}^{n} y_i^{2v_i}\right) dy.$$

d. From **c.**, we have the following equality for $g(x) = 1$, namely,

$$\int_{\mathbb{R}_n^+} T_x^y f(x) \left(\prod_{i=1}^{n} y_i^{2v_i}\right) dy = \int_{\mathbb{R}_n^+} f(y) \left(\prod_{i=1}^{n} y_i^{2v_i}\right) dy.$$

e. $(f * g)(x) = (g * f)(x)$.

The Fourier-Bessel transformation and its inverse transformation are defined as follows [7], [8]

$$(F_B f)(x) = C_v \int_{\mathbb{R}_n^+} f(y) \left(\prod_{i=1}^n j_{v_i - \frac{1}{2}}(x_i, y_i) \, y_i^{2v_i} \right) dy$$

$$\left(F_B^{-1} f\right)(x) = (F_B f)(-x), \qquad C_v = \left(\prod_{i=1}^n 2^{v_i - \frac{1}{2}} \Gamma \left(v_i + \frac{1}{2} \right) \right)^{-1},$$

where $j_{v_i - \frac{1}{2}}(x_i, y_i)$ is the normalized Bessel function which is the eigenfunction of the Bessel differential operator. There are the following identities for the Fourier-Bessel transformation [4], [5].

$$F_B \delta(x) = 1$$

$$F_B(f * g)(x) = F_B f(x) \cdot F_B g(x).$$

Lemma 1.1. *There is the following equality for Fourier Bessel transformation*

$$F_B \left(|x|^{-\alpha} \right) = 2^{n + 2|v| - 2\alpha} \Gamma \left(\frac{n + 2|v| - \alpha}{2} \right) \left[\Gamma \left(\frac{\alpha}{2} \right) \right]^{-1} |x|^{\alpha - n - 2|v|}.$$

where $|v| = v_1 + \cdots + v_n$.

The proof of this lemma is given in [7].

The proof of the following Lemma 1.2 and Lemma 1.3 can be easily seen in our paper [9].

Lemma 1.2. *If $\square_B^k U(x) = \delta$ for $x \in \Gamma_+ = \{ x \in \mathbb{R}_n^+ : x_1 > 0, x_2 > 0, \ldots, x_n > 0 \text{ and } u > 0 \}$, where $\square_B^k$ is the Bessel-ultra hyperbolic operator iterated $k-$times defined by (1.1), then $U(x) = R_{2k}^H(x)$ is the unique elementary solution of the operator $\square_B^k$ where*

$$(1.12) \qquad R_{2k}^H(x) = \frac{u^{\left(\frac{2k - n - 2|v|}{2} \right)}}{K_n(2k)}$$

$$= \frac{\left(x_1^2 + x_2^2 + \cdots + x_p^2 - x_{p+1}^2 - \cdots - x_{p+q}^2 \right)^{\left(\frac{2k - n - 2|v|}{2} \right)}}{K_n(2k)}$$

for

$$K_n(2k) = \frac{\pi^{\frac{n + 2|v| - 1}{2}} \Gamma \left(\frac{2 + 2k - n - 2|v|}{2} \right) \Gamma \left(\frac{1 - 2k}{2} \right) \Gamma(2k)}{\Gamma \left(\frac{2 + 2k - p - 2|v|}{2} \right) \Gamma \left(\frac{p - 2k}{2} \right)}.$$

For any complex number α, we define the function (1.12) as follows

$$(1.13) \qquad R_\alpha^H(u) = \frac{u^{\left(\frac{\alpha - n - 2|v|}{2} \right)}}{K_n(\alpha)},$$

where the constant $K_n(\alpha)$ is given by the formula

$$K_n(\alpha) = \frac{\pi^{\frac{n + 2|v| - 1}{2}} \Gamma \left(\frac{2 + \alpha - n - 2|v|}{2} \right) \Gamma \left(\frac{1 - \alpha}{2} \right) \Gamma(\alpha)}{\Gamma \left(\frac{2 + \alpha - p - 2|v|}{2} \right) \Gamma \left(\frac{p - \alpha}{2} \right)}.$$

Now R_α^H is an ordinary function if $\text{Re}(\alpha) \geq n$ and is a distribution of α if $\text{Re}(\alpha) < n$.

Now, if $p = 1$ then (1.13) reduces to the function $M_\alpha(u)$ say, defined by

$$(1.14) \qquad M_\alpha(u) = \frac{u^{\left(\frac{\alpha - n - 2|v|}{2}\right)}}{H_n(\alpha)}$$

where $u = x_1^2 - x_2^2 - \cdots - x_n^2$ and

$$H_n(\alpha) = \pi^{\frac{n+2|v|-1}{2}} 2^{\alpha-1} \Gamma\left(\frac{\alpha - n - 2|v|}{2}\right).$$

The function $M_\alpha(u)$ is called the Bessel hyperbolic kernel of Marcel Riesz.

Lemma 1.3. *Given the equation $\Delta_B^k U(x) = \delta$ for $x \in \mathbb{R}_n^+$, where Δ_B^k is the Laplace-Bessel operator iterated k times defined by (1.2), then $U(x) = (-1)^k R_{2k}^e(x)$ is an elementary solution of the operator Δ_B^k where,*

$$(1.15) \qquad R_{2k}^e(x) = \frac{2^{n+2|v|-4k} \Gamma\left(\frac{n+2|v|-2k}{2}\right)}{\prod_{i=1}^n 2^{v_i - \frac{1}{2}} \Gamma\left(v_i + \frac{1}{2}\right) \Gamma(k)} |x|^{2k-n-2|v|}.$$

For any complex number β, we define the function (1.15) as follows

$$(1.16) \qquad R_\beta^e(v) = \frac{2^{-\beta} \Gamma\left(\frac{n+2|v|-\beta}{2}\right)}{\prod_{i=1}^n 2^{v_i - \frac{1}{2}} \Gamma\left(v_i + \frac{1}{2}\right) \Gamma\left(\frac{\beta}{2}\right)} v^{\frac{\beta-n-2|v|}{2}}$$

for $\Gamma(\beta) = 2^{\beta-1} \pi^{-\frac{1}{2}} \Gamma\left(\frac{\beta}{2}\right) \Gamma\left(\frac{\beta+1}{2}\right)$ and $v = x_1^2 + x_2^2 + \cdots + x_n^2$.

The function $R_\beta^e(v)$ is called the Bessel elliptic kernel of Marcel Riesz and is an ordinary function if $\mathrm{Re}(\beta) \geq n$ and is a distribution of β if $\mathrm{Re}(\beta) < n$.

Let $x = (x_1, x_2, \ldots, x_n)$ be a point of $\mathbb{C}^n$ and write

$$w = x_1^2 + x_2^2 + \cdots + x_p^2 - i(x_{p+1}^2 + x_{p+1}^2 + \cdots + x_{p+q}^2)$$

and

$$z = x_1^2 + x_2^2 + \cdots + x_p^2 + i(x_{p+1}^2 + x_{p+1}^2 + \cdots + x_{p+q}^2), \quad p + q = n.$$

For any complex numbers λ and τ, we define the functions as follows

$$(1.17) \qquad S_\lambda(w) = \frac{2^{-\lambda} \Gamma\left(\frac{n+2|v|-\lambda}{2}\right)}{\prod_{i=1}^n 2^{v_i - \frac{1}{2}} \Gamma\left(v_i + \frac{1}{2}\right) \Gamma\left(\frac{\lambda}{2}\right)} w^{\frac{\lambda-n-2|v|}{2}}$$

and

$$(1.18) \qquad T_\tau(z) = \frac{2^{-\tau} \Gamma\left(\frac{n+2|v|-\tau}{2}\right)}{\prod_{i=1}^n 2^{v_i - \frac{1}{2}} \Gamma\left(v_i + \frac{1}{2}\right) \Gamma\left(\frac{\tau}{2}\right)} z^{\frac{\tau-n-2|v|}{2}}.$$

Lemma 1.4. *The convolution $R_{2k}^H(u) * (-1)^k R_{2k}^e(v)$ is an elementary solution of the operator $\Diamond_B^k$ iterated k–times and is defined by (1.3).*

Proof. We need to show that $\Diamond_B^k U(x) = \delta$, for $U(x) = R_{2k}^H(u) * (-1)^k R_{2k}^e(v)$, can be written as $\Diamond_B^k U(x) = \Box_B^k \Delta_B^k U(x)$ by (1.3). $\Delta_B^k U(x) = R_{2k}^H(u)$ is a unique elementary solution of the operator $\Box_B^k$ for n odd with p odd and q even, or for n even with p odd and q odd. By the method of $B-$convolution, we have

$$\Delta_B^k \delta * U(x) = R_{2k}^H(u).$$

$B-$convolving both sides by $(-1)^k R_{2k}^e(v)$, we obtain

$$\left((-1)^k R_{2k}^e(v) * \Delta_B^k \delta \right) * U(x) = (-1)^k R_{2k}^e(v) * R_{2k}^H(u)$$

or

$$\Delta_B^k \left((-1)^k R_{2k}^e(v) \right) * U(x) = (-1)^k R_{2k}^e(v) * R_{2k}^H(u).$$

It follows that $U(x) = R_{2k}^H(u) * (-1)^k R_{2k}^e(v)$ by Lemma 1.3. This completes the proof. $\square$

Lemma 1.5. *Let $R_{2k}^e(v)$ and $R_{2m}^e(v)$ be defined by (1.15), then*

   a) $R_{2k}^e(v) * R_{2m}^e(v) = R_{2k+2m}^e(v)$, *for* $2k + 2m \neq n + 2|v| + 2r$, $r = 0, 1, 2, \ldots$

   b) $\Box_B^k R_{2m}^e(v) = R_{2m-2k}^e(v)$, *where k and m are a nonnegative integer,*

   c) $\Box_B^k \delta = R_{-2k}^e$, *where k is a nonnegative integer.*

Proof.
   a) The proof of Lemma 1.5(a) can be seen in [9].

   b) By Lemma 1.5(a) and [10] we have

$$\delta * R_{2m}^e = R_{2k}^e * R_{2m-2k}^e$$
$$\Box_B^k R_{2k}^e * R_{2m}^e = R_{2k}^e * R_{2m-2k}^e$$
$$R_{2k}^e * \Box_B^k R_{2m}^e = R_{2k}^e * R_{2m-2k}^e$$

and

$$\Box_B^k R_{2m}^e(x) = R_{2m-2k}^e.$$

   c) For $k \in \mathbb{N}$ we have the following equality [9]

$$F_B(\Box_B^k \delta) = C_v (-1)^k |x|^k.$$

Therefore from the inverse Fourier-Bessel transform and Lemma 1.1 we obtain

$$\Box_B^k \delta = \frac{2^{n+2|v|-4k} \Gamma\left(\frac{n+2|v|-4k}{2} \right)}{\prod_{i=1}^n 2^{v_i - \frac{1}{2}} \Gamma\left(v_i + \frac{1}{2} \right) \Gamma(-k)} v^{\frac{-2k-n-2|v|}{2}}$$

or equality

$$\Box_B^k \delta = R_{-2k}^e$$

and when $k = 0$, one has

$$R_0^e = \delta.$$

$\square$

Lemma 1.6.

i) The functions $(-1)^k(-i)^{\frac{q}{2}}S_{2k}(w)$ and $(-1)^k(i)^{\frac{q}{2}}T_{2k}(z)$ are the elementary solutions of the operators Λ_1^k and Λ_2^k, respectively, where $S_{2k}(w)$ and $T_{2k}(z)$ are defined by (1.17) and (1.18), respectively, with $\lambda = \tau = 2k$. The operators Λ_1^k and Λ_2^k are defined by (1.5) and (1.6), respectively.

ii) The functions $(-1)^k(-i)^{\frac{q}{2}}S_{-2k}(w)$ and $(-1)^k(i)^{\frac{q}{2}}T_{-2k}(z)$ are the inverses in the $B-$convolution algebras of $(-1)^k(-i)^{\frac{q}{2}}S_{2k}(w)$ and $(-1)^k(i)^{\frac{q}{2}}T_{2k}(z)$, respectively.

Proof.
i) We need to show that

$$\Lambda_1^k\left[(-1)^k(-i)^{\frac{q}{2}}S_{2k}(w)\right] = \delta$$

and

$$\Lambda_2^k\left[(-1)^k(i)^{\frac{q}{2}}T_{2k}(z)\right] = \delta.$$

Firstly, we have to show that

(1.19)
$$\Lambda_1^k S_\lambda(w) = (-1)^k S_{\lambda-2k}(w),$$

(1.20)
$$\Lambda_2^k T_\tau(z) = (-1)^k T_{\tau-2k}(z)$$

and

(1.21)
$$S_{-2k}(w) = (-1)^k(i)^{\frac{q}{2}}\Lambda_1^k\delta,$$

(1.22)
$$T_{-2k}(z) = (-1)^k(-i)^{\frac{q}{2}}\Lambda_2^k\delta.$$

Now, for $k = 1$,

$$\Lambda_1^k S_\lambda(w) = \left(\sum_{i=1}^{p} B_{x_i} + i\sum_{j=p+1}^{p+q} B_{x_j}\right) S_\lambda(w),$$

where $S_\lambda(w)$ is defined by (1.17) and $B_{x_i} = \frac{\partial^2}{\partial x_i^2} + \frac{2v_i}{x_i}\frac{\partial}{\partial x_i}$. By direct computation, we obtain

$$\Lambda_1 S_\lambda(w) = \frac{2^{-\lambda}\Gamma\left(\frac{n+2|v|-\lambda}{2}\right)}{\prod\limits_{i=1}^{n} 2^{v_i-\frac{1}{2}}\Gamma\left(v_i+\frac{1}{2}\right)\Gamma\left(\frac{\lambda}{2}\right)}(\lambda - n - 2|v|)(\lambda - 2)w^{\frac{\lambda-2-n-2|v|}{2}}$$

$$= (-1)\frac{2^{-(\lambda-2)}\Gamma\left(\frac{n+2|v|-(\lambda-2)}{2}\right)}{\prod\limits_{i=1}^{n} 2^{v_i-\frac{1}{2}}\Gamma\left(v_i+\frac{1}{2}\right)\Gamma\left(\frac{\lambda-2}{2}\right)}w^{\frac{\lambda-2-n-2|v|}{2}}$$

using the properties of Gamma functions. Thus $\Lambda_1 S_\lambda(w) = -S_{\lambda-2}(w)$. By repeating k−times in operating Λ_1 to $S_\lambda(w)$, we obtain

$$\Lambda_1^k S_\lambda(w) = (-1)^k S_{\lambda-2k}(w).$$

Similarly,

$$\Lambda_2^k T_\tau(z) = (-1)^k T_{\tau-2k}(z).$$

Thus we obtain (1.21) and (1.22) as required. Now consider

$$w = x_1^2 + x_2^2 + \cdots + x_p^2 - i(x_{p+1}^2 + x_{p+1}^2 + \cdots + x_{p+q}^2), \quad p + q = n$$

by changing the variable

$$x_1 = y_1, x_2 = y_2, \ldots, x_p = y_p,$$

$$x_{p+1} = \frac{y_{p+1}}{\sqrt{-i}}, \quad x_{p+2} = \frac{y_{p+2}}{\sqrt{-i}}, \quad \ldots, \quad x_{p+q} = \frac{y_{p+q}}{\sqrt{-i}}.$$

We thus have

$$w = y_1^2 + y_2^2 + \cdots + y_{p+1}^2 + \cdots + y_{p+q}^2.$$

Denote $w = r^2 = y_1^2 + y_2^2 + \cdots + y_n^2$ and consider the generalized function $w^\eta = r^{2\eta}$ where η is any complex number. Now

$$\langle w^\eta, \varphi \rangle = \int_{\mathbb{R}_n^+} w^\eta \varphi(x) dx,$$

where $\varphi \in D$, the space of infinitely differentiable functions with compact supports. Thus

$$\langle w^\eta, \varphi \rangle = \int_{\mathbb{R}_n} r^{2\eta} \varphi \frac{\partial(x_1, x_2, \ldots, x_n)}{\partial(y_1, y_2, \ldots, y_n)} dy_1 dy_2 \ldots dy_n = \frac{1}{(-i)^{\frac{q}{2}}} \int_{\mathbb{R}_n} w^\eta \varphi dy = \langle w^\eta, \varphi \rangle.$$

By Gelfand and Shilov [2], the functional $r^{2\eta}$ has simple poles at $\eta = \frac{-n-2|v|}{2} - k$, k is nonnegative and for $k = 0$ we can find the residue of $r^{2\eta}$ at $\eta = \frac{-n-2|v|}{2}$ and by [2], we have

$$\operatorname*{res}_{\eta=\frac{-n-2|v|}{2}} r^{2\eta} = \frac{2\pi^{\frac{n+2|v|}{2}}}{\Gamma\left(\frac{n+2|v|}{2}\right)}\delta(x).$$

Thus

(1.23) $$\operatorname*{res}_{\eta=\frac{-n-2|v|}{2}} w^\eta = (i)^{2(\frac{q}{2})}\frac{\pi^{\frac{n+2|v|}{2}}}{\Gamma\left(\frac{n+2|v|}{2}\right)}\delta(x).$$

We next find the residues of w^η at $\eta = \frac{-n-2|v|}{2} - k$. Now, by direct computation we have

$$\Lambda_1 w^{\eta+1} = 2(\eta+1)(2\eta+n+2|v|)w^\eta,$$

where w is defined by (1.16) and Λ_1 is defined by (1.5). By k-fold iteration, we have

$$\Lambda_1^k w^{\eta+1} = 4^k(\eta+1)(\eta+2)\cdots(\eta+k)\left(\eta + \frac{n+2|v|}{2}\right)$$
$$\times \left(\eta + \frac{n+2|v|}{2} + 1\right)\cdots\left(\eta + \frac{n+2|v|}{2} + k - 1\right)w^\eta$$

or

$$w^\eta = \frac{1}{4^k(\eta+1)(\eta+2)\cdots(\eta+k)\left(\eta+\frac{n+2|v|}{2}\right)\left(\eta+\frac{n+2|v|}{2}+1\right)\cdots\left(\eta+\frac{n+2|v|}{2}+k-1\right)}\Lambda_1^k w^{\eta+1}.$$

Thus we have

$$\operatorname*{res}_{\eta=\frac{-n-2|v|}{2}} w^\eta = \frac{1}{4^k k\left(\eta+\frac{n+2|v|}{2}k-1\right)\left(\eta+\frac{n+2|v|}{2}+k-2\right)\cdots\frac{n+2|v|}{2}}\operatorname*{res}_{\eta=\frac{-n-2|v|}{2}}\Lambda_1^k w^{\eta+1}.$$

By (1.23) and the properties of Gamma functions, we have

$$(1.24) \qquad \operatorname*{res}_{\eta=\frac{-n-2|v|}{2}} w^\eta = \frac{2(i)^{\frac{q}{2}}\pi^{\frac{n+2|v|}{2}}}{4^k\Gamma\left(\frac{n+2|v|}{2}+k\right)}\Lambda_1^k\delta(x).$$

Now we consider $S_{-2k}(w)$. We obtain

$$S_{-2k}(w) = \lim_{\eta\to-2k} S(w)$$

$$= \pi^{-\frac{n+2|v|}{2}}\frac{\lim_{\eta\to-2k} w^{\frac{\eta-n-2|v|}{2}}}{\lim_{\eta\to-2k}\Gamma\left(\frac{\eta}{2}\right)}\lim_{\eta\to-2k}\left(2^{-\eta}\Gamma\left(\frac{n+2|v|-\eta}{2}\right)\right)$$

$$= \pi^{-\frac{n+2|v|}{2}}\frac{\lim_{\eta\to-2k}(\eta+2k)w^{\frac{\eta-n-2|v|}{2}}}{\lim_{\eta\to-2k}(\eta+2k)\Gamma\left(\frac{\eta}{2}\right)}2^{2k}\Gamma\left(\frac{n+2|v|+2k}{2}\right)$$

$$= 4^k\pi^{-\frac{n+2|v|}{2}}\frac{\operatorname*{res}_{\eta=-2k} w^{\frac{\eta-n-2|v|}{2}}}{\operatorname*{res}_{\eta=-2k}\Gamma\left(\frac{\eta}{2}\right)}\Gamma\left(\frac{n+2|v|+2k}{2}\right).$$

Since $\operatorname*{res}_{\eta=-\frac{n+2|v|}{2}-k} w^\eta = \operatorname*{res}_{\eta=-2k} w^{\frac{\eta-n-2|v|}{2}}$ and $\operatorname*{res}_{\eta=-2k}\Gamma(\frac{\eta}{2}) = \frac{2(-1)^k}{k!}$ by (1.24) and the properties of the Gamma function we have

$$S_{-2k}(w) = (-1)^k(i)^{\frac{q}{2}}\Lambda_1^k\delta.$$

Similarly

$$T_{-2k}(z) = (-1)^k(-i)^{\frac{q}{2}}\Lambda_2^k\delta.$$

Thus we have

$$(1.25) \qquad S_0(w) = (i)^{\frac{q}{2}}\delta(x) \quad \text{and} \quad T_0(z) = (-i)^{\frac{q}{2}}\delta(x).$$

Now, from (1.19)

$$\Lambda_1^k S_{2k}(w) = (-1)^k S_0(w) \quad \text{for } \eta = 2k.$$

Thus, by (1.25) we have

$$\Lambda_1^k(-1)^k(-i)^{\frac{q}{2}}S_{2k}(w) = \delta(x).$$

It follows that $(-1)^k(-i)^{\frac{q}{2}}S_{2k}(w)$ is an elementary solution of the operator Λ_1^k. Similarly $(-1)^k(i)^{\frac{q}{2}}T_{2k}(z)$ is also an elementary solution of Λ_2^k.

ii) We need to show that

$$\left[(-1)^k(-i)^{\frac{q}{2}}S_{-2k}(w)\right] * \left[(-1)^k(-i)^{\frac{q}{2}}S_{2k}(w)\right] = \delta$$

and

$$\left[(-1)^k(i)^{\frac{q}{2}}T_{-2k}(z)\right] * \left[(-1)^k(i)^{\frac{q}{2}}T_{2k}(z)\right] = \delta.$$

Now, from (1.22) $(-1)^k(-i)^{\frac{q}{2}}S_{-2k}(w) = \Lambda_1^k\delta$, $B-$convolving both sides by $(-1)^k(-i)^{\frac{q}{2}}S_{2k}(w)$, we have

$$\left[(-1)^k(-i)^{\frac{q}{2}}S_{2k}(w)\right] * \left[(-1)^k(-i)^{\frac{q}{2}}S_{-2k}(w)\right] = \left[(-1)^k(-i)^{\frac{q}{2}}S_{2k}(w)\right] * \Lambda_1^k\delta$$

$$= \Lambda_1^k\left[(-1)^k(-i)^{\frac{q}{2}}S_{2k}(w)\right] * \delta$$

$$= \delta * \delta = \delta$$

by Lemma 1.6(i).

Similarly we can obtain

$$\left[(-1)^k(i)^{\frac{q}{2}}T_{-2k}(z)\right] * \left[(-1)^k(i)^{\frac{q}{2}}T_{2k}(z)\right] = \delta.$$

$\square$

Theorem 1.7. *Given the equation*

(1.26) $$\oplus_B^k K(x) = \delta,$$

where $\oplus_B^k$ is the operator iterated $k-$times defined by (1.4), δ is the Dirac-delta distribution, $x = (x_1, x_2, \ldots, x_n) \in \mathbb{R}_n^+$ and k is a nonnegative integer. Then we have

(1.27) $$K(x) = \left[R_{2k}^H(u) * (-1)^k R_{2k}^e(v)\right] * (-1)^k(-i)^{\frac{q}{2}}S_{2k}(w) * (-1)^k(i)^{\frac{q}{2}}T_{2k}(z)$$

as an elementary solution of (1.26) where $R_{2k}^H(u)$, $R_{2k}^e(v)$, $S_{2k}(w)$ and $T_{2k}(z)$ are defined by (1.13), (1.16), (1.17) and (1.18), respectively, with $\alpha = \beta = \eta = \tau = 2k$, k is a nonnegative integer.

Moreover, from (1.27) we have

(1.28) $$(-1)^k R_{-2k}^e(v) * \left[(-1)^k(-i)^{\frac{q}{2}}S_{-2k}(w)\right] * \left[(-1)^k(i)^{\frac{q}{2}}T_{-2k}(z)\right] * K(x) = R_{2k}^H(u)$$

as an elementary solution of the operator $\square_B^k$ iterated $k-$times defined by (1.1) and in particular from (1.27) and (1.28) with $p = 1$, $q = n - 1$, $k = 1$ and $x_1 = t$, we have

(1.29) $$(-1)^k R_{-2}^e(v) * \left[(-1)^k(-i)^{\frac{q}{2}}S_{-2}(w)\right] * \left[(-1)^k(i)^{\frac{q}{2}}T_{-2}(z)\right] * K(x) = M_2(u)$$

as an elementary solution of the Bessel wave operator defined by (1.8), where $M_2(u)$ is defined by (1.14) with $\alpha = 2$. Also, for $q = 0$ then (1.26) becomes

(1.30) $$\triangle_{B,p}^{1k}K(x) = \delta$$

and by (1.27) we have

(1.31)
$$K(x) = (-1)^k R_{2k}^e(v) * (-1)^k R_{2k}^e(v) * (-1)^k R_{2k}^e(v) * (-1)^k R_{2k}^e(v)$$
$$= (-1)^{4k} R_{4k}^e(v) = R_{8k}^e(v)$$

is an elementary solution of (1.30). where $\triangle_{B,p}^{4k}$ is the Laplacian Bessel of $p-$dimension, iterated $4k-$times and is defined by (1.10) and $v = x_1^2 + x_2^2 + \cdots + x_p^2$.

Proof. From (1.26) and (1.4) we have

$$\oplus_B^k K(x) = \left(\lozenge_B^k \Lambda_1^k \Lambda_2^k \right) K(x) = \delta$$

$B-$convolving both sides of the above equation by the $B-$convolution

$$\left[R_{2k}^H(u) * (-1)^k R_{2k}^e(v) \right] * (-1)^k (-i)^{\frac{q}{2}} S_{2k}(w) * (-1)^k (i)^{\frac{q}{2}} T_{2k}(z)$$

and the properties of the $B-$convolution with derivatives, we have

$$\lozenge_B^k \left[R_{2k}^H(u) * (-1)^k R_{2k}^e(v) \right] * \Lambda_1^k \left[(-1)^k (-i)^{\frac{q}{2}} S_{2k}(w) \right] * \Lambda_2^k \left[(-1)^k (i)^{\frac{q}{2}} T_{2k}(z) \right] * K(x)$$
$$= \left[R_{2k}^H(u) * (-1)^k R_{2k}^e(v) \right] * (-1)^k (-i)^{\frac{q}{2}} S_{2k}(w) * (-1)^k (i)^{\frac{q}{2}} T_{2k}(z)$$

Thus

$$\delta * \delta * \delta * K(x) = K(x) = \left[R_{2k}^H(u) * (-1)^k R_{2k}^e(v) \right] * (-1)^k (-i)^{\frac{q}{2}} S_{2k}(w) * (-1)^k (i)^{\frac{q}{2}} T_{2k}(z)$$

by Lemma 1.4 and Lemma 1.6*(i)*.

Thus we have (1.27) as required. Now we will relate the elementary solution $K(x)$ given by (1.27) to the elementary solution of the Bessel wave equation defined by (1.8) and the Laplacian Bessel defined by (1.10). Now from (1.27) and by Lemma 1.5 and Lemma 1.6*(ii)* *and the properties of inverses in the $B-$convolution algebra, we have*

$$(-1)^k R_{-2k}^e(v) * \left[(-1)^k (-i)^{\frac{q}{2}} S_{-2k}(w) \right] * \left[(-1)^k (i)^{\frac{q}{2}} T_{-2k}(z) \right] * K(x)$$
$$= \delta * \delta * R_{2k}^H(u) = R_{2k}^H(u).$$

Actually, by Lemma 1.2 $R_{2k}^H(u)$ is an elementary solution of the Bessel ultra-hyperbolic operator $\Box_B^k$ iterated $k-$times defined by (1.1).

In particular, by putting $p = 1, q = n - 1, k = 1$ and $x_1 = t$ in (1.27) and (1.28), $R_2^H(u)$ reduces to $M_2(u)$ where $M_2(u)$ is defined by (1.14) with $\alpha = 2$. Thus we have

$$(-1)^k R_{-2}^e(v) * \left[(-1)^k (-i)^{\frac{q}{2}} S_{-2}(w) \right] * \left[(-1)^k (i)^{\frac{q}{2}} T_{-2}(z) \right] * K(x) = M_2(u)$$

as elementary solution of the Bessel wave operator defined by (1.8), where $u = t^2 - x_2^2 - \cdots - x_{n-1}^2$.

Also, for $q = 0$ by Lemma 1.3 we obtain

$$K(x) = (-1)^{4k} R_{4k}^e(v) = R_{8k}^e(v)$$

as elementary solution of (1.30), where $v = x_1^2 + x_2^2 + \cdots + x_p^2$. On the other hand, we can also find $K(x)$ from (1.27), since $q = 0$, we have $R_{2k}^H(u)$ reduces to $(-1)^k R_{2k}^e(v)$ and $(-1)^k S_{2k}(w)$ reduces to $(-1)^k R_{2k}^e(v)$, also $(-1)^k T_{2k}(z)$ reduces to $(-1)^k R_{2k}^e(v)$, where $v = x_1^2 + x_2^2 + \cdots + x_p^2$.

Thus, by (1.27) for $q = 0$, we have

$$K(x) = (-1)^k R_{2k}^e(v) * (-1)^k R_{2k}^e(v) * (-1)^k R_{2k}^e(v) * (-1)^k R_{2k}^e(v) = (-1)^{4k} R_{4k}^e(v) = R_{8k}^e(v)$$

by [1].

This completes the proof. □

REFERENCES

[1] W.F. Donoghue, *Distributions and Fourier Transforms*, Acad. Press, New York, 1969.

[2] I.M. Gelfand and G.E. Shilov, *Generalized Function*, Acad. Press, New York, 1964.

[3] A. Kananthai, On the operator $\oplus^k$ related to the wave equation and Laplacian, *Applied Math. and Computation*, **132** (2002), 219–229.

[4] I.A. Kipriyanov, *Doklady Academyy Nauk of the USSR*, **158**(2) (1964), 274–278.

[5] I.A. Kipriyanov, *Tr. Math. Im. V.A. Steklova Akad. Nauk SSSR*, **89** (1967), 130–213.

[6] B.M. Levitan, Expansion in Fourier series and integrals with Bessel functions (in Russian), *Uspeki Mat., Nauka* (N.S), **6**(2)(42) (1951), 102–143.

[7] H. Yildirim, *Riesz Potentials Generated by a Generalized shift operator*, Ankara Uni. Graduate School of Natural and Applied Sciences, Dept. of Math., Ph.D. thesis, 1995.

[8] H. Yildirim and M.Z. Sarikaya, On the generalized Riesz type potentials, *Jour. of Inst. of Math. and Comp. Sci.*, **14**(3) (2001), 217–224.

[9] H. Yildirim, M.Z. Sarikaya and S. Ozturk, The solutions of the n-dimensional Bessel diamond operator and the Fourier-Bessel transform of their convolution, *Proc. Indian Acad. Sci.* (Math. Sci.), **114**(4) (2004), 375–387.

[10] S.E. Trione, On Marcel Riesz's ultra-hyperbolic type, *Trabajoc Matematica*, **116** (1987) (preprint).

In: Advances in Inequalities for Special Functions   ISBN 978-1-60021-919-1
Editors: P. Cerone and S. S. Dragomir, pp. 161–167 © 2008 Nova Science Publishers, Inc.

Inequalities for Walsh Polynomials with Semi-monotone Coefficients of Higher Order

Živorad Tomovski

Department of Mathematics
Faculty of Mathematics and Natural Sciences
Skopje 1000, Macedonia
E-mail address: tomovski@iunona.pmf.ukim.edu.mk

ABSTRACT. Using the concept of majorant sequence (see [5, ch.XXI], [6], [8], [9], [10]), some new inequalities for Walsh polynomials with p–times complex semi-monotone and p–times complex monotone sequence are given. Inequalities for p–times monotone sequences of nonnegative real numbers are also obtained. These results generalize some inequalities for Walsh polynomials with semi-monotone and semi-convex coefficients, given by the author of the present paper in [10].

1991 Mathematics Subject Classification: 26D05, 42C10

Key words and phrases: Walsh polynomials, Petrović inequality, $m-$ times complex semi-monotone sequence, Cesáro sums, majorant sequence.

1 INTRODUCTION

Let $I = [0, 1)$. Denote by $\{w_n(x)\}_{n=0}^{\infty}$ the Paley-Walsh orthonormal system defined on I. Thus $w_0(x) \equiv 1$, and for each positive integer n with dyadic development

$$n = \sum_{i=0}^{p} 2^{\nu_i}, \qquad \nu_1 > \nu_2 > \cdots > \nu_p \geq 0,$$

we have

$$w_n(x) = \prod_{i=0}^{p} r_{\nu_i}(x),$$

where $\{r_n(x)\}_{n=0}^{\infty}$ denotes the Rademacher system of functions defined by (see, e.g. [1, p. 60], [4, p. 9-10])

$$r_\nu(x) = sign \sin 2^\nu \pi x \qquad (\nu = 0, 1, 2, \ldots; \; 0 \leq x < 1).$$

Let $D_j^0(x) = w_j(x)$ and $D_j^k(x)$ denote the Cesáro sums of order k of the sequence $\{D_j^0(x)\}$ (see [11] for this terminology). Then

$$D_j^k(x) = \sum_{r=0}^{j} D_r^{k-1}(x) \qquad (j \geq 0, k \geq 1).$$

For $k = 1$ we get well-known Walsh-Dirichlet kernel $D_j(x)$ of order j. Consider the Walsh polynomials $\sum_{k=n}^{m} \lambda_k w_k(x)$ with complex valued coefficients $\{\lambda_k\}$. The finite-order differences $\Delta^m \lambda_n$ are defined by $\Delta \lambda_n = \lambda_n - \lambda_{n+1}$ and $\Delta^m \lambda_n = \Delta\left(\Delta^{m-1}\lambda_n\right) = \Delta^{m-1}\lambda_n - \Delta^{m-1}\lambda_{n+1}$, $m = 2, 3, \ldots$, $n = 1, 2, \ldots$. Petrovič [7] proved the following complementary triangle inequality for a sequence of complex numbers $\{\lambda_1, \lambda_2, \ldots, \lambda_n\}$.

Theorem 1.1. *Let α be a real number and $0 < \theta < \frac{\pi}{2}$. If $\{\lambda_1, \lambda_2, \ldots, \lambda_n\}$ are complex numbers such that $\alpha - \theta \leq \arg \lambda_\nu \leq \alpha + \theta$, $\nu = 1, 2, \ldots, n$, then*

$$\left|\sum_{\nu=1}^{n} \lambda_\nu\right| \geq (\cos\theta) \sum_{\nu=1}^{n} |\lambda_\nu|.$$

For $0 < \theta < \frac{\pi}{2}$ denote by $K(\theta)$ the cone $K(\theta) = \{z : |\arg z| \leq \theta\}$. Let $\{b_k\}$ be a positive nondecreasing sequence. The sequence of complex numbers $\{u_k\}$ is said to be $m-$**times complex semi-monotone** if there exists a cone $K(\theta)$ such that $\Delta^i\left(\frac{u_k}{b_k}\right) \in K(\theta)$ or $\Delta^i(u_k b_k) \in K(\theta)$, for all $i = 1, 2, \ldots, m$. We note that Fejér in [3] introduced a similar definition for a sequence of real numbers. Specifically for $b_k = 1$, the sequence $\{u_k\}$ shall be called $m-$**times complex monotone.** The definitions for complex semi-monotone and complex semi-convex sequences (cases $m = 1$ and $m = 2$) were introduced by the author in [8, 9, 10]. Using the concept of majorant sequence (see [8, 9, 10]) the author obtained new bounding inequalities for Walsh polynomials with semi-monotone and semi-convex coefficients. In this paper we shall present similar bounding inequalities for Walsh polynomials with $m-$ times complex semi-monotone sequences.

2 Preliminaries

Set $\bigoplus_{s=\alpha}^{\beta} n_s = 2^{-\left(\sum_{s=\alpha}^{\beta} n_s\right)}$ $(\alpha \leq \beta)$. Let $I(n_1, n_2, \ldots, n_k)$ denote the open interval

$$\left(\sum_{j=1}^{k} \bigoplus_{s=j}^{k} n_s, \sum_{j=1}^{k} \bigoplus_{s=j}^{k} n_s + \bigoplus_{s=1}^{k} n_s\right).$$

Then the interval $I(n_1, n_2, \ldots, n_k)$ can be obtained in the following way (see [2]). Divide the open interval $(0, 1)$ into the open subintervals $I(1), I(2), I(3), \ldots$ with the partition points $\frac{1}{2}, \frac{1}{4}, \frac{1}{8}, \ldots$, where $I(1) = \left(\frac{1}{2}, 1\right), I(2) = \left(\frac{1}{4}, \frac{1}{2}\right), I(3) = \left(\frac{1}{8}, \frac{1}{4}\right), \ldots$. Take the interval $I(n_k)$. Then $I(n_k) = \left(2^{-n_k}, 2^{-n_k+1}\right)$. Divide the interval $I(n_k)$ into the open subintervals $I(1, n_k), I(2, n_k), I(3, n_k)$, with the partition points $2^{-n_k} + 2^{-n_k-1}, 2^{-n_k} + 2^{-n_k-2}, 2^{-n_k} + 2^{-n_k-3}, \ldots$, where

$$I(1, n_k) = \left(2^{-n_k} + 2^{-n_k-1}, 2^{-n_k+1}\right)$$
$$I(2, n_k) = \left(2^{-n_k} + 2^{-n_k-2}, 2^{-n_k} + 2^{-n_k-1}\right)$$
$$I(3, n_k) = \left(2^{-n_k} + 2^{-n_k-3}, 2^{-n_k} + 2^{-n_k-2}\right)$$

and so on. We have $|I(1, n_k)| = \frac{|I(n_k)|}{2}$, $|I(2, n_k)| = \frac{|I(n_k)|}{4}$, $|I(3, n_k)| = \frac{I(n_k)}{8}$, where $|\cdot|$ denotes the length of the interval. Continue this process for $I(n_{k-1}, n_k), I(n_{k-2}, n_{k-1}, n_k), \ldots$ after k steps, we get $I(n_1, n_2, \ldots n_k)$. Set $E_0 = \varnothing$ and $E_1 = \{0\}$. For $k \geq 2$, let E_k be the set consisting of 0 and those partition points to get all $I(n_1, n_2, \ldots n_k)$, where $n_1, n_2, \ldots, n_{k-1} \geq 1$. Then E_k is a countable subset of I and $I \backslash E_k = \cup I(n_1, n_2, \ldots, n_{k-1})$, where the union is disjoint and runs over all positive integers $n_1, n_2, \ldots, n_{k-1}$. Chen and Wu in [2] introduced the sequence $\{Q_k(x) : k \geq 0\}$ of rational functions defined on $[0,1)$ below. Set $Q_0(x) = 1$ and $Q_1(x) = \frac{2}{x}$. For $k \geq 2$, define

$$
Q_k(x) = \begin{cases} 0, & x \in E_k \\ \rho_k \left(x - \sum_{j=1}^{k-1} \bigoplus_{s=j}^{k-1} n_s \right)^{-k}, & x \in I(n_1, n_2, \ldots, n_k) \end{cases}
$$

where $n_1, n_2, \ldots, n_{k-1}$ run over all possibilities of positive integers, and the numbers ρ_k are defined by the recursive formulas: $\rho_0 = 1$, $\rho_1 = 2$, and for $k \geq 2$,

$$
\rho_k = 2^k \left(1 + \sum_{\substack{\alpha+\beta<k+1 \\ \alpha<k, \beta\geq 2}} 2^{-\alpha} (k-\beta+2)^{2\alpha} \rho_\alpha \right).
$$

In [2, p. 403], Chen and Wu proved that $Q_\alpha(x) \leq \rho_\alpha \left(\frac{Q_k(x)}{\rho_k} \right)^{\frac{\alpha}{k}}$, $(1 \leq \alpha \leq k-1)$. Hence $\left(\frac{Q_\alpha(x)}{\rho_\alpha} \right)^{\frac{1}{\alpha}} \leq \left(\frac{Q_k(x)}{\rho_k} \right)^{\frac{1}{k}}$, so that

$$
\frac{1}{x - \sum_{j=1}^{\alpha-1} \bigoplus_{r=j}^{\alpha-1} n_r} \leq \frac{1}{x - \sum_{j=1}^{k-1} \bigoplus_{r=j}^{k-1} n_r}.
$$

Since $\frac{1}{x - \sum_{j=1}^{k-1} \bigoplus_{r=j}^{k-1} n_r} > 1$ for all $x \in [0,1)$, we obtain

$$
\left(\frac{1}{x - \sum_{j=1}^{\alpha-1} \bigoplus_{r=j}^{\alpha-1} n_r} \right)^\alpha \leq \left(\frac{1}{x - \sum_{j=1}^{k-1} \bigoplus_{r=j}^{k-1} n_r} \right)^\alpha \leq \left(\frac{1}{x - \sum_{j=1}^{k-1} \bigoplus_{r=j}^{k-1} n_r} \right)^k,
$$

for all $x \in [0,1)$. It is obvious that $\{\rho_k\}$ is a monotone increasing sequence, namely $\rho_\alpha \leq \rho_k$ for all $\alpha \leq k$. Hence

$$
\frac{\rho_\alpha}{\left(x - \sum_{j=1}^{\alpha-1} \bigoplus_{r=j}^{\alpha-1} n_r \right)^\alpha} \leq \frac{\rho_k}{\left(x - \sum_{j=1}^{k-1} \bigoplus_{r=j}^{k-1} n_r \right)^k},
$$

so that $Q_\alpha(x) \leq Q_k(x)$, for all $x \in [0,1)$ and all $1 \leq \alpha \leq k$.

3   Main Results

Theorem 3.1. *Let $\{u_k\}$ be a $p-$times complex semi-monotone sequence.*

i) If $\Delta^i \left(\frac{u_k}{b_k} \right) \in K(\theta)$, for all $i = 1, 2, \ldots, p$, then

$$
\left| \sum_{k=n}^m u_k w_k(x) \right| \leq \frac{b_m Q_p(x)}{\cos\theta} \left[\left| \Delta^{p-1} \left(\frac{u_n}{b_n} \right) \right| + \left| \Delta^{p-1} \left(\frac{u_{m+1}}{b_{m+1}} \right) \right| \right.
$$

$$
\left. + \left| \sum_{s=1}^{p-1} \Delta^s \left(\frac{u_{m+1}}{b_{m+1}} \right) \right| + \left| \frac{u_{m+1}}{b_{m+1}} \right| + \left| \sum_{s=1}^{p-1} \Delta^s \left(\frac{u_n}{b_n} \right) \right| + \left| \frac{u_n}{b_n} \right| \right].
$$

ii) If $\Delta^i (u_k b_k) \in K(\theta)$, for all $i = 1, 2, \ldots, p$, then

$$
\left| \sum_{k=n}^m u_k w_k(x) \right| \leq \frac{b_n^{-1} Q_p(x)}{\cos\theta} \left[\left| \Delta^{p-1}(u_n b_n) \right| + \left| \Delta^{p-1}(u_{m+1} b_{m+1}) \right| \right.
$$

$$
\left. + \left| \sum_{s=1}^{p-1} \Delta^s (u_{m+1} b_{m+1}) \right| + |u_{m+1} b_{m+1}| + \left| \sum_{s=1}^{p-1} \Delta^s (u_n b_n) \right| + |u_n b_n| \right].
$$

Proof. i) Let $B_j^0(x) = b_j w_j(x)$ and $B_j^k(x)$ denote the Cesáro sums of order k of the sequence $\{B_j^0(x)\}$. Then $B_j^k(x) = \sum_{u=0}^j B_u^{k-1}(x)$, $j \geq 0$, $k \geq 1$. Summation by parts gives

$$\sum_{k=n}^m \frac{u_k}{b_k}(b_k w_k) = \sum_{k=n}^m \Delta^p\left(\frac{u_k}{b_k}\right) B_k^p(x) + \sum_{s=0}^{p-1}\left[\Delta^s\left(\frac{u_{m+1}}{b_{m+1}}\right) B_m^{s+1}(x) - \Delta^s\left(\frac{u_n}{b_n}\right) B_{n-1}^{s+1}(x)\right].$$

Hence,

$$\left|\sum_{k=n}^m \frac{u_k}{b_k}(b_k w_k)\right| \leq b_m \left|\sum_{k=n}^m \Delta^p\left(\frac{u_k}{b_k}\right) D_k^p(x)\right| + b_m\left|\sum_{s=0}^{p-1}\Delta^s\left(\frac{u_{m+1}}{b_{m+1}}\right) D_m^{s+1}(x)\right|$$

$$+ b_m\left|\sum_{s=0}^{p-1}\Delta^s\left(\frac{u_n}{b_n}\right) D_{n-1}^{s+1}(x)\right|$$

$$\leq b_m\left[\sum_{k=n}^m\left|\Delta^p\left(\frac{u_k}{b_k}\right)\right| |D_k^p(x)| + \sum_{s=0}^{p-1}\left|\Delta^s\left(\frac{u_{m+1}}{b_{m+1}}\right)\right| |D_m^{s+1}(x)|\right.$$

$$\left. + \sum_{s=0}^{p-1}\left|\Delta^s\left(\frac{u_n}{b_n}\right)\right| |D_{n-1}^{s+1}(x)|\right]$$

$$\leq b_m\left[Q_p(x)\sum_{k=n}^m\left|\Delta^p\left(\frac{u_k}{b_k}\right)\right| + \sum_{s=0}^{p-1}\left|\Delta^s\left(\frac{u_{m+1}}{b_{m+1}}\right)\right| Q_{s+1}(x)\right.$$

$$\left. + \sum_{s=0}^{p-1}\left|\Delta^s\left(\frac{u_n}{b_n}\right)\right| Q_{s+1}(x)\right]$$

$$\leq b_m Q_p(x)\left[\sum_{k=n}^m\left|\Delta^p\left(\frac{u_k}{b_k}\right)\right| + \sum_{s=0}^{p-1}\left|\Delta^s\left(\frac{u_{m+1}}{b_{m+1}}\right)\right| + \sum_{s=0}^{p-1}\left|\Delta^s\left(\frac{u_n}{b_n}\right)\right|\right]$$

$$\leq \frac{b_m Q_p(x)}{\cos\theta}\left[\left|\sum_{k=n}^{m}\Delta^p\left(\frac{u_k}{b_k}\right)\right|+\left|\sum_{s=1}^{p-1}\Delta^s\left(\frac{u_{m+1}}{b_{m+1}}\right)\right|\right.$$

$$\left.+\left|\frac{u_{m+1}}{b_{m+1}}\right|+\left|\sum_{s=1}^{p-1}\Delta^s\left(\frac{u_n}{b_n}\right)\right|+\left|\frac{u_n}{b_n}\right|\right]$$

$$=\frac{b_m Q_p(x)}{\cos\theta}\left[\left|\Delta^{p-1}\left(\frac{u_n}{b_n}\right)-\Delta^{p-1}\left(\frac{u_{m+1}}{b_{m+1}}\right)\right|+\left|\sum_{s=1}^{p-1}\Delta^s\left(\frac{u_{m+1}}{b_{m+1}}\right)\right|\right.$$

$$\left.+\left|\frac{u_{m+1}}{b_{m+1}}\right|+\left|\sum_{s=1}^{p-1}\Delta^s\left(\frac{u_n}{b_n}\right)\right|+\left|\frac{u_n}{b_n}\right|\right]$$

$$\leq\frac{b_m Q_p(x)}{\cos\theta}\left[\left|\Delta^{p-1}\left(\frac{u_n}{b_n}\right)\right|+\left|\Delta^{p-1}\left(\frac{u_{m+1}}{b_{m+1}}\right)\right|+\left|\sum_{s=1}^{p-1}\Delta^s\left(\frac{u_{m+1}}{b_{m+1}}\right)\right|\right.$$

$$\left.+\left|\frac{u_{m+1}}{b_{m+1}}\right|+\left|\sum_{s=1}^{p-1}\Delta^s\left(\frac{u_n}{b_n}\right)\right|+\left|\frac{u_n}{b_n}\right|\right].$$

ii) Let $\widetilde{B}_j^0(x)=\frac{w_j(x)}{b_j}$ and $\widetilde{B}_j^k(x)$ denote the Cesáro sums of order k of the sequence $\left\{\widetilde{B}_j^0(x)\right\}$. Then

$$\widetilde{B}_j^k(x)=\sum_{u=0}^{j}\widetilde{B}_u^{k-1}(x),\quad j\geq0,k\geq1.$$

Summation by parts gives,

$$\sum_{k=n}^{m}u_k b_k\left(b_k^{-1}w_k\right)=\sum_{k=n}^{m}\Delta^p\left(u_k b_k\right)\widetilde{B}_k^p(x)$$

$$+\sum_{s=0}^{p-1}\left[\Delta^s\left(u_{m+1}b_{m+1}\right)\widetilde{B}_m^{s+1}(x)-\Delta^s\left(u_n b_n\right)\widetilde{B}_{n-1}^{s+1}(x)\right].$$

Then

$$\left|\sum_{k=n}^{m}u_k b_k\left(b_k^{-1}w_k\right)\right|\leq b_n^{-1}\left|\sum_{k=n}^{m}\Delta^p\left(u_k b_k\right)D_k^p(x)\right|$$

$$+b_n^{-1}\left|\sum_{s=0}^{p-1}\Delta^s\left(u_{m+1}b_{m+1}\right)D_m^{s+1}(x)\right|+b_n^{-1}\left|\sum_{s=0}^{p-1}\Delta^s\left(u_n b_n\right)D_{n-1}^{s+1}(x)\right|$$

$$\leq b_n^{-1}\sum_{k=n}^{m}\left|\Delta^p\left(u_k b_k\right)\right|\left|D_k^p(x)\right|+b_n^{-1}\sum_{s=0}^{p-1}\left|\Delta^s\left(u_{m+1}b_{m+1}\right)\right|\left|D_m^{s+1}(x)\right|$$

$$+b_n^{-1}\sum_{s=0}^{p-1}\left|\Delta^s\left(u_n b_n\right)\right|\left|D_{n-1}^{s+1}(x)\right|$$

$$\leq b_n^{-1}Q_p(x)\left[\sum_{k=n}^{m}\left|\Delta^p\left(u_k b_k\right)\right|+\sum_{s=0}^{p-1}\left|\Delta^s\left(u_{m+1}b_{m+1}\right)\right|+\sum_{s=0}^{p-1}\left|\Delta^s\left(u_n b_n\right)\right|\right]$$

$$\leq \frac{b_n^{-1} Q_p(x)}{\cos \theta} \left[\left| \sum_{k=n}^{m} \Delta^p(u_k b_k) \right| + \left| \sum_{s=1}^{p-1} \Delta^s(u_{m+1} b_{m+1}) \right| \right.$$

$$+ \left| u_{m+1} b_{m+1} \right| + \left| \sum_{s=1}^{p-1} \Delta^s(u_n b_n) \right| + \left| u_n b_n \right| \Bigg]$$

$$\leq \frac{b_n^{-1} Q_p(x)}{\cos \theta} \Big[\left| \Delta^{p-1}(u_n b_n) \right| + \left| \Delta^{p-1}(u_{m+1} b_{m+1}) \right|$$

$$+ \left| \sum_{s=1}^{p-1} \Delta^s(u_{m+1} b_{m+1}) \right| + \left| u_{m+1} b_{m+1} \right| + \left| \sum_{s=1}^{p-1} \Delta^s(u_n b_n) \right| + \left| u_n b_n \right| \Big].$$

$\square$

If $b_k = 1$, $k = n, n+1, \ldots, m$, from Theorem 3.1, we obtain the following corollary.

Corollary 3.2. *Let $\{u_k\}$ be a $p-$times complex monotone sequence, then*

$$\left| \sum_{k=n}^{m} u_k w_k(x) \right|$$

$$\leq \frac{Q_p(x)}{\cos \theta} \left[\left| \Delta^{p-1} u_n \right| + \left| \Delta^{p-1} u_{m+1} \right| + \left| \sum_{s=1}^{p-1} \Delta^s u_{m+1} \right| + \left| u_{m+1} \right| \left| \sum_{s=1}^{p-1} \Delta^s u_n \right| + \left| u_n \right| \right].$$

Corollary 3.3.

  i) *If $\{a_k\}$ is a nonnegative sequence such that $\left\{ a_k b_k^{-1} \right\}$ is a $p-$times monotone sequence, then*

$$\left| \sum_{k=n}^{m} u_k w_k(x) \right| \leq b_m Q_p(x) \left[\sum_{k=n}^{m} \Delta^p \left(\frac{a_k}{b_k} \right) + \sum_{s=0}^{p-1} \Delta^s \left(\frac{a_{m+1}}{b_{m+1}} \right) + \sum_{s=0}^{p-1} \Delta^s \left(\frac{a_n}{b_n} \right) \right].$$

  ii) *If $\{a_k\}$ is a nonnegative sequence such that $\{a_k b_k\}$ is a $p-$times monotone sequence, then*

$$\left| \sum_{k=n}^{m} u_k w_k(x) \right| \leq b_n^{-1} Q_p(x) \left[\sum_{k=n}^{m} \Delta^p(a_k b_k) + \sum_{s=0}^{p-1} \Delta^s(a_{m+1} b_{m+1}) + \sum_{s=0}^{p-1} \Delta^s(a_n b_n) \right].$$

REFERENCES

[1] G. Aleksits, *Convergence Problems of Orthogonal Series*, Pergamon Press, New York-Oxford-Paris, 1961.

[2] C.-P. Chen and C.-T. Wu, Double Walsh series with coefficients of bounded variation of higher order, *Trans. Amer. Math. Soc.*, **350**(1) (1998), 395–417.

[3] L. Fejer, Trigonometrische Reihen und Potenzreihen mit mehrfach monotoner Koeffizientenfolge. *Trans. Amer. Math. Soc.*, **39** (1936), 18–59

[4] B.I. Golubov, A.V. Efimov and V.A. Skvorcov, *Walsh Series and Transformations*, Science, Moscow (1987) (Russian).

[5] D.S. Mitrinović, J. Pečarić and A.M. Fink, *Classical and New Inequalities in Analysis*, Kluwer, 1993.

[6] D.S. Mitrinović and J. Pečarić, On an inequality of G.K. Lebed, *Prilozi MANU, Od. Mat. Tehn. Nauki*, **12** (1991), 15–19.

[7] M. Petrović, Theoreme sur les integrales curvilignes, *Publ. Math. Univ. Belgrade*, **2** (1933), 45–59.

[8] Ž. Tomovski, On some inequalities of Mitrinović and Pečarić, *Prilozi MANU, Od. Mat. Tehn. Nauki*, **22** (2001), 21–28.

[9] Ž. Tomovski, Some inequalities for complex trigonometric polynomials with special coefficients, *J. Inequal. Pure and Appl. Math.*, **4**(4) (2003), Art. 78,.

[10] Ž. Tomovski, Inequalities for Walsh polynomials with semi-monotone and semi-convex coefficients, *J. Inequal. Pure and Appl. Math.*, **6**(4) (2005), Art. 98.

[11] A. Zygmund, *Trigonometric Series* (2nd ed.), Vol. **1**, Cambridge Univ.Press, Cambridge, 1959.